Birth of Our Solar System

Our solar system was born from the gravitational collapse of an interstellar cloud of gas about $4\frac{1}{2}$ billion years ago, or about September 3 on the cosmic calendar. The Sun formed at the center of the cloud while the planets, including Earth, formed in a disk surrounding it.

Life on Earth

We do not know exactly when life arose on Earth, but fossil evidence indicates that it was within a few hundred million years after Earth's formation. Nearly three billion more years passed before complex plant and animal life evolved.

H

On
an
of
the

SEPTEMBER	OCTOBER	NOVEMBER	DECEMBER

SEP 3

SEP 22

DEC 17

DEC 26

DEC 30

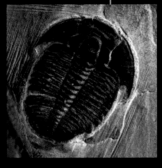

This rock formation in West Greenland holds the oldest known evidence of life on Earth, dating to more than 3.85 billion years ago, or September 22 on the cosmic calendar.

Fossil evidence shows a remarkable increase in animal diversity beginning about 540 million years ago — December 17 on the cosmic calendar. We call this the Cambrian explosion.

Dinosaurs arose about 225 million years ago — December 26 on the cosmic calendar. Mammals arose around the same time.

Dinosaurs went extinct, probably due to an asteroid or comet impact, about 65 million years ago, which was only yesterday (December 30) on the cosmic calendar.

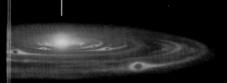

the solar system may have looked like shortly before forming.

uman History

the cosmic calendar, our hominid
estors arose only a few hours ago, and all
ecorded human history has occurred in just
last 15 seconds before midnight.

You

The average human life span is only about
two-tenths of a second on the cosmic
calendar.

On the cosmic calendar, our ancestors began to
master agriculture only 25 seconds ago ...

*Our early ancestors had
smaller brains, but probably
were walking upright by
about 5 million years
ago—December 31, 9 PM
on the cosmic calendar.*

*Modern humans arose about
40,000 years ago, which is
only about two minutes ago
(December 31, 11:58 PM) on
the cosmic calendar.*

*...the Egyptians built the pyramids only 11 seconds
ago ...*

*...we learned that Earth is a planet orbiting the Sun
only 1 second ago ...*

11:59:59.95 PM

*...and a typical college student was born only 0.05
second ago.*

Jeffrey Bennett • Megan Donahue • Nicholas Schneider
Mark Voit

The Cosmic Perspective

Second Custom Edition for University of California Berkeley

Taken From:
The Cosmic Perspective, Seventh Edition
by Jeffrey Bennett, Megan Donahue, Nicholas Schneider, and Mark Voit

Cover Art: Courtesy of Photodisc/Getty Images.

Taken from:

The Cosmic Perspective, Seventh Edition
by Jeffrey Bennett, Megan Donahue, Nicholas Schneider, and Mark Voit
Copyright © 2014, 2010, 2008, 2006 by Pearson Education, Inc.
Published by Pearson
Upper Saddle River, New Jersey 07458

This special edition published in cooperation with Pearson Learning Solutions.

Pearson Learning Solutions, 501 Boylston Street, Suite 900, Boston, MA 02116
A Pearson Education Company
www.pearsoned.com

Printed in the United States of America

2 3 4 5 6 7 8 9 10 V092 18 17 16 15 14

000200010271767604

CW

ISBN 10: 1-269-21957-X
ISBN 13: 978-1-269-21957-0

DEDICATION

To all who have ever wondered about the mysteries
of the universe. We hope this book will answer some
of your questions—and that it will also raise new
questions in your mind that will keep you curious
and interested in the ongoing human adventure
of astronomy. And, especially, to Michaela, Emily,
Sebastian, Grant, Nathan, Brooke, and Angela.
The study of the universe begins at birth, and we
hope that you will grow up in a world with far less
poverty, hatred, and war so that all people will have
the opportunity to contemplate the mysteries of the
universe into which they are born.

BRIEF CONTENTS

DETAILED CONTENTS

PART I
DEVELOPING PERSPECTIVE

PART IV
A DEEPER LOOK AT NATURE

PART V
STARS

PREFACE

We humans have gazed into the sky for countless generations. We have wondered how our lives are connected to the Sun, Moon, planets, and stars that adorn the heavens. Today, through the science of astronomy, we know that these connections go far deeper than our ancestors ever imagined. This book tells the story of modern astronomy and the new perspective, *The Cosmic Perspective*, that astronomy gives us of ourselves and our planet.

This book grew out of our experience teaching astronomy to both college students and the general public over the past 30 years. During this time, a flood of new discoveries fueled a revolution in our understanding of the cosmos but had little impact on the basic organization and approach of most astronomy textbooks. We felt the time had come to rethink how to organize and teach the major concepts in astronomy to reflect this revolution in scientific understanding. This book is the result.

Who Is This Book For?

The Cosmic Perspective is designed as a textbook for college courses in introductory astronomy, but is suitable for anyone who is curious about the universe. We assume no prior knowledge of astronomy or physics, and the book is especially suited to students who do not intend to major in mathematics or science.

The Cosmic Perspective provides a comprehensive survey of modern astronomy, and it contains enough material for a two-semester introductory astronomy sequence. It may also be used for one-semester survey courses if professors choose their areas of emphasis. However, instructors of one-term courses may also wish to consider our two shorter versions of this book: *The Essential Cosmic Perspective*, which covers a smaller set of topics and is tailored to meet the needs of comprehensive one-semester survey courses in astronomy, and *The Cosmic Perspective Fundamentals*, which covers only the most fundamental topics in astronomy and is designed for courses that address a more limited set of topics.

New to This Edition

The underlying philosophy, goals, and structure of *The Cosmic Perspective* remain the same as in past editions, but we have thoroughly updated the text and made a number of other improvements. Here, briefly, is a list of the significant changes you'll find in the seventh edition:

- **Major Chapter-Level Changes:** We have made numerous significant changes to both update science and improve the pedagogical flow in this edition. The full list is too long to put here, but major changes include the following:

- **Chapter 1** has been reorganized so that Section 1.1 now focuses on our cosmic address and the scale of space, while Section 1.2 focuses on our cosmic origins and the scale of time. We believe these changes will make it easier for students to learn key ideas that they'll need for the rest of their course in astronomy.

- In **Chapter 3**, we have significantly reorganized and rewritten Sections 3.1 and 3.2, with the goal of making it easier for students to focus on the key take-away ideas in each of these sections.

- In **Chapter 5**, we have consolidated the last two sections from the prior edition into a single Section 5.4, thereby making it easier for students to understand all the key ideas that we learn from spectra.

- **Chapter 8** has been significantly reorganized and rewritten so that the four major features of the solar system introduced in Chapter 7 are now all explained in a single section, making it much easier for students to draw connections between the features and how they are natural consequences of the nebular theory.

- **Chapter 13** has been completely rewritten to incorporate new developments in the study of extrasolar planets and planetary systems, including results from the *Kepler* mission. In the time since the last edition was published, the number of known extrasolar planets has more than quintupled, the number of known Earth-size planets has gone from zero to many, and our general picture of planetary systems has evolved to the point where we can now make strong statistical statements about planets throughout the universe.

- In **Chapter 20**, we have reorganized so that Hubble's law is introduced along with other distance measurement techniques in Section 20.2, and Section 20.3 now focuses on the age of the universe.

- **Chapters 22 and 23** have been thoroughly reorganized so that we now cover the Big Bang theory before we cover dark matter, dark energy, and the fate of the universe. This change was motivated by the spectacular progress in cosmic microwave background observations during the past decade and allows light-element abundances and microwave background observations to be presented as primary evidence that dark matter consists of exotic particles.

- **Mathematical Insight** boxes have been substantially reworked throughout the book. Although we have kept the same basic mathematical content and level, we have revised them to make the explanations shorter and simpler, and therefore more accessible to students.

- **Fully Updated Science:** Astronomy is a fast-moving field, and numerous new developments have occurred since the prior edition was published. In addition to the major chapter-level changes above, other scientific updates in this edition include

  - New results and images from spacecraft exploring our solar system, including *Phoenix*, the *Mars Reconnaissance Orbiter*, and *Curiosity* at Mars; *Venus Express* at Venus; *Cassini* at Saturn; *MESSENGER* at Mercury; *Stardust* and *Dawn* at Vesta; *SOHO* and *TRACE* at the Sun; and more
  - Recent results from major space observatories, including Hubble, Kepler, Spitzer, Chandra, and Fermi
  - Updated data and models on topics including global warming, cycling of gas in the Milky Way, and galaxy formation and evolution
  - New research on the timing and possible origin of life on Earth

- **New Group Work Questions:** The end-of-chapter exercise sets now include a subsection of problems that can be easily done in class to foster peer learning and in-class participation.

- **New Content in MasteringAstronomy®:** We have reached the point where *The Cosmic Perspective* is no longer just a textbook; rather it is a "learning package" that combines a printed book with deeply integrated, interactive media developed to support every chapter of our book. For students, the MasteringAstronomy Study Area provides a wealth of tutorials and activities to build understanding, while quizzes and exercises allow them to test what they've learned. For instructors, the MasteringAstronomy Item Library provides the unprecedented ability to quickly build, post, and automatically grade pre- and post-lecture diagnostic tests, weekly homework assignments, and exams of appropriate difficulty, duration, and content coverage. It also provides the ability to record detailed information on the step-by-step work of every student directly into a powerful and easy-to-use gradebook, and to evaluate results with a sophisticated suite of diagnostics. Among the changes you'll find to the MasteringAstronomy site for this edition are numerous new and revised interactive figures, including many narrated video tours; numerous new tutorials in the Item Library; and a fully updated set of reading, concept, and visual quizzes in both the Study Area and the Item Library.

Themes of *The Cosmic Perspective*

The Cosmic Perspective offers a broad survey of modern understanding of the cosmos and of how we have built that understanding. Such a survey can be presented in a number of different ways. We have chosen to interweave a few key themes throughout the book, each selected to help make the subject more appealing to students who may never have taken any formal science courses and who may begin the course with little understanding of how science works. We built our book around the following five key themes:

- *Theme 1: We are a part of the universe and thus can learn about our origins by studying the universe.* This is the overarching theme of *The Cosmic Perspective*, as we continually emphasize that learning about the universe helps us understand ourselves. Studying the intimate connections between human life and the cosmos gives students a reason to care about astronomy and also deepens their appreciation of the unique and fragile nature of our planet and its life.

- *Theme 2: The universe is comprehensible through scientific principles that anyone can understand.* The universe is comprehensible because the same physical laws appear to be at work in every aspect, on every scale, and in every age of the universe. Moreover, while professional scientists generally have discovered the laws, anyone can understand their fundamental features. Students can learn enough in one or two terms of astronomy to comprehend the basic reasons for many phenomena that they see around them—phenomena ranging from seasonal changes and phases of the Moon to the most esoteric astronomical images that appear in the news.

- *Theme 3: Science is not a body of facts but rather a process through which we seek to understand the world around us.* Many students assume that science is just a laundry list of facts. The long history of astronomy can show them that science is a process through which we learn about our universe—a process that is not always a straight line to the truth. That is why our ideas about the cosmos sometimes change as we learn more, as they did dramatically when we first recognized that Earth is a planet going around the Sun rather than the center of the universe. In this book, we continually emphasize the nature of science so that students can understand how and why modern theories have gained acceptance and why these theories may still change in the future.

- *Theme 4: A course in astronomy is the beginning of a lifelong learning experience.* Building upon the prior themes, we emphasize that what students learn in their astronomy course is not an end but a beginning. By remembering a few key physical principles and understanding the nature of science, students can follow astronomical developments for the rest of their lives. We therefore seek to motivate students enough that they will continue to participate in the ongoing human adventure of astronomical discovery.

- *Theme 5: Astronomy affects each of us personally with the new perspectives it offers.* We all conduct the daily business of our lives with reference to some "world view"—a set of personal beliefs about our place and purpose in the universe that we have developed through a combination of schooling, religious training, and personal thought. This world view shapes our beliefs and many of our actions. Although astronomy does not mandate a particular set of beliefs, it does provide perspectives on the architecture of the universe that can influence how we view ourselves and our world, and these perspectives can potentially affect our behavior. For example, someone who believes Earth to be at the center of the universe might treat our planet quite differently from someone who views it as a tiny and fragile world in the vast cosmos. In many respects, the role of astronomy in shaping world views may be to represent the deepest connection between the universe and the everyday lives of humans.

Pedagogical Principles of *The Cosmic Perspective*

No matter how an astronomy course is taught, it is very important to present material according to a clear set of pedagogical principles. The following list briefly summarizes the major pedagogical principles that we apply throughout this book. (The *Instructor Guide* describes these principles in more detail.)

- *Stay focused on the big picture.* Astronomy is filled with interesting facts and details, but they are meaningless unless they fit into a big picture view of the universe. We therefore take care to stay focused on the big picture (essentially the themes discussed above) at all times. A major benefit of this approach is that although students may forget individual facts and details after the course is over, the big picture framework should stay with them for life.
- *Always provide context first.* We all learn new material more easily when we understand why we are learning it. In essence, this is simply the idea that it is easier to get somewhere when you know where you are going. We therefore begin the book (Chapter 1) with a broad overview of modern understanding of the cosmos, so that students can know what they will be studying in the rest of the book. We maintain this "context first" approach throughout the book by always telling students what they will be learning, and why, before diving into the details.
- *Make the material relevant.* It's human nature to be more interested in subjects that seem relevant to our lives. Fortunately, astronomy is filled with ideas that touch each of us personally. For example, the study of our solar system helps us better understand and appreciate our planet Earth, and the study of stars and galaxies helps us learn how we have come to exist. By emphasizing our personal connections to the cosmos, we make the material more meaningful, inspiring students to put in the effort necessary to learn it.
- *Emphasize conceptual understanding over "stamp collecting" of facts.* If we are not careful, astronomy can appear to be an overwhelming collection of facts that are easily forgotten when the course ends. We therefore emphasize a few key conceptual ideas that we use over and over again. For example, the laws of conservation of energy and conservation of angular momentum (introduced in Section 4.3) reappear throughout the book, and we find that the wide variety of features found on the terrestrial planets can be understood through just a few basic geological processes. Research shows that, long after the course is over, students are far more likely to retain such conceptual learning than individual facts or details.

- *Proceed from the more familiar and concrete to the less familiar and abstract.* It's well known that children learn best by starting with concrete ideas and then generalizing to abstractions later. The same is true for many adults. We therefore always try to "build bridges to the familiar"— that is, to begin with concrete or familiar ideas and then gradually draw more general principles from them.
- *Use plain language.* Surveys have found that the number of new terms in many introductory astronomy books is larger than the number of words taught in many first-year courses on a foreign language. In essence, this means the books are teaching astronomy in what looks to students like a foreign language! Clearly, it is much easier for students to understand key astronomical concepts if they are explained in plain English without resorting to unnecessary jargon. We have gone to great lengths to eliminate jargon as much as possible or, at minimum, to replace standard jargon with terms that are easier to remember in the context of the subject matter.
- *Recognize and address student misconceptions.* Students do not arrive as blank slates. Most students enter our courses not only lacking the knowledge we hope to teach but often holding misconceptions about astronomical ideas. Therefore, to teach correct ideas, we must also help students recognize the paradoxes in their prior misconceptions. We address this issue in a number of ways, the most obvious being the presence of many Common Misconceptions boxes. These summarize commonly held misconceptions and explain why they cannot be correct.

The Topical (Part) Structure of *The Cosmic Perspective*

The Cosmic Perspective is organized into seven broad topical areas (the seven Parts in the table of contents), each approached in a distinctive way designed to help maintain the focus on the themes discussed earlier. Here, we summarize the guiding philosophy through which we have approached each topic. Every Part concludes with one of our two-page Cosmic Context spreads, which tie together into a coherent whole the diverse ideas covered in the individual chapters.

Part I: Developing Perspective (Chapters 1–3, S1)

Guiding Philosophy: Introduce the big picture, the process of science, and the historical context of astronomy.

The basic goal of these chapters is to give students a big picture overview and context for the rest of the book, and to help them develop an appreciation for the process of science and how science has developed through history. Chapter 1 outlines our modern understanding of the cosmos, so that students gain perspective on the entire universe before diving into its details. Chapter 2 introduces basic sky phenomena, including seasons and phases of the Moon, and provides perspective on how phenomena we experience every day are tied to the broader cosmos. Chapter 3 discusses the nature of science, offering a historical perspective on the development of science and giving students perspective on how science works and how it differs from nonscience. The supplementary (optional) Chapter S1 goes into more detail about the sky, including celestial timekeeping and navigation.

The *Cosmic Context* figure for Part I appears on pp. 108–109.

Part II: Key Concepts for Astronomy (Chapters 4–6)

Guiding Philosophy: Connect the physics of the cosmos to everyday experiences.

These chapters lay the groundwork for understanding astronomy through what is sometimes called the "universality of physics"— the idea that a few key principles governing matter, energy, light, and motion explain both the phenomena of our daily lives and the mysteries of the cosmos. Each chapter begins with a section on science in everyday life in which we remind students how much they already know about scientific phenomena from their everyday experiences. We then build on this everyday knowledge to help students learn the formal principles of physics needed for the rest of their study of astronomy. Chapter 4 covers the laws of motion, the crucial conservation laws of angular momentum and energy, and the universal law of gravitation. Chapter 5 covers the nature of light and matter, the formation of spectra, and the Doppler effect. Chapter 6 covers telescopes and astronomical observing techniques.

The *Cosmic Context* figure for Part II appears on pp. 188–189.

Part III: Learning from Other Worlds (Chapters 7–13)

Guiding Philosophy: We learn about our own world and existence by studying about other planets in our solar system and beyond.

This set of chapters begins in Chapter 7 with a broad overview of the solar system, including a 10-page tour that highlights some of the most important and interesting features of the Sun and each of the planets in our solar system. In the remaining chapters of this Part, we seek to explain these features through a true *comparative planetology* approach, in which the discussion emphasizes the *processes* that shape the planets rather than the "stamp collecting" of facts about them. Chapter 8 uses the concrete features of the solar system presented in Chapter 7 to build student understanding of the current theory of solar system formation. Chapters 9 and 10 focus on the terrestrial planets, covering key ideas of geology and atmospheres, respectively. In both chapters, we start with examples from our own planet Earth to help students understand the types of features that are found throughout the terrestrial worlds and the fundamental processes that explain how these features came to be. We then complete each of these chapters by summarizing how the various processes have played out on each individual world. Chapter 11 covers the jovian planets and their moons and rings. Chapter 12 covers small bodies in the solar system, including asteroids, comets, and dwarf planets. It also covers cosmic collisions, including the impact linked to the extinction of the dinosaurs and a discussion of how seriously we should take the ongoing impact threat. Finally, Chapter 13 turns to the exciting topic of other planetary systems that have been discovered in recent years. Note that Part III is essentially independent of Parts IV through VII, and thus can be covered either before or after them.

The *Cosmic Context* figure for Part III appears on pp. 396–397.

Part IV: A Deeper Look at Nature (Chapters S2–S4)

Guiding Philosophy: Ideas of relativity and quantum mechanics are accessible to anyone.

Nearly all students have at least heard of things like the prohibition on faster-than-light travel, curvature of spacetime, and the uncertainty principle. But few (if any) students enter an introductory astronomy course with any idea of what these things mean, and they are naturally curious about them. Moreover, a basic understanding of the ideas of relativity and quantum mechanics makes it possible to gain a much deeper appreciation of many of the most important and interesting topics in modern astronomy including black holes, gravitational lensing, and the overall geometry of the universe. The three chapters of Part IV cover special relativity (Chapter S2), general relativity (Chapter S3), and key astronomical ideas of quantum mechanics (Chapter S4). The main thrust throughout is to demystify relativity and quantum mechanics by convincing students that they are capable of understanding the key ideas despite the reputation of these subjects for being hard or counterintuitive. ***These chapters are labeled "supplementary" because coverage of them is optional.*** Covering them will give your students a deeper understanding of the topics that follow on stars, galaxies, and cosmology, but the later chapters are self-contained so that they may be covered without having covered Part IV at all.

The *Cosmic Context* figure for Part IV appears on pp. 462–463.

Part V: Stars (Chapters 14–18)

Guiding Philosophy: We are intimately connected to the stars.

These are our chapters on stars and stellar life cycles. Chapter 14 covers the Sun in depth so that it can serve as a concrete model for building an understanding of other stars. Chapter 15 describes the general properties of other stars, how we measure these properties, and how we classify stars with the H-R diagram. Chapter 16 covers star birth, and the rest of stellar evolution is discussed in Chapter 17. Chapter 18 covers the end points of stellar evolution: white dwarfs, neutron stars, and black holes, along with a discussion of gamma-ray bursts.

The *Cosmic Context* figure for Part V appears on pp. 576–577.

Part VI: Galaxies and Beyond (Chapters 19–23)

Guiding Philosophy: Present galaxy evolution and cosmology together as intimately related topics.

These chapters cover galaxies and cosmology. Chapter 19 presents the Milky Way as a paradigm for galaxies in much the same way that Chapter 14 uses the Sun as a paradigm for stars.

Chapter 20 presents the properties of galaxies and shows how the quest to measure galactic distances led to Hubble's law and laid the foundation for modern cosmology. Chapter 21 discusses how the current state of knowledge regarding galaxy evolution has emerged from our ability to look back through time. Chapter 22 then presents the Big Bang theory and the evidence supporting it, setting the stage for Chapter 23, which explores dark matter and its role in galaxy formation, as well as dark energy and its implications for the fate of the universe.

The *Cosmic Context* figure for Part VI appears on pp. 694–695.

Part VII: Life on Earth and Beyond (Chapter 24)

Guiding Philosophy: The study of life on Earth helps us understand the search for life in the universe.

This Part consists of a single chapter. It may be considered optional, to be used as time allows. Those who wish to teach a more detailed course on astrobiology may wish to consider the text *Life in the Universe*, by Bennett and Shostak.

The *Cosmic Context* figure for Part VII appears on pp. 722–723.

Pedagogical Features of *The Cosmic Perspective*

Alongside the main narrative, *The Cosmic Perspective* includes a number of pedagogical devices designed to enhance student learning:

- **Learning Goals** Presented as key questions, motivational learning goals begin every chapter, and every section of every chapter is carefully written to address the specific learning goal in the title. This helps students stay focused on the big picture and stay motivated by the understanding they will gain.
- **Chapter Summary** The end-of-chapter summary offers a concise review of the learning goal questions, helping reinforce student understanding of key concepts from the chapter. Thumbnail figures are included to remind students of key illustrations and photos in the chapter.
- **Annotated Figures** Key figures in each chapter now include the research-proven technique of "annotation"— carefully crafted text placed on the figure (in blue) to guide students through interpreting graphs, following process figures, and translating between different representations.
- **Cosmic Context Two-Page Figures** These two-page spreads provide visual summaries of key processes and concepts.
- **Wavelength/Observatory Icons** For astronomical images, simple icons indicate whether the image is a photo, artist's impression, or computer simulation; whether a photo came from ground-based or space-based observations; and the wavelength band used to take the photo.
- **MasteringAstronomy® Resources** Specific resources from the MasteringAstronomy site, such as Interactive Figures or Photos and Self-Guided Tutorials, are referenced above specific section titles to direct students to help when they need it.

- **Think About It** This feature, which appears throughout the book as short questions integrated into the narrative, gives students the opportunity to reflect on important new concepts. It also serves as an excellent starting point for classroom discussions.
- **See It for Yourself** This feature also occurs throughout the book, integrated into the narrative, and gives students the opportunity to conduct simple observations or experiments that will help them understand key concepts.
- **Common Misconceptions** These boxes address popularly held but incorrect ideas related to the chapter material.
- **Special Topic Boxes** These boxes contain supplementary discussion topics related to the chapter material but not prerequisite to the continuing discussion.
- **Mathematical Insight Boxes** These boxes contain most of the mathematics used in the book and can be covered or skipped depending on the level of mathematics that you wish to include in your course. The Mathematical Insights use a three-step problem-solving strategy—Understand, Solve, and Explain—that gives students a consistent and explicit structure for solving quantitative homework problems.
- **The Big Picture** Every chapter narrative ends with this feature. It helps students put what they've learned in the chapter into the context of the overall goal of gaining a broader perspective on ourselves and our planet.
- **Visual Skills Check** This set of questions is designed to help students build their skills at interpreting the many types of visual information used in astronomy. Answers to these questions appear in Appendix J.
- **End-of-Chapter Exercises** Each chapter includes an extensive set of exercises that can be used for study, discussion, or assignment. All of the end-of-chapter exercises are organized into the following subsets:

  - Review Questions: Questions that students should be able to answer from the reading alone.
  - Does It Make Sense? (or similar title): A set of short statements for which students are expected to determine whether each statement makes sense, and to explain why or why not. These exercises are generally easy once students understand a particular concept, but very difficult otherwise; thus, they are an excellent probe of comprehension.
  - Quick Quiz: A short multiple-choice quiz that allows students to check their progress.
  - Process of Science Questions: Essay or discussion questions that help students focus on how science progresses over time.
  - NEW! Group Work Exercises: Questions designed for collaborative learning in class.
  - Short-Answer/Essay Questions: Questions that go beyond the Review Questions in asking for conceptual interpretation.
  - Quantitative Problems: Problems that require some mathematics, usually based on topics covered in the Mathematical Insight boxes.
  - Discussion Questions: Open-ended questions for class discussions.

- **Cross-References** When a concept is covered in greater detail elsewhere in the book, we include a boldface cross-reference in brackets to the relevant section (e.g., [**Section 5.2**]).
- **Glossary** A detailed glossary makes it easy for students to look up important terms.
- **Appendixes** The appendixes include a number of useful references and tables including key constants (Appendix A), key formulas (Appendix B), key mathematical skills (Appendix C), numerous data tables and star charts (Appendixes D–I), and answers to the Visual Skills Check questions (Appendix J).

MasteringAstronomy®—A New Paradigm in Astronomy Teaching

What is the single most important factor in student success in astronomy? Both research and common sense reveal the same answer: *study time*. No matter how good the teacher or how good the textbook, students learn only when they spend adequate time studying. Unfortunately, limitations on resources for grading have prevented most instructors from assigning much homework despite its obvious benefits to student learning. And limitations on help and office hours have made it difficult for students to make sure they use self-study time effectively. That, in a nutshell, is why we have created MasteringAstronomy. For students, it provides adaptive learning designed to coach them *individually*—responding to their errors with specific, targeted feedback and providing optional hints for those who need additional guidance. For professors, MasteringAstronomy provides unprecedented ability to automatically monitor and record students' step-by-step work and evaluate the effectiveness of assignments and exams. As a result, we believe that MasteringAstronomy can change the way astronomy courses are taught: It is now possible, even in large classes, to ensure that each student spends his or her study time on optimal learning activities outside of class.

MasteringAstronomy provides students with a wealth of self-study resources including interactive tutorials targeting the most difficult concepts of the course, interactive versions of key figures and photos, self-study quizzes, and other activities for self-assessment covering every chapter. For professors, MasteringAstronomy provides a library of tutoring activities that is periodically updated based on the performance of students nationwide. You can create assignments tailored to your specific class goals from among hundreds of activities and problems including pre- and post-lecture diagnostic quizzes, tutoring activities, end-of-chapter problems from this textbook, and test bank questions. Visit the MasteringAstronomy website to learn more.

Finally, in a world where everyone claims to have the best website, we'd like to point out three reasons why you'll discover that MasteringAstronomy really does stand out from the crowd:

- MasteringAstronomy specifically supports the structure and pedagogy of *The Cosmic Perspective*. You'll find the same concepts emphasized in the book and on the website, using the same terminology and the same pedagogical approaches. This type of consistency will ensure that students focus on the concepts, without the risk of becoming confused by different presentations.
- Nearly all MasteringAstronomy content has been developed either directly by *The Cosmic Perspective* author team or by this author team in close collaboration with outstanding educators including Jim Dove, Jim Cooney, Jonathan Williams, Richard Gelderman, Lauren Jones, Ed Prather, Tim Slater, and Daniel Loranz. The direct involvement of *The Cosmic Perspective* authors ensures that you can expect the same high level of quality in our website that you have come to expect in our textbook.
- The MasteringAstronomy platform uses the same unique student-driven engine as the highly successful MasteringPhysics® product (the most widely adopted physics homework and tutorial system), developed by a group led by MIT physicist David Pritchard. This robust platform gives instructors unprecedented power not only to tailor content to their own courses but also to evaluate the effectiveness of assignments and exams.

Additional Supplements for The Cosmic Perspective

The Cosmic Perspective is much more than just a textbook. It is a complete package of teaching, learning, and assessment resources designed to help both teachers and students. In addition to MasteringAstronomy (described above), the following supplements are available with this book:

- *SkyGazer 5.0* (Access code card ISBN 0-321-76518-4, CD ISBN 0-321-89843-5) Based on Voyager IV, one of the world's most popular planetarium programs, SkyGazer 5.0 makes it easy for students to learn constellations and explore the wonders of the sky through interactive exercises and demonstrations. Accompanying activities are available in *LoPresto's Astronomy Media Workbook*, seventh edition. Both SkyGazer and LoPresto's workbook are available for download. Ask your Pearson sales representative for details.
- *Starry Night™ College* (ISBN 0-321-71295-1) Now available as an additional option with *The Cosmic Perspective*, Starry Night™ College has been acclaimed as the world's most realistic desktop planetarium software. This special version has an easy-to-use point-and-click interface and is available as an additional bundle. The *Starry Night Activity Workbook*, consisting of thirty-five worksheets for homework or lab, based on Starry Night Planetarium software, is available for download in the MasteringAstronomy Study Area or with a Starry Night College access code. Ask your Pearson sales representative for details.
- *Astronomy Active Learning In-Class Tutorials* (ISBN 0-805-38296-8) by Marvin L. De Jong. This workbook provides fifty 20-minute in-class tutorial activities to choose from. Designed for use in large lecture classes, these activities are also suitable for labs. These short, structured activities are designed for students to complete on their own or in peer-learning groups. Each activity

targets specific learning objectives such as understanding Newton's laws, understanding Mars's retrograde motion, tracking stars on the H-R diagram, or comparing the properties of planets.

- **Lecture Tutorials for Introductory Astronomy** (0-321-82046-0), by Prather, Slater, Adams and Brissenden, includes forty-four lecture tutorials to engage students in critical reasoning and spark classroom discussion.
- **Sky and Telescope: Special Student Supplement** (0-321-70620-X), which includes nine articles with assessment insert covering general review, Process of Science, Scale of the Universe, and Our Place in the Universe, is available for bundling. Ask your Pearson representative for details.
- **Observation Exercises in Astronomy** (ISBN 0-321-63812-3) This workbook by Lauren Jones includes fifteen observation activities that can be used with a number of different planetarium software packages.

Instructor-Only Supplements

Several additional supplements are available for instructors only. Contact your local Pearson sales representative to find out more about the following supplements:

- **Instructor Resources** This comprehensive collection of instructor resources includes high-resolution JPEGs of all images from the book; Interactive Figures and Photos™ based on figures in the text; additional applets and animations to illustrate key concepts; PowerPoint® Lecture Outlines that incorporate figures, photos, checkpoint questions, and multimedia; and PRS-enabled clicker quizzes based on the book and book-specific interactive media, to make preparing for lectures quick and easy. These resources are located in MasteringAstronomy for easy use.
- **Clickers in the Astronomy Classroom** (ISBN 0-805-39616-0) This 100-page handbook by Douglas Duncan provides everything you need to know to successfully introduce or enhance your use of CRS (clicker) quizzing in your astronomy class—the research-proven benefits, common pitfalls to avoid, and a wealth of thought-provoking astronomy questions for every week of your course.
- **Instructor Guide** (ISBN 0-321-89659-9) The *Instructor Guide* contains a detailed overview of the text, sample syllabi for courses of different emphasis and duration, suggested teaching strategies, answers or discussion points for all Think About It and See It For Yourself questions in the text, solutions to all end-of-chapter problems, and a detailed reference guide summarizing media resources available for every chapter and section of the book.
- **Test Bank** (ISBN 0-321-84100-X) Available in both Word and TestGen formats on the Instructor Resource Center and MasteringAstronomy, the Test Bank contains a broad set of multiple-choice, true/false, and free-response questions for each chapter. The Test Bank is also assignable through MasteringAstronomy.

Acknowledgments

Our textbook carries only four author names, but in fact it is the result of hard work by a long list of committed individuals. We could not possibly list everyone who has helped, but we would like to call attention to a few people who have played particularly important roles. First, we thank our editors and friends at Pearson, who have stuck with us through thick and thin, including Adam Black, Nancy Whilton, Jim Smith, Michael Gillespie, Will Moore, Christy Lesko, Mary O'Connell, and Corinne Benson. Special thanks to our production teams, especially Sally Lifland; our art and design team, led by Mark Ong; and our Web team, led by Deb Perry, Kate Brayton, Wendy Romaniecki, Amir Said, and Caroline Power.

We've also been fortunate to have an outstanding group of reviewers, whose extensive comments and suggestions helped us shape the book. We thank all those who have reviewed drafts of the book in various stages, including

Marilyn Akins, *Broome Community College*
Christopher M. Anderson, *University of Wisconsin*
John Anderson, *University of North Florida*
Peter S. Anderson, *Oakland Community College*
Keith Ashman
Simon P. Balm, *Santa Monica College*
Nadine Barlow, *Northern Arizona University*
John Beaver, *University of Wisconsin at Fox Valley*
Peter A. Becker, *George Mason University*
Timothy C. Beers, *National Optical Astronomy Observatory*
Jim Bell, *Cornell University*
Priscilla J. Benson, *Wellesley College*
Bernard W. Bopp, *University of Toledo*
Sukanta Bose, *Washington State University*
David Brain, *University of Colorado*
David Branch, *University of Oklahoma*
John C. Brandt, *University of New Mexico*
James E. Brau, *University of Oregon*
Jean P. Brodie, *UCO/Lick Observatory, University of California, Santa Cruz*
Erik Brogt, *University of Canterbury*
James Brooks, *Florida State University*
Daniel Bruton, *Stephen F. Austin State University*
Amy Campbell, *Louisiana State University*
Eugene R. Capriotti, *Michigan State University*
Eric Carlson, *Wake Forest University*
David A. Cebula, *Pacific University*
Supriya Chakrabarti, *University of Massachusetts, Lowell*
Kwang-Ping Cheng, *California State University Fullerton*
Dipak Chowdhury, *Indiana University—Purdue University Fort Wayne*
Chris Churchill, *New Mexico State University*
Josh Colwell, *University of Central Florida*
Anita B. Corn, *Colorado School of Mines*
Philip E. Corn, *Red Rocks Community College*
Kelli Corrado, *Montgomery County Community College*
Peter Cottrell, *University of Canterbury*
John Cowan, *University of Oklahoma*
Kevin Crosby, *Carthage College*

Christopher Crow, *Indiana University—Purdue University Fort Wayne*

Manfred Cuntz, *University of Texas at Arlington*

Christopher De Vries, *California State University Stanislaus*

John M. Dickey, *University of Minnesota*

Bryan Dunne, *University of Illinois, Urbana-Champaign*

Suzan Edwards, *Smith College*

Robert Egler, *North Carolina State University at Raleigh*

Paul Eskridge, *Minnesota State University*

David Falk, *Los Angeles Valley College*

Timothy Farris, *Vanderbilt University*

Robert A. Fesen, *Dartmouth College*

Tom Fleming, *University of Arizona*

Douglas Franklin, *Western Illinois University*

Sidney Freudenstein, *Metropolitan State College of Denver*

Martin Gaskell, *University of Nebraska*

Richard Gelderman, *Western Kentucky University*

Harold A. Geller, *George Mason University*

Donna Gifford, *Pima Community College*

Mitch Gillam, *Marion L. Steele High School*

Bernard Gilroy, *The Hun School of Princeton*

Owen Gingerich, *Harvard–Smithsonian* (Historical Accuracy Reviewer)

David Graff, *U.S. Merchant Marine Academy*

Richard Gray, *Appalachian State University*

Kevin Grazier, *Jet Propulsion Laboratory*

Robert Greeney, *Holyoke Community College*

Henry Greenside, *Duke University*

Alan Greer, *Gonzaga University*

John Griffith, *Lin-Benton Community College*

David Griffiths, *Oregon State University*

David Grinspoon, *Denver Museum of Nature and Science*

John Gris, *University of Delaware*

Bruce Gronich, *University of Texas at El Paso*

Thomasana Hail, *Parkland University*

Jim Hamm, *Big Bend Community College*

Charles Hartley, *Hartwick College*

J. Hasbun, *University of West Georgia*

Joe Heafner, *Catawba Valley Community College*

Scott Hildreth, *Chabot College*

Mark Hollabaugh, *Normandale Community College*

Richard Holland, *Southern Illinois University, Carbondale*

Joseph Howard, *Salisbury University*

James Christopher Hunt, *Prince George's Community College*

Richard Ignace, *University of Wisconsin*

James Imamura, *University of Oregon*

Douglas R. Ingram, *Texas Christian University*

Assad Istephan, *Madonna University*

Bruce Jakosky, *University of Colorado*

Adam G. Jensen, *University of Colorado*

Adam Johnston, *Weber State University*

Lauren Jones, *Gettysburg College*

William Keel, *University of Alabama*

Julia Kennefick, *University of Arkansas*

Steve Kipp, *University of Minnesota, Mankato*

Kurtis Koll, *Cameron University*

Ichishiro Konno, *University of Texas at San Antonio*

John Kormendy, *University of Texas at Austin*

Eric Korpela, *University of California, Berkeley*

Kevin Krisciunas, *Texas A&M*

Ted La Rosa, *Kennesaw State University*

Kristine Larsen, *Central Connecticut State University*

Ana Marie Larson, *University of Washington*

Stephen Lattanzio, *Orange Coast College*

Larry Lebofsky, *University of Arizona*

Patrick Lestrade, *Mississippi State University*

Nancy Levenson, *University of Kentucky*

David M. Lind, *Florida State University*

Abraham Loeb, *Harvard University*

Michael LoPresto, *Henry Ford Community College*

William R. Luebke, *Modesto Junior College*

Darrell Jack MacConnell, *Community College of Baltimore City*

Marie Machacek, *Massachusetts Institute of Technology*

Loris Magnani, *University of Georgia*

Steven Majewski, *University of Virginia*

Phil Matheson, *Salt Lake Community College*

John Mattox, *Fayetteville State University*

Marles McCurdy, *Tarrant County College*

Stacy McGaugh, *Case Western University*

Barry Metz, *Delaware County Community College*

William Millar, *Grand Rapids Community College*

Dinah Moche, *Queensborough Community College of City University, New York*

Stephen Murray, *University of California, Santa Cruz*

Zdzislaw E. Musielak, *University of Texas at Arlington*

Charles Nelson, *Drake University*

Gerald H. Newsom, *Ohio State University*

Brian Oetiker, *Sam Houston State University*

John P. Oliver, *University of Florida*

Stacy Palen, *Weber State University*

Russell L. Palma, *Sam Houston State University*

Bryan Penprase, *Pomona College*

Eric S. Perlman, *Florida Institute of Technology*

Peggy Perozzo, *Mary Baldwin College*

Charles Peterson, *University of Missouri, Columbia*

Cynthia W. Peterson, *University of Connecticut*

Jorge Piekarewicz, *Florida State University*

Lawrence Pinsky, *University of Houston*

Stephanie Plante, *Grossmont College*

Jascha Polet, *California State Polytechnic University, Pomona*

Matthew Price, *Oregon State University*

Harrison B. Prosper, *Florida State University*

Monica Ramirez, *Aims College, Colorado*

Christina Reeves-Shull, *Richland College*

Todd M. Rigg, *City College of San Francisco*

Elizabeth Roettger, *DePaul University*

Roy Rubins, *University of Texas at Arlington*

Carl Rutledge, *East Central University*

Bob Sackett, *Saddleback College*

Rex Saffer, *Villanova University*

John Safko, *University of South Carolina*

James A. Scarborough, *Delta State University*

Britt Scharringhausen, *Ithaca College*

Ann Schmiedekamp, *Pennsylvania State University, Abington*

Joslyn Schoemer, *Denver Museum of Nature and Science*
James Schombert, *University of Oregon*
Gregory Seab, *University of New Orleans*
Larry Sessions, *Metropolitan State College of Denver*
Anwar Shiekh, *Colorado Mesa University*
Ralph Siegel, *Montgomery College, Germantown Campus*
Philip I. Siemens, *Oregon State University*
Caroline Simpson, *Florida International University*
Paul Sipiera, *William Harper Rainey College*
Earl F. Skelton, *George Washington University*
Evan Skillman, *University of Minnesota*
Michael Skrutskie, *University of Virginia*
Mark H. Slovak, *Louisiana State University*
Norma Small-Warren, *Howard University*
Dale Smith, *Bowling Green State University*
James R. Sowell, *Georgia Technical University*
Kelli Spangler, *Montgomery County Community College*
John Spencer, *Lowell Observatory*
Darryl Stanford, *City College of San Francisco*
George R. Stanley, *San Antonio College*
John Stolar, *West Chester University*
Jack Sulentic, *University of Alabama*
C. Sean Sutton, *Mount Holyoke College*
Beverley A. P. Taylor, *Miami University*
Brett Taylor, *Radford University*
Donald M. Terndrup, *Ohio State University*
Frank Timmes, *Arizona State University*
David Trott, *Metro State College*
David Vakil, *El Camino College*
Trina Van Ausdal, *Salt Lake Community College*
Licia Verde, *Institute of Cosmological Studies, Barcelona*
Nicole Vogt, *New Mexico State University*
Darryl Walke, *Rariton Valley Community College*
Fred Walter, *State University of New York, Stony Brook*
James Webb, *Florida International University*
Mark Whittle, *University of Virginia*
Paul J. Wiita, *The College of New Jersey*
Lisa M. Will, *Mesa Community College*
Jonathan Williams, *University of Hawaii*
J. Wayne Wooten, *Pensacola Junior College*
Scott Yager, *Brevard College*
Andrew Young, *Casper College*
Arthur Young, *San Diego State University*
Min S. Yun, *University of Massachusetts, Amherst*
Dennis Zaritsky, *University of Arizona*
Robert L. Zimmerman, *University of Oregon*

In addition, we thank the following colleagues who helped us clarify technical points or checked the accuracy of technical discussions in the book:

Nahum Arav, *Virginia Technical University*
Phil Armitage, *University of Colorado*
Thomas Ayres, *University of Colorado*
Cecilia Barnbaum, *Valdosta State University*
Rick Binzel, *Massachusetts Institute of Technology*
Howard Bond, *Space Telescope Science Institute*
David Brain, *University of Colorado*
Humberto Campins, *University of Central Florida*
Robin Canup, *Southwest Research Institute*

Clark Chapman, *Southwest Research Institute*
Kelly Cline, *Carroll College*
Josh Colwell, *University of Central Florida*
Mark Dickinson, *National Optical Astronomy Observatory*
Jim Dove, *Metropolitan State College of Denver*
Dan Fabrycky, *University of Chicago*
Harry Ferguson, *Space Telescope Science Institute*
Andrew Hamilton, *University of Colorado*
Todd Henry, *Georgia State University*
Dennis Hibbert, *Everett Community College*
Dave Jewitt, *University of California, Los Angeles*
Julia Kregenow, *Penn State University*
Emily Lakdawalla, *The Planetary Society*
Hal Levison, *Southwest Research Institute*
Mario Livio, *Space Telescope Science Institute*
J. McKim Malville, *University of Colorado*
Geoff Marcy, *University of California Berkeley and San Francisco State University*
Mark Marley, *Ames Research Center*
Linda Martel, *University of Hawaii*
Kevin McLin, *University of Colorado*
Michael Mendillo, *Boston University*
Steve Mojzsis, *University of Colorado*
Francis Nimmo, *University of California, Santa Cruz*
Tyler Nordgren, *University of Redlands*
Rachel Osten, *Space Telescope Science Institute*
Bob Pappalardo, *Jet Propulsion Laboratory*
Bennett Seidenstein, *Arundel High School*
Michael Shara, *American Museum of Natural History*
Brad Snowder, *Western Washington University*
Bob Stein, *Michigan State University*
Glen Stewart, *University of Colorado*
John Stolar, *West Chester University*
Jeff Taylor, *University of Hawaii*
Dave Tholen, *University of Hawaii*
Nick Thomas, *University of Bern*
Dimitri Veras, *Cambridge University*
John Weiss, *Carleton College*
Francis Wilkin, *Union College*
Jeremy Wood, *Hazard Community College*
Jason Wright, *Penn State University*
Don Yeomans, *Jet Propulsion Laboratory*

Finally, we thank the many people who have greatly influenced our outlook on education and our perspective on the universe over the years, including Tom Ayres, Fran Bagenal, Forrest Boley, Robert A. Brown, George Dulk, Erica Ellingson, Katy Garmany, Jeff Goldstein, David Grinspoon, Robin Heyden, Don Hunten, Geoffrey Marcy, Joan Marsh, Catherine McCord, Dick McCray, Dee Mook, Cherilynn Morrow, Charlie Pellerin, Carl Sagan, Mike Shull, John Spencer, and John Stocke.

Jeff Bennett
Megan Donahue
Nick Schneider
Mark Voit

ABOUT THE AUTHORS

Jeffrey Bennett

Jeffrey Bennett holds a B.A. (1981) in biophysics from the University of California, San Diego, and an M.S. and Ph.D. (1987) in astrophysics from the University of Colorado, Boulder. He has taught at every level from preschool through graduate school, including more than 50 college classes in astronomy, physics, mathematics, and education. He served 2 years as a visiting senior scientist at NASA headquarters, where he created NASA's "IDEAS" program, started a program to fly teachers aboard NASA's airborne observatories (including *SOFIA*), and worked on numerous educational programs for the Hubble Space Telescope and other space science missions. He also proposed the idea for and helped develop both the Colorado Scale Model Solar System on the CU-Boulder campus and the *Voyage* Scale Model Solar System on the National Mall in Washington, D.C. (He is pictured here with the model Sun.) In addition to this astronomy textbook, he is also lead author of college-level textbooks in astrobiology, mathematics, and statistics (all from Pearson); of critically acclaimed books for the general public including *Beyond UFOs* (Princeton University Press, 2008/2011) and *Math for Life* (Roberts & Co., 2012); and of the award-winning children's books *Max Goes to the Moon, Max Goes to Mars, Max Goes to Jupiter*, and *The Wizard Who Saved the World*. When not working, he enjoys participating in masters swimming and in the daily adventures of life with his wife, Lisa; his children, Grant and Brooke; and his dog, Cosmo. His personal website is www.jeffreybennett.com.

Megan Donahue

Megan Donahue is a professor in the Department of Physics and Astronomy at Michigan State University and a Fellow of the American Association for the Advancement of Science. Her current research is mainly about using X-ray, UV, infrared, and visible light to study clusters of galaxies: their contents—dark matter, hot gas, galaxies, active galactic nuclei—and what they reveal about the contents of the universe and how galaxies form and evolve. She grew up on a farm in Nebraska and received an S.B. in physics from MIT, where she began her research career as an X-ray astronomer. She has a Ph.D. in astrophysics from the University of Colorado. Her Ph.D. thesis on theory and optical observations of intergalactic and intracluster gas won the 1993 Trumpler Award from the Astronomical Society for the Pacific for an outstanding astrophysics doctoral dissertation in North America. She continued postdoctoral research as a Carnegie Fellow at Carnegie Observatories in Pasadena, California, and later as an STScI Institute Fellow at Space Telescope. Megan was a staff astronomer at the Space Telescope Science Institute until 2003, when she joined the MSU faculty. Megan is married to Mark Voit, and they collaborate on many projects, including this textbook and the raising of their children, Michaela, Sebastian, and Angela. Between the births of Sebastian and Angela, Megan qualified for and ran the Boston Marathon. These days, Megan runs trails, orienteers, and plays piano and bass guitar whenever her children allow it.

Nicholas Schneider

Nicholas Schneider is an associate professor in the Department of Astrophysical and Planetary Sciences at the University of Colorado and a researcher in the Laboratory for Atmospheric and Space Physics. He received his B.A. in physics and astronomy from Dartmouth College in 1979 and his Ph.D. in planetary science from the University of Arizona in 1988. In 1991, he received the National Science Foundation's Presidential Young Investigator Award. His research interests include planetary atmospheres and planetary astronomy. One research focus is the odd case of Jupiter's moon Io. Another is the mystery of Mars's lost atmosphere, which he hopes to answer by serving as science lead on the Imaging UV Spectrograph on NASA's *MAVEN* mission. Nick enjoys teaching at all levels and is active in efforts to improve undergraduate astronomy education. In 2010 he received the Boulder Faculty Assembly's Teaching Excellence Award. Off the job, Nick enjoys exploring the outdoors with his family and figuring out how things work.

Mark Voit

Mark Voit is a professor in the Department of Physics and Astronomy at Michigan State University and a Fellow of the American Association for the Advancement of Science. He earned his A.B. in astrophysical sciences at Princeton University and his Ph.D. in astrophysics at the University of Colorado in 1990. He continued his studies at the California Institute of Technology, where he was a research fellow in theoretical astrophysics, and then moved on to Johns Hopkins University as a Hubble Fellow. Before going to Michigan State, Mark worked in the Office of Public Outreach at the Space Telescope, where he developed museum exhibitions about the Hubble Space Telescope and helped design NASA's award-winning HubbleSite. His research interests range from interstellar processes in our own galaxy to the clustering of galaxies in the early universe. He is married to coauthor Megan Donahue, and cooks terrific meals for her and their three children. Mark likes getting outdoors whenever possible and particularly enjoys running, mountain biking, canoeing, orienteering, and adventure racing. He is also author of the popular book *Hubble Space Telescope: New Views of the Universe.*

HOW TO SUCCEED
IN YOUR ASTRONOMY COURSE

If Your Course Is	Time for Reading the Assigned Text (per week)	Time for Homework or Self-Study (per week)	Time for Review and Test Preparation (average per week)	Total Study Time (per week)
3 credits	2 to 4 hours	2 to 3 hours	2 hours	6 to 9 hours
4 credits	3 to 5 hours	2 to 4 hours	3 hours	8 to 12 hours
5 credits	3 to 5 hours	3 to 6 hours	4 hours	10 to 15 hours

The Key to Success: Study Time

The single most important key to success in any college course is to spend enough time studying. A general rule of thumb for college classes is that you should expect to study about 2 to 3 hours per week *outside* of class for each unit of credit. For example, based on this rule of thumb, a student taking 15 credit hours should expect to spend 30 to 45 hours each week studying outside of class. Combined with time in class, this works out to a total of 45 to 60 hours spent on academic work—not much more than the time a typical job requires, and you get to choose your own hours. Of course, if you are working while you attend school, you will need to budget your time carefully.

As a rough guideline, your studying time in astronomy might be divided as shown in the table above. If you find that you are spending fewer hours than these guidelines suggest, you can probably improve your grade by studying longer. If you are spending more hours than these guidelines suggest, you may be studying inefficiently; in that case, you should talk to your instructor about how to study more effectively.

Using This Book

Each chapter in this book is designed to make it easy for you to study effectively and efficiently. To get the most out of each chapter, you might wish to use the following study plan.

- A textbook is not a novel, and you'll learn best by reading the elements of this text in the following order:

  1. Start by reading the Learning Goals and the introductory paragraphs at the beginning of the chapter so that you'll know what you are trying to learn.
  2. Get an overview of key concepts by studying the illustrations and reading their captions and annotations. The illustrations highlight almost all of the major concepts, so this "illustrations first" strategy gives you an opportunity to survey the concepts before you read about them in depth. You will find the two-page Cosmic Context figures especially useful. Also watch for the Interactive Figure icons—when you see one, go to the MasteringAstronomy® website to try the interactive version.

  3. Read the chapter narrative, trying the Think About It questions and the See It for Yourself activities as you go along, but save the boxed features (Common Misconceptions, Special Topics, Mathematical Insights) to read later. As you read, make notes on the pages to remind yourself of ideas you'll want to review later. Avoid using a highlight pen (or a highlighting tool if you are using an e-book), which makes it too easy to highlight mindlessly. For a printed book, underlining with pen or pencil is far more effective, because it forces you to take greater care and therefore helps keep you alert as you study; be careful to underline selectively—it won't help you later if you've underlined everything. For an e-book, write notes to remind yourself why you marked a block of text as particularly important.
  4. After reading the chapter once, go back through and read the boxed material. You should read all of the Common Misconceptions and Special Topics boxes; whether you choose to read the Mathematical Insights is up to you and your instructor. Also watch for the MasteringAstronomy tutorial icons throughout the chapter; if a concept is giving you trouble, go to the MasteringAstronomy site to try the relevant tutorial.
  5. Finally, turn your attention to the Chapter Summary. The best way to use the summary is to try to answer the Learning Goal questions for yourself before reading the short answers given in the summary.

- After completing the reading as outlined above, test your understanding with the end-of-chapter exercises. A good way to begin is to make sure you can answer all of the Review Questions; if you don't know an answer, look back through the chapter until you figure it out. Then try the Does It Make Sense? and Quick Quiz questions.
- You can further check your understanding and get feedback on difficulties by trying the online quizzes in the Study Area at the MasteringAstronomy site. Each chapter has three quizzes: a Reading Quiz, a Concept Quiz, and a Visual Quiz. Try the Reading Quiz first. Once you clear up any difficulties you have with it, try the Concept and Visual quizzes.

- If your course has a quantitative emphasis, work through all of the examples in the Mathematical Insights before trying the quantitative problems for yourself. Remember that you should always try to answer questions qualitatively before you begin plugging numbers into a calculator. For example, make an order-of-magnitude estimate of what your answer should be so that you'll know your calculation is on the right track, and be sure that your answer makes sense and has the appropriate units.
- If you have done all the above, you will have already made use of numerous resources on the MasteringAstronomy site. Don't stop there; visit the site again and make use of other resources that will help you further build your understanding. These resources have been developed specifically to help you learn the most important ideas in your astronomy course, and they have been extensively tested to make sure they are effective. They really do work, and the only way you'll gain their benefits is by going to the website and using them.

General Strategies for Studying

- Budget your time effectively. Studying 1 or 2 hours each day is more effective, and far less painful, than studying all night before homework is due or before exams.
- Engage your brain. Learning is an active process, not a passive experience. Whether you are reading, listening to a lecture, or working on assignments, always make sure that your mind is actively engaged. If you find your mind drifting or find yourself falling asleep, make a conscious effort to revive yourself, or take a break if necessary.
- Don't miss class. Listening to lectures and participating in discussions is much more effective than reading someone else's notes. Active participation will help you retain what you are learning. Also, be sure to complete any assigned reading *before* the class in which it will be discussed. This is crucial, since class lectures and discussions are designed to help reinforce key ideas from the reading.
- Take advantage of resources offered by your professor, whether it be e-mail, office hours, review sessions, online chats, or other opportunities to talk to and get to know your professor. Most professors will go out of their way to help you learn in any way that they can.
- Start your homework early. The more time you allow yourself, the easier it is to get help if you need it. If a concept gives you trouble, do additional reading or studying beyond what has been assigned. And if you still have trouble, ask for help: You surely can find friends, peers, or teachers who will be glad to help you learn.
- Working together with friends can be valuable in helping you understand difficult concepts. However, be sure that you learn *with* your friends and do not become dependent on them.
- Don't try to multitask. A large body of research shows that human beings simply are not good at multitasking: When we attempt it, we do more poorly at all of the individual tasks. And in case you think you are an exception, the same research found that those people who believed they were best at multitasking were actually the worst! So when it is time to study, turn off your electronic devices, find a quiet spot, and give your work a focused effort at concentration.

Preparing for Exams

- Study the Review Questions, and rework problems and other assignments; try additional questions to be sure you understand the concepts. Study your performance on assignments, quizzes, or exams from earlier in the term.
- Work through the relevant online tutorials and chapter quizzes available at the MasteringAstronomy site.
- Study your notes from lectures and discussions. Pay attention to what your instructor expects you to know for an exam.
- Reread the relevant sections in the textbook, paying special attention to notes you have made on the pages.
- Study individually *before* joining a study group with friends. Study groups are effective only if every individual comes prepared to contribute.
- Don't stay up too late before an exam. Don't eat a big meal within an hour of the exam (thinking is more difficult when blood is being diverted to the digestive system).
- Try to relax before and during the exam. If you have studied effectively, you are capable of doing well. Staying relaxed will help you think clearly.

Presenting Homework and Writing Assignments

All work that you turn in should be of *collegiate quality:* neat and easy to read, well organized, and demonstrating mastery of the subject matter. Future employers and teachers will expect this quality of work. Moreover, although submitting homework of collegiate quality requires "extra" effort, it serves two important purposes directly related to learning:

1. The effort you expend in clearly explaining your work solidifies your learning. In particular, research has shown that writing and speaking trigger different areas of your brain. Writing something down—even when you think you already understand it—reinforces your learning by involving other areas of your brain.
2. If you make your work clear and self-contained (that is, make it a document that you can read without referring to the questions in the text), you will have a much more useful study guide when you review for a quiz or exam.

The following guidelines will help ensure that your assignments meet the standards of collegiate quality:

- Always use proper grammar, proper sentence and paragraph structure, and proper spelling. Do not use texting shorthand.
- Make all answers and other writing fully self-contained. A good test is to imagine that a friend will be reading

your work and to ask yourself whether the friend will understand exactly what you are trying to say. It is also helpful to read your work out loud to yourself, making sure that it sounds clear and coherent.

- In problems that require calculation:
  - Be sure to *show your work* clearly so that both you and your instructor can follow the process you used to obtain an answer. Also, use standard mathematical symbols, rather than "calculator-ese." For example, show multiplication with the × symbol (not with an asterisk), and write 10^5, not 10^5 or 10E5.
  - *Check that word problems have word answers.* That is, after you have completed any necessary calculations, make sure that any problem stated in words is answered with one or more *complete sentences* that describe the point of the problem and the meaning of your solution.

- Express your word answers in a way that would be *meaningful* to most people. For example, most people would find it more meaningful if you expressed a result of 720 hours as 1 month. Similarly, if a precise calculation yields an answer of 9,745,600 years, it may be more meaningfully expressed in words as "nearly 10 million years."

- Include illustrations whenever they help explain your answer, and make sure your illustrations are neat and clear. For example, if you graph by hand, use a ruler to make straight lines. If you use software to make illustrations, be careful not to make them overly cluttered with unnecessary features.

- If you study with friends, be sure that you turn in your own work stated in your own words—you should avoid anything that might give even the *appearance* of possible academic dishonesty.

FOREWORD

THE MEANING OF
THE COSMIC PERSPECTIVE

by Neil deGrasse Tyson

© Neil deGrasse Tyson

*Astrophysicist Neil deGrasse Tyson is the Frederick P. Rose Director of New York City's Hayden Planetarium at the American Museum of Natural History. He has written numerous books and articles, hosts the PBS series NOVA scienceNOW, and was named one of the "Time 100"—*Time *Magazine's list of the 100 most influential people in the world. He contributed this essay about the meaning of "The Cosmic Perspective," abridged from his 100th essay written for* Natural History *magazine.*

Of all the sciences cultivated by mankind, Astronomy is acknowledged to be, and undoubtedly is, the most sublime, the most interesting, and the most useful. For, by knowledge derived from this science, not only the bulk of the Earth is discovered . . .; but our very faculties are enlarged with the grandeur of the ideas it conveys, our minds exalted above [their] low contracted prejudices.

—*James Ferguson,* Astronomy Explained Upon Sir Isaac Newton's Principles, and Made Easy To Those Who Have Not Studied Mathematics (1757)

Long before anyone knew that the universe had a beginning, before we knew that the nearest large galaxy lies two and a half million light-years from Earth, before we knew how stars work or whether atoms exist, James Ferguson's enthusiastic introduction to his favorite science rang true.

But who gets to think that way? Who gets to celebrate this cosmic view of life? Not the migrant farm worker. Not the sweatshop worker. Certainly not the homeless person rummaging through the trash for food. You need the luxury of time not spent on mere survival. You need to live in a nation whose government values the search to understand humanity's place in the universe. You need a society in which intellectual pursuit can take you to the frontiers of discovery, and in which news of your discoveries can be routinely disseminated.

When I pause and reflect on our expanding universe, with its galaxies hurtling away from one another, embedded with the ever-stretching, four-dimensional fabric of space and time, sometimes I forget that uncounted people walk this Earth without food or shelter, and that children are disproportionately represented among them.

When I pore over the data that establish the mysterious presence of dark matter and dark energy throughout the universe, sometimes I forget that every day—every twenty-four-hour rotation of Earth—people are killing and being killed. In the name of someone's ideology.

When I track the orbits of asteroids, comets, and planets, each one a pirouetting dancer in a cosmic ballet choreographed by the forces of gravity, sometimes I forget that too many people act in wanton disregard for the delicate interplay of Earth's atmosphere, oceans, and land, with consequences that our children and our children's children will witness and pay for with their health and well-being.

And sometimes I forget that powerful people rarely do all they can to help those who cannot help themselves.

I occasionally forget those things because, however big the world is—in our hearts, our minds, and our outsize atlases—the universe is even bigger. A depressing thought to some, but a liberating thought to me.

Consider an adult who tends to the traumas of a child: a broken toy, a scraped knee, a schoolyard bully. Adults know that kids have no clue what constitutes a genuine problem, because inexperience greatly limits their childhood perspective.

As grown-ups, dare we admit to ourselves that we, too, have a collective immaturity of view? Dare we admit that our thoughts and behaviors spring from a belief that the world revolves around us? Part the curtains of society's racial, ethnic, religious, national, and cultural conflicts, and you find the human ego turning the knobs and pulling the levers.

Now imagine a world in which everyone, but especially people with power and influence, holds an expanded view of our place in the cosmos. With that perspective, our problems would shrink—or never arise at all—and we could celebrate our earthly differences while shunning the behavior of our predecessors who slaughtered each other because of them.

■ ■ ■

Back in February 2000, the newly rebuilt Hayden Planetarium featured a space show called "Passport to the Universe," which took visitors on a virtual zoom from New York City to the edge of the cosmos. En route the audience saw Earth, then the solar system, then the 100 billion stars of the Milky Way galaxy shrink to barely visible dots on the planetarium dome.

I soon received a letter from an Ivy League professor of psychology who wanted to administer a questionnaire to visitors, assessing the depth of their depression after viewing the show. Our show, he wrote, elicited the most dramatic feelings of smallness he had ever experienced.

How could that be? Every time I see the show, I feel alive and spirited and connected. I also feel large, knowing that the goings-on within the three-pound human brain are what enabled us to figure out our place in the universe.

Allow me to suggest that it's the professor, not I, who has misread nature. His ego was too big to begin with, inflated by delusions of significance and fed by cultural assumptions that human beings are more important than everything else in the universe.

In all fairness to the fellow, powerful forces in society leave most of us susceptible. As was I . . . until the day I learned in biology class that more bacteria live and work in one centimeter of my colon than the number of people who have ever existed in the world. That kind of information makes you think twice about who—or what—is actually in charge.

From that day on, I began to think of people not as the masters of space and time but as participants in a great cosmic chain of being, with a direct genetic link across species both living and extinct, extending back nearly 4 billion years to the earliest single-celled organisms on Earth.

■ ■ ■

Need more ego softeners? Simple comparisons of quantity, size, and scale do the job well.

Take water. It's simple, common, and vital. There are more molecules of water in an eight-ounce cup of the stuff than there are cups of water in all the world's oceans. Every cup that passes through a single person and eventually rejoins the world's water supply holds enough molecules to mix 1,500 of them into every other cup of water in the world. No way around it: some of the water you just drank passed through the kidneys of Socrates, Genghis Khan, and Joan of Arc.

How about air? Also vital. A single breathful draws in more air molecules than there are breathfuls of air in Earth's entire atmosphere. That means some of the air you just breathed passed through the lungs of Napoleon, Beethoven, Lincoln, and Billy the Kid.

Time to get cosmic. There are more stars in the universe than grains of sand on any beach, more stars than seconds have passed since Earth formed, more stars than words and sounds ever uttered by all the humans who ever lived.

Want a sweeping view of the past? Our unfolding cosmic perspective takes you there. Light takes time to reach Earth's observatories from the depths of space, and so you see objects and phenomena not as they are but as they once were. That means the universe acts like a giant time machine: the farther away you look, the further back in time you see—back almost to the beginning of time itself. Within that horizon of reckoning, cosmic evolution unfolds continuously, in full view.

Want to know what we're made of? Again, the cosmic perspective offers a bigger answer than you might expect. The chemical elements of the universe are forged in the fires of high-mass stars that end their lives in stupendous explosions, enriching their host galaxies with the chemical arsenal of life as we know it. We are not simply in the universe. The universe is in us. Yes, we are stardust.

■ ■ ■

Again and again across the centuries, cosmic discoveries have demoted our self-image. Earth was once assumed to be astronomically unique, until astronomers learned that Earth is just another planet orbiting the Sun. Then we presumed the Sun was unique, until we learned that the countless stars of the night sky are suns themselves. Then we presumed our galaxy, the Milky Way, was the entire known universe, until we established that the countless fuzzy things in the sky are other galaxies, dotting the landscape of our known universe.

The cosmic perspective flows from fundamental knowledge. But it's more than just what you know. It's also about having the wisdom and insight to apply that knowledge to assessing our place in the universe. And its attributes are clear:

- The cosmic perspective comes from the frontiers of science, yet is not solely the provenance of the scientist. It belongs to everyone.
- The cosmic perspective is humble.
- The cosmic perspective is spiritual—even redemptive—but is not religious.
- The cosmic perspective enables us to grasp, in the same thought, the large and the small.
- The cosmic perspective opens our minds to extraordinary ideas but does not leave them so open that our brains spill out, making us susceptible to believing anything we're told.
- The cosmic perspective opens our eyes to the universe, not as a benevolent cradle designed to nurture life but as a cold, lonely, hazardous place.
- The cosmic perspective shows Earth to be a mote, but a precious mote and, for the moment, the only home we have.
- The cosmic perspective finds beauty in the images of planets, moons, stars, and nebulae but also celebrates the laws of physics that shape them.
- The cosmic perspective enables us to see beyond our circumstances, allowing us to transcend the primal search for food, shelter, and sex.
- The cosmic perspective reminds us that in space, where there is no air, a flag will not wave—an indication that perhaps flag waving and space exploration do not mix.

■ The cosmic perspective not only embraces our genetic kinship with all life on Earth but also values our chemical kinship with any yet-to-be discovered life in the universe, as well as our atomic kinship with the universe itself.

■ ■ ■

At least once a week, if not once a day, we might each ponder what cosmic truths lie undiscovered before us, perhaps awaiting the arrival of a clever thinker, an ingenious experiment, or an innovative space mission to reveal them. We might further ponder how those discoveries may one day transform life on Earth.

Absent such curiosity, we are no different from the provincial farmer who expresses no need to venture beyond the county line, because his forty acres meet all his needs. Yet if all our predecessors had felt that way, the farmer would instead be a cave dweller, chasing down his dinner with a stick and a rock.

During our brief stay on planet Earth, we owe ourselves and our descendants the opportunity to explore—in part because it's fun to do. But there's a far nobler reason. The day our knowledge of the cosmos ceases to expand, we risk regressing to the childish view that the universe figuratively and literally revolves around us. In that bleak world, arms-bearing, resource-hungry people and nations would be prone to act on their "low contracted prejudices." And that would be the last gasp of human enlightenment—until the rise of a visionary new culture that could once again embrace the cosmic perspective.

KEY TO WAVELENGTH ICONS ON FIGURES

You'll see the following icons on figures throughout the book. They are used to indicate the wavelength of light shown in each image, and to identify photo-realistic artworks and images made by computer simulations.

(palette icon)	Indicates an artist's representation
(computer icon)	Indicates a graphic generated using computer simulations
RAD	Indicates an image based on data from an observatory on Earth observing radio waves
RADIO	Indicates an image based on data from a spacecraft observing radio waves
IR	Indicates an image based on data from an observatory on Earth observing infrared light
IR	Indicates an image based on data from a spacecraft observing infrared light
VIS	Indicates an image based on data from an observatory on Earth observing visible light
VIS	Indicates an image based on data from a spacecraft observing visible light
VIS	Indicates an image based on data from a rover observing visible light
UV	Indicates an image based on data from a spacecraft observing ultraviolet light
X-ray	Indicates an image based on data from a spacecraft observing X rays
gamma	Indicates an image based on data from a spacecraft observing gamma rays

1

A MODERN VIEW OF THE UNIVERSE

LEARNING GOALS

1.1 THE SCALE OF THE UNIVERSE

- What is our place in the universe?
- How big is the universe?

1.2 THE HISTORY OF THE UNIVERSE

- How did we come to be?
- How do our lifetimes compare to the age of the universe?

1.3 SPACESHIP EARTH

- How is Earth moving through space?
- How do galaxies move within the universe?

1.4 THE HUMAN ADVENTURE OF ASTRONOMY

- How has the study of astronomy affected human history?

We shall not cease from exploration
And the end of all our exploring
Will be to arrive where we started
And know the place for the first time.
　　　　　—*T. S. Eliot*

Far from city lights on a clear night, you can gaze upward at a sky filled with stars. Lie back and watch for a few hours, and you will observe the stars marching steadily across the sky. Confronted by the seemingly infinite heavens, you might wonder how Earth and the universe came to be. If you do, you will be sharing an experience common to humans around the world and in thousands of generations past.

Modern science offers answers to many of our fundamental questions about the universe and our place within it. We now know the basic content and scale of the universe. We know the age of Earth and the approximate age of the universe. And, although much remains to be discovered, we are rapidly learning how the simple ingredients of the early universe developed into the incredible diversity of life on Earth.

In this first chapter, we will survey the scale, history, and motion of the universe. This "big picture" perspective on our universe will provide a base on which you'll be able to build a deeper understanding in the rest of the book.

1.1 THE SCALE OF THE UNIVERSE

For most of human history, our ancestors imagined Earth to be stationary and located at the center of a relatively small universe. These ideas made sense at a time when understanding was built upon everyday experience. After all, we cannot feel the constant motion of Earth as it rotates on its axis and orbits the Sun, and if you observe the sky you'll see that the Sun, Moon, planets, and stars all appear to revolve around us each day. Nevertheless, we now know that Earth is a planet orbiting a rather average star in a vast universe.

The historical path to this knowledge was long and complex. In later chapters, we'll see that the ancient belief in an Earth-centered (or *geocentric*) universe changed only when people were confronted by strong evidence to the contrary, and we'll explore how the method of learning that we call *science* enabled us to acquire this evidence. First, however, it's useful to have a general picture of the universe as we know it today.

What is our place in the universe?

Take a look at the remarkable photo that opens this chapter (on page 1). This photo, taken by the Hubble Space Telescope, shows a piece of the sky so small that you could block your view of it with a grain of sand held at arm's length. Yet it encompasses an almost unimaginable expanse of both space and time: Nearly every object within it is a *galaxy* filled with billions of stars, and some of the smaller smudges are galaxies so far away that their light has taken billions of years to reach us. Let's begin our study of astronomy by exploring what a photo like this one tells us about our own place in the universe.

Our Cosmic Address The galaxies that we see in the Hubble Space Telescope photo are just one of several levels of structure in our universe. A good way to build context on these levels is to consider what we might call our "cosmic address," illustrated in FIGURE 1.1.

Earth is a planet in our **solar system**, which consists of the Sun, the planets and their moons, and countless smaller objects that include rocky *asteroids* and icy *comets*. Keep in mind that our Sun is a *star*, just like the stars we see in our night sky.

Our solar system belongs to the huge, disk-shaped collection of stars called the **Milky Way Galaxy**. A **galaxy** is a great island of stars in space, containing between a few hundred million and a trillion or more stars. The Milky Way is a relatively large galaxy, containing more than 100 billion stars. Our solar system is located a little over halfway from the galactic center to the edge of the galactic disk.

Billions of other galaxies are scattered throughout space. Some galaxies are fairly isolated, but many others are found in groups. Our Milky Way, for example, is one of the two largest among about 40 galaxies in the **Local Group.** Groups of galaxies with more than a few dozen members are often called **galaxy clusters.**

On a very large scale, galaxies and galaxy clusters appear to be arranged in giant chains and sheets with huge voids between them; the background of Figure 1.1 shows this large-scale structure. The regions in which galaxies and galaxy clusters are most tightly packed are called **superclusters,** which are essentially clusters of galaxy clusters. Our Local Group is located in the outskirts of the Local Supercluster.

Together, all these structures make up our **universe.** In other words, the universe is the sum total of all matter and energy, encompassing the superclusters and voids and everything within them.

Astronomical Distance Measurements Notice that Figure 1.1 is labeled with an approximate size for each structure in kilometers. In astronomy, many of the distances are so large that kilometers are not the most convenient unit. Instead, we often use two other units:

- One **astronomical unit (AU)** is Earth's average distance from the Sun, which is about 150 million kilometers (93 million miles). We commonly describe distances within our solar system in astronomical units.

- One **light-year (ly)** is the distance that light can travel in 1 year, which is about 10 trillion kilometers (6 trillion miles). We generally use light-years to describe the distances of stars and galaxies.

Universe

approx. size: 10^{21} km ≈ 100 million ly

Local Supercluster

approx. size: 3×10^{19} km ≈ 3 million ly

Local Group

approx. size: 10^{18} km ≈ 100,000 ly

Milky Way Galaxy

Solar System
(*not to scale*)

Earth

approx. size: 10^{10} km ≈ 60 AU

approx. size: 10^4 km

FIGURE 1.1 Our cosmic address. These diagrams show key levels of structure in our universe. For a more detailed view, see the "You Are Here in Space" foldout diagram in the front of the book.

Be sure to note that a light-year is a unit of *distance*, not of time. Light travels at the speed of light, which is 300,000 kilometers per second. We therefore say that one *light-second* is about 300,000 kilometers, because that is the distance light travels in one second. Similarly, one light-minute is the distance that light travels in one minute, one light-hour is the distance that light travels in one hour, and so on. Mathematical Insight 1.1 shows that light travels about 10 trillion kilometers in one year, so that distance represents a light-year.

Looking Back in Time The speed of light is extremely fast by earthly standards. It is so fast that if you could make light go in circles, it could circle Earth nearly eight times in a single second. Nevertheless, even light takes time to travel the vast distances in space. Light takes a little more than 1 second to reach Earth from the Moon, and about 8 minutes to reach Earth from the Sun. Stars are so far away that their light takes years to reach us, which is why we measure their distances in light-years.

Consider Sirius, the brightest star in the night sky, which is located about 8 light-years away. Because it takes light 8 years to travel this distance, we see Sirius not as it is today, but rather as it was 8 years ago. The effect is more dramatic at greater distances. The Orion Nebula (FIGURE 1.2) is a giant cloud in which stars and planets are forming. It is located about 1500 light-years from Earth, which means we see it as it looked about 1500 years ago—about the time of the fall of the Roman Empire. If any major events have occurred in the Orion Nebula since that time, we cannot yet know about them because the light from these events has not yet reached us.

The general idea that light takes time to travel through space leads to a remarkable fact:

The farther away we look in distance, the further back we look in time.

The Andromeda Galaxy (FIGURE 1.3) is about 2.5 million light-years away, which means we see it as it looked about 2.5 million years ago. We see more distant galaxies as they were even further in the past. Some of the galaxies in the Hubble Space Telescope photo that opens the chapter are billions of light-years away, meaning we see them as they were billions of years ago.

SEE IT FOR YOURSELF

The glow from the central region of the Andromeda Galaxy is faintly visible to the naked eye and easy to see with binoculars. Use a star chart to find it in the night sky. Contemplate the fact that you are seeing light that spent 2.5 million years in space before reaching your eyes. If students on a planet in the Andromeda Galaxy were looking at the Milky Way, what would they see? Could they know that we exist here on Earth?

Basic Astronomical Definitions

ASTRONOMICAL OBJECTS

star A large, glowing ball of gas that generates heat and light through nuclear fusion in its core. Our Sun is a star.

planet A moderately large object that orbits a star and shines primarily by reflecting light from its star. According to a definition adopted in 2006, an object can be considered a planet only if it (1) orbits a star, (2) is large enough for its own gravity to make it round, and (3) has cleared most other objects from its orbital path. An object that meets the first two criteria but has not cleared its orbital path, like Pluto, is designated a **dwarf planet.**

moon (or **satellite**) An object that orbits a planet. The term *satellite* is also used more generally to refer to any object orbiting another object.

asteroid A relatively small and rocky object that orbits a star.

comet A relatively small and ice-rich object that orbits a star.

small solar system body An asteroid, comet, or other object that orbits a star but is too small to qualify as a planet or dwarf planet.

COLLECTIONS OF ASTRONOMICAL OBJECTS

solar system The Sun and all the material that orbits it, including planets, dwarf planets, and small solar system bodies. Although the term *solar system* technically refers only to our own star system (*solar* means "of the Sun"), it is often applied to other star systems as well.

star system A star (sometimes more than one star) and any planets and other materials that orbit it.

galaxy A great island of stars in space, containing from a few hundred million to a trillion or more stars, all held together by gravity and orbiting a common center.

cluster (or **group**) **of galaxies** A collection of galaxies bound together by gravity. Small collections (up to a few dozen galaxies) are generally called *groups*, while larger collections are called *clusters.*

supercluster A gigantic region of space in which many groups and clusters of galaxies are packed more closely together than elsewhere in the universe.

universe (or **cosmos**) The sum total of all matter and energy—that is, all galaxies and everything between them.

observable universe The portion of the entire universe that can be seen from Earth, at least in principle. The observable universe is probably only a tiny portion of the entire universe.

ASTRONOMICAL DISTANCE UNITS

astronomical unit (AU) The average distance between Earth and the Sun, which is about 150 million kilometers. More technically, 1 AU is the length of the semimajor axis of Earth's orbit.

light-year The distance that light can travel in 1 year, which is about 9.46 trillion kilometers.

TERMS RELATING TO MOTION

rotation The spinning of an object around its axis. For example, Earth rotates once each day around its axis, which is an imaginary line connecting the North and South Poles.

orbit (revolution) The orbital motion of one object around another due to gravity. For example, Earth orbits the Sun once each year.

expansion (of the universe) The increase in the average distance between galaxies as time progresses.

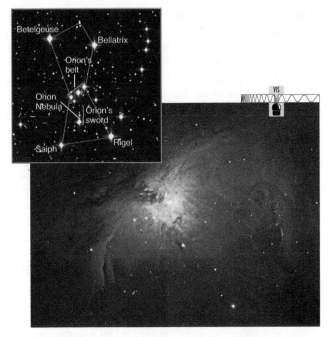

FIGURE 1.2 The Orion Nebula, located about 1500 light-years away. The inset shows its location in the constellation Orion.

FIGURE 1.3 The Andromeda Galaxy (M31). When we look at this galaxy, we see light that has been traveling through space for 2.5 million years.

It's also amazing to realize that any "snapshot" of a distant galaxy is a picture of both space and time. For example, because the Andromeda Galaxy is about 100,000 light-years in diameter, the light we currently see from the far side of the galaxy must have left on its journey to us some 100,000 years before the light we see from the near side. Figure 1.3 therefore shows different parts of the galaxy spread over a time period of 100,000 years. When we study the universe, it is impossible to separate space and time.

The Observable Universe As we'll discuss in Section 1.2, astronomers estimate that the universe is about 14 billion years old. This fact, combined with the fact that looking deep into space means looking far back in time, places a limit on the portion of the universe that we can see, even in principle. **FIGURE 1.4** shows the idea. If we look at a galaxy that is 7 billion light-years away, we see it as it looked 7 billion years

ago*—which means we see it as it was when the universe was half its current age. If we look at a galaxy that is 12 billion light-years away (like the most distant ones in the Hubble Space Telescope photo), we see it as it was 12 billion years ago, when the universe was only 2 billion years old. And if we tried to look beyond 14 billion light-years, we'd be looking to a time more than 14 billion years ago—which is before the universe existed and therefore means that there is nothing to see. This distance of 14 billion light-years therefore marks the boundary (or *horizon*) of our **observable universe**—the portion of the entire universe that we can potentially observe. Note that this fact does not put any limit on the size of the

---

*As we'll see in Chapter 20, distances to faraway galaxies must be defined carefully in an expanding universe; distances like those given here are based on the time it has taken a galaxy's light to reach us (called the *lookback time*).

Far: We see a galaxy 7 billion light-years away as it was 7 billion years ago—when the universe was about half its current age of 14 billion years.

Farther: We see a galaxy 12 billion light-years away as it was 12 billion years ago—when the universe was only about 2 billion years old.

The limit of our observable universe: Light from nearly 14 billion light-years away shows the universe as it looked shortly after the Big Bang, before galaxies existed.

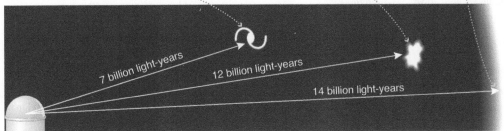

Beyond the observable universe: We cannot see anything farther than 14 billion light-years away, because its light has not had enough time to reach us.

7 billion light-years

12 billion light-years

14 billion light-years

FIGURE 1.4 **interactive figure** The farther away we look in space, the further back we look in time. The age of the universe therefore puts a limit on the size of the *observable* universe—the portion of the entire universe that we can observe, at least in principle.

entire universe, which may be far larger than our observable universe. We simply have no hope of seeing or studying anything beyond the bounds of our observable universe.

 Scale of the Universe Tutorial, Lessons 1–3

How big is the universe?

Figure 1.1 put numbers on the sizes of different structures in the universe, but these numbers have little meaning for most people—after all, they are literally astronomical. Therefore, to help you develop a greater appreciation of our modern view of the universe, we'll discuss a few ways of putting these numbers into perspective.

The Scale of the Solar System One of the best ways to develop perspective on cosmic sizes and distances is to imagine our solar system shrunk down to a scale that would allow you to walk through it. The Voyage scale model solar system in Washington, D.C., makes such a walk possible (FIGURE 1.5). The Voyage model shows the Sun and the planets, and the distances between them, at *one ten-billionth* of their actual sizes and distances.

FIGURE 1.6a shows the Sun and planets at their correct sizes (but not distances) on the Voyage scale. The model Sun is about the size of a large grapefruit, Jupiter is about the size of a marble, and Earth is about the size of the ball point in a pen. You can immediately see some key facts about our solar system. For example, the Sun is far larger than any of the planets; in mass, the Sun outweighs all the planets combined by a factor of nearly 1000. The planets also vary considerably in size: The storm on Jupiter known as the Great Red Spot (visible near Jupiter's lower left in the painting) could swallow up the entire Earth.

The scale of the solar system is even more remarkable when you combine the sizes shown in Figure 1.6a with the distances illustrated by the map of the Voyage model in FIGURE 1.6b. For example, the ball-point-size Earth is located about 15 meters (16.5 yards) from the grapefruit-size Sun, which means you can picture Earth's orbit as a circle of radius 15 meters around a grapefruit.

MATHEMATICAL INSIGHT 1.1

How Far Is a Light-Year?
An Introduction to Astronomical Problem Solving

 Math Review Video: Problem Solving Part 1

We can develop greater insight into astronomical ideas by applying mathematics. The key to using mathematics is to approach problems in a clear and organized way. One simple approach uses the following three steps:

Step 1 Understand the problem: Ask yourself what the solution will look like (for example, what units will it have? will it be big or small?) and what information you need to solve the problem. Draw a diagram or think of a simpler analogous problem to help you decide how to solve it.

Step 2 Solve the problem: Carry out the necessary calculations.

Step 3 Explain your result: Be sure that your answer makes sense, and consider what you've learned by solving the problem.

You can remember this process as "Understand, Solve, and Explain," or USE for short. You may not always need to write out the three steps explicitly, but they may help if you are stuck.

EXAMPLE: How far is a light-year?

SOLUTION: Let's use the three-step process.

Step 1 Understand the problem: The question asks how *far*, so we are looking for a *distance*. In this case, the definition of a light-year tells us that we are looking for the *distance that light can travel in 1 year*. We know that light travels at the speed of light, so we are looking for an equation that gives us distance from speed. If you don't remember this equation, just think of a simpler but analogous problem, such as

"If you drive at 50 kilometers per hour, how far will you travel in 2 hours?" You'll realize that you simply multiply the speed by the time: distance = speed × time. In this case, the speed is the speed of light, or 300,000 km/s, and the time is 1 year.

Step 2 Solve the problem: From Step 1, our equation is that 1 light-year is the speed of light times one year. To make the units consistent, we convert 1 year to seconds by remembering that there are 60 seconds in 1 minute, 60 minutes in 1 hour, 24 hours in 1 day, and 365 days in 1 year. (See Appendix C.3 to review unit conversions.) We now carry out the calculations:

$$1 \text{ light-year} = (\text{speed of light}) \times (1 \text{ yr})$$
$$= \left(300{,}000 \frac{\text{km}}{\text{s}}\right) \times \left(1 \text{ yr} \times \frac{365 \text{ days}}{1 \text{ yr}}\right.$$
$$\left. \times \frac{24 \text{ hr}}{1 \text{ day}} \times \frac{60 \text{ min}}{1 \text{ hr}} \times \frac{60 \text{ s}}{1 \text{ min}}\right)$$
$$= 9{,}460{,}000{,}000{,}000 \text{ km } (9.46 \text{ trillion km})$$

Step 3 Explain your result: In sentence form, our answer is "One light-year is about 9.46 trillion kilometers." This answer makes sense: It has the expected units of distance (kilometers) and it is a long way, which we expect for the distance that light can travel in a year. We say "about" in the answer because we know it is not exact. For example, a year is not exactly 365 days long. In fact, for most purposes, we can approximate the answer further as "One light-year is about 10 trillion kilometers."

FIGURE 1.5 This photo shows the pedestals housing the Sun (the gold sphere on the nearest pedestal) and the inner planets in the Voyage scale model solar system (Washington, D.C.). The model planets are encased in the sidewalk-facing disks visible at about eye level on the planet pedestals. The building at the left is the National Air and Space Museum.

Perhaps the most striking feature of our solar system when we view it to scale is its emptiness. The Voyage model shows the planets along a straight path, so we'd need to draw each planet's orbit around the model Sun to show the full extent of our planetary system. Fitting all these orbits would require an area measuring more than a kilometer on a side—an area equivalent to more than 300 football fields arranged in a grid. Spread over this large area, only the grapefruit-size Sun, the planets, and a few moons would be big enough to see. The rest of it would look virtually empty (that's why we call it *space!*).

Seeing our solar system to scale also helps put space exploration into perspective. The Moon, the only other world on which humans have ever stepped (FIGURE 1.7), lies only about 4 centimeters ($1\frac{1}{2}$ inches) from Earth in the Voyage model. On this scale, the palm of your hand can cover the entire region of the universe in which humans have so far traveled. The trip to Mars is more than 150 times as far as the trip to the Moon, even when Mars is on the same side of its orbit as Earth. And while you can walk from the Sun to Pluto in a few minutes on the Voyage scale, the *New Horizons* spacecraft that is making the real journey will have been in space nearly a decade when it flies past Pluto in July 2015.

a The scaled sizes (but not distances) of the Sun, planets, and two largest known dwarf planets.

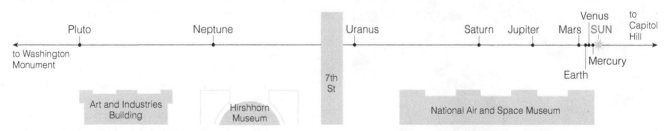

b Locations of the Sun and planets in the Voyage model, Washington, D.C.; the distance from the Sun to Pluto is about 600 meters (1/3 mile). Planets are lined up in the model, but in reality each planet orbits the Sun independently and a perfect alignment never occurs.

FIGURE 1.6 interactive figure The Voyage scale model represents the solar system at *one ten-billionth* of its actual size. Pluto is included in the Voyage model, which was built before the International Astronomical Union reclassified Pluto as a dwarf planet.

FIGURE 1.7 This famous photograph from the first Moon landing (*Apollo 11* in July 1969) shows astronaut Buzz Aldrin, with Neil Armstrong reflected in his visor. Armstrong was the first to step onto the Moon's surface, saying, "That's one small step for a man, one giant leap for mankind."

FIGURE 1.8 This photograph and diagram show the constellation Centaurus, which is visible from tropical and southern latitudes. Alpha Centauri's real distance of 4.4 light-years is 4400 kilometers on the 1-to-10-billion Voyage scale.

Distances to the Stars If you visit the Voyage model in Washington, D.C., you can walk the roughly 600-meter distance from the Sun to Pluto in just a few minutes. How much farther would you have to walk to reach the next star on this scale?

Amazingly, you would need to walk to California. If this answer seems hard to believe, you can check it for yourself. A light-year is about 10 trillion kilometers, which becomes 1000 kilometers on the 1-to-10-billion scale (because 10 trillion ÷ 10 billion = 1000). The nearest star system to our own, a three-star system called Alpha Centauri (**FIGURE 1.8**), is

about 4.4 light-years away. That distance is about 4400 kilometers (2700 miles) on the 1-to-10-billion scale, or roughly equivalent to the distance across the United States.

The tremendous distances to the stars give us some perspective on the technological challenge of astronomy. For example, because the largest star of the Alpha Centauri system is roughly the same size and brightness as our Sun, viewing it in the night sky is somewhat like being in Washington, D.C., and seeing a very bright grapefruit in San Francisco (neglecting the problems introduced by the curvature of Earth). It may seem

remarkable that we can see the star at all, but the blackness of the night sky allows the naked eye to see it as a faint dot of light. It looks much brighter through powerful telescopes, but we still cannot see features of the star's surface.

Now, consider the difficulty of detecting *planets* orbiting nearby stars, which is equivalent to looking from Washington, D.C., and trying to find ball points or marbles orbiting grapefruits in California or beyond. When you consider this challenge, it is all the more remarkable to realize that we now have technology capable of finding such planets [**Section 13.1**].

The vast distances to the stars also offer a sobering lesson about interstellar travel. Although science fiction shows like *Star Trek* and *Star Wars* make such travel look easy, the reality is far different. Consider the *Voyager 2* spacecraft. Launched in 1977, *Voyager 2* flew by Jupiter in 1979, Saturn in 1981, Uranus in 1986, and Neptune in 1989. It is now bound for the stars at a speed of close to 50,000 kilometers per hour—about 100 times as fast as a speeding bullet. But even at this speed, *Voyager 2* would take about 100,000 years to reach Alpha Centauri if it were headed in that direction (which it's not). Convenient interstellar travel remains well beyond our present technology.

The Size of the Milky Way Galaxy The vast separation between our solar system and Alpha Centauri is typical of

COMMON MISCONCEPTIONS

Confusing Very Different Things

Most people are familiar with the terms *solar system* and *galaxy*, but few realize how incredibly different they are. Our solar system is a single star system, while our galaxy is a collection of more than 100 billion star systems—so many that it would take thousands of years just to count them. Moreover, if you look at the sizes in Figure 1.1, you'll see that our galaxy is about 100 million times larger in diameter than our solar system. So be careful; numerically speaking, mixing up *solar system* and *galaxy* is a gigantic mistake!

the separations among star systems in our region of the Milky Way Galaxy. We therefore cannot use the 1-to-10-billion scale for thinking about distances beyond the nearest stars, because more distant stars would not fit on Earth with this scale. To visualize the galaxy, let's reduce our scale by another factor of 1 billion (making it a scale of 1 to 10^{19}).

On this new scale, each light-year becomes 1 millimeter, and the 100,000-light-year diameter of the Milky Way Galaxy becomes 100 meters, or about the length of a football field. Visualize a football field with a scale model of our galaxy centered over midfield. Our entire solar system is a microscopic dot located around the

---

MATHEMATICAL INSIGHT 1.2

The Scale of Space and Time

 Math Review Video: Scientific Notation, Parts 1 to 3

Making a scale model usually requires nothing more than division. For example, in a 1-to-20 architectural scale model, a building that is actually 6 meters tall will be only $6 \div 20 = 0.3$ meter tall. The idea is the same for astronomical scaling, except that we usually divide by such large numbers that it's easier to work in *scientific notation*—that is, with the aid of powers of 10. (See Appendixes C.1 and C.2 to review these concepts.)

EXAMPLE 1: How big is the Sun on a 1-to-10-billion scale?

SOLUTION:

Step 1 Understand: We are looking for the scaled *size* of the Sun, so we simply need to divide its actual radius by 10 billion, or 10^{10}. Appendix E.1 gives the Sun's radius as 695,000 km, or 6.95×10^5 km in scientific notation.

Step 2 Solve: We carry out the division:

$$\text{scaled radius} = \frac{\text{actual radius}}{10^{10}}$$
$$= \frac{6.95 \times 10^5 \, \text{km}}{10^{10}}$$
$$= 6.95 \times 10^{(5-10)} \, \text{km} = 6.95 \times 10^{-5} \, \text{km}$$

Notice that we used the rule that dividing powers of 10 means subtracting their exponents [**Appendix C.1**].

Step 3 Explain: We have found an answer, but because most of us don't have a good sense of what 10^{-5} kilometer looks like, the answer will be more meaningful if we convert it to units that will be easier to interpret. In this case, because there are 1000 (10^3) meters in a kilometer and 100 (10^2) centimeters in a meter, we convert to centimeters:

$$6.95 \times 10^{-5} \, \text{km} \times \frac{10^3 \, \text{m}}{1 \, \text{km}} \times \frac{10^2 \, \text{cm}}{1 \, \text{m}} = 6.95 \, \text{cm}$$

We've found that on the 1-to-10-billion scale the Sun's radius is about 7 centimeters, which is a diameter of about 14 centimeters—about the size of a large grapefruit.

EXAMPLE 2: What scale allows the 100,000-light-year diameter of the Milky Way Galaxy to fit on a 100-meter-long football field?

SOLUTION:

Step 1 Understand: We want to know *how many times larger* the actual diameter of the galaxy is than 100 meters, so we'll divide the actual diameter by 100 meters. To carry out the division, we'll need both numbers in the same units. We can put the galaxy's diameter in meters by using the fact that a light-year is about 10^{13} kilometers (see Mathematical Insight 1.1) and a kilometer is 10^3 meters; because we are working with powers of 10, we'll write the galaxy's 100,000-light-year diameter as 10^5 ly.

Step 2 Solve: We now convert the units and carry out the division:

$$\frac{\text{galaxy diameter}}{\text{football field diameter}} = \frac{10^5 \, \text{ly} \times \frac{10^{13} \, \text{km}}{1 \, \text{ly}} \times \frac{10^3 \, \text{m}}{1 \, \text{km}}}{10^2 \, \text{m}}$$
$$= 10^{(5+13+3-2)} = 10^{19}$$

Note that the answer has no units, because it simply tells us how many times larger one thing is than the other.

Step 3 Explain: We've found that we need a scale of 1 to 10^{19} to make the galaxy fit on a football field.

20-yard line. The 4.4-light-year separation between our solar system and Alpha Centauri becomes just 4.4 millimeters on this scale—smaller than the width of your little finger. If you stood at the position of our solar system in this model, millions of star systems would lie within reach of your arms.

Another way to put the galaxy into perspective is to consider its number of stars—more than 100 billion. Imagine that tonight you are having difficulty falling asleep (perhaps because you are contemplating the scale of the universe). Instead of counting sheep, you decide to count stars. If you are able to count about one star each second, how long would it take you to count 100 billion stars in the Milky Way? Clearly, the answer is 100 billion (10^{11}) seconds, but how long is that? Amazingly, 100 billion seconds is more than 3000 years. (You can confirm this by dividing 100 billion by the number of seconds in 1 year.) You would need thousands of years just to *count* the stars in the Milky Way Galaxy, and this assumes you never take a break—no sleeping, no eating, and absolutely no dying!

The Observable Universe As incredible as the scale of our galaxy may seem, the Milky Way is only one of roughly 100 billion galaxies in the observable universe. Just as it would take thousands of years to count the stars in the Milky Way, it would take thousands of years to count all the galaxies.

Think for a moment about the total number of stars in all these galaxies. If we assume 100 billion stars per galaxy, the total number of stars in the observable universe is roughly 100 billion × 100 billion, or 10,000,000,000,000,000,000,000 (10^{22}). How big is this number? Visit a beach. Run your hands through the fine-grained sand. Imagine counting each tiny grain of sand as it slips through your fingers. Then imagine counting every grain of sand on the beach and continuing to count *every* grain of dry sand on *every* beach on Earth (see Mathematical Insight 1.3). If you could actually complete this task, you would find that the number of grains of sand is comparable to the number of stars in the observable universe (FIGURE 1.9).

MATHEMATICAL INSIGHT 1.3

Order of Magnitude Estimation

In astronomy, numbers are often so large that an estimate can be useful even if it's good only to about the nearest power of 10. For example, when we multiplied 100 billion stars per galaxy by 100 billion galaxies to estimate that there are about 10^{22} stars in the observable universe, we knew that the "ballpark" nature of these numbers means the actual number of stars could easily be anywhere from about 10^{21} to 10^{23}. Estimates good to about the nearest power of 10 are called **order of magnitude estimates**.

EXAMPLE: Verify the claim that the number of grains of (dry) sand on all the beaches on Earth is comparable to the number of stars in the observable universe.

SOLUTION:

Step 1 Understand: To verify the claim, we need to estimate the number of grains of sand and see if it is close to our estimate of 10^{22} stars. We can estimate the total number of sand grains by dividing the *total volume* of sand on Earth's beaches by the *average volume* of an individual sand grain. Volume is equal to length times width times depth, so the total volume is the total length of sandy beach on Earth multiplied by the typical width and depth of dry sand. That is,

$$\text{total sand grains} = \frac{\text{total volume of beach sand}}{\text{average volume of 1 sand grain}}$$
$$= \frac{\text{beach length} \times \text{beach width} \times \text{beach depth}}{\text{average volume of 1 sand grain}}$$

We now need numbers to put into the equation. We can estimate the average volume of an individual sand grain by measuring out a small volume of sand, counting the number of grains in this volume, and then dividing the volume by the number of grains. If you do this, you'll find that a reasonable order of magnitude estimate is one-tenth of a cubic millimeter, or 10^{-10} m³, per sand grain. We can estimate beach width and depth from experience or photos of beaches. Typical widths are about 20 to 50 meters and typical sand depth is about 2 to 5 meters, so we can make the numbers easy by assuming that the product of beach width times depth is about 100 square meters, or 10^2 m². The total length of sandy beach on Earth is more difficult to estimate, but you can look online and find that it is less than about 1 million kilometers, or 10^9 m.

Step 2 Solve: We already have our equation and all the numbers we need, so we just put them in; note that we group beach width and depth together, since we estimated them together in Step 1:

$$\text{total sand grains} = \frac{\text{beach length} \times (\text{beach width} \times \text{beach depth})}{\text{average volume of 1 sand grain}}$$
$$= \frac{10^9 \text{ m} \times 10^2 \text{ m}^2}{10^{-10} \text{ m}^3}$$
$$= 10^{[9+2-(-10)]} = 10^{21}$$

Step 3 Explain: Our order of magnitude estimate for the total number of grains of dry sand on all the beaches on Earth is 10^{21}, which is within a factor of 10 of the estimated 10^{22} stars in the observable universe. Because both numbers could easily be off by a factor of 10 or more, we cannot say with certainty that one is larger than the other, but the numbers are clearly comparable.

FIGURE 1.9 The number of stars in the observable universe is comparable to the number of grains of dry sand on all the beaches on Earth.

1.2 THE HISTORY OF THE UNIVERSE

Our universe is vast not only in space, but also in time. In this section, we will briefly discuss the history of the universe as we understand it today.

Before we begin, you may wonder how we can claim to know anything about what the universe was like in the distant past. We'll devote much of the rest of this textbook to understanding how science enables us to do this, but you already know part of the answer: Because looking farther into space means looking further back in time, we can actually *see* parts of the universe as they were long ago, simply by looking far enough away. In other words, our telescopes act somewhat like time machines, enabling us to observe the history of the universe. At great distances, we see the universe as it was long ago, when it was much younger than it is today.

How did we come to be?

FIGURE 1.10 (pages 12–13) summarizes the history of the universe according to modern science. Let's start at the upper left of the figure, and discuss the key events and what they mean.

The Big Bang, Expansion, and the Age of the Universe Telescopic observations of distant galaxies show that the entire universe is *expanding,* meaning that average distances between galaxies are increasing with time. This fact implies that galaxies must have been closer together in the past, and if we go back far enough, we must reach the point at which the expansion began. We call this beginning the **Big Bang,** and scientists use the observed rate of expansion to calculate that it occurred about 14 billion years ago. The three cubes in the upper left portion of Figure 1.10 represent the expansion of a small piece of the universe through time.

The universe as a whole has continued to expand ever since the Big Bang, but on smaller size scales the force of gravity has drawn matter together. Structures such as galaxies and galaxy clusters occupy regions where gravity has won out against the overall expansion. That is, while the universe as a whole continues to expand, individual galaxies and galaxy clusters (and objects within them such as stars and planets) do *not* expand. This idea is also illustrated by the three cubes in Figure 1.10. Notice that as the cube as a whole grew larger, the matter within it clumped into galaxies and galaxy clusters. Most galaxies, including our own Milky Way, formed within a few billion years after the Big Bang.

Stellar Lives and Galactic Recycling Within galaxies like the Milky Way, gravity drives the collapse of clouds of gas and dust to form stars and planets. Stars are not living organisms, but they nonetheless go through "life cycles." A star is born when gravity compresses the material in a cloud to the point at which the center becomes dense enough and hot enough to generate energy by **nuclear fusion,** the process in which lightweight atomic nuclei smash together and stick (or fuse) to make heavier nuclei. The star "lives" as long as it can shine with energy from fusion, and "dies" when it exhausts its usable fuel.

In its final death throes, a star blows much of its content back out into space. The most massive stars die in titanic explosions called *supernovae.* The returned matter mixes with other matter floating between the stars in the galaxy, eventually becoming part of new clouds of gas and dust from which new generations of stars can be born. Galaxies therefore function as cosmic recycling plants, recycling material expelled from dying stars into new generations of stars and planets. This cycle is illustrated in the lower right of Figure 1.10. Our own solar system is a product of many generations of such recycling.

Star Stuff The recycling of stellar material is connected to our existence in an even deeper way. By studying stars of different ages, we have learned that the early universe contained only the simplest chemical elements: hydrogen and helium (and a trace of lithium). We and Earth are made primarily of other elements, such as carbon, nitrogen, oxygen, and iron. Where did these other elements come from? Evidence shows that they were manufactured by stars, some through the nuclear fusion that makes stars shine, and others through nuclear reactions accompanying the explosions that end stellar lives.

By the time our solar system formed, about $4\frac{1}{2}$ billion years ago, earlier generations of stars had already converted about 2% of our galaxy's original hydrogen and helium into heavier elements. Therefore, the cloud that gave birth to our solar system was made of about 98% hydrogen and helium and 2% other elements. This 2% may sound small, but it was more than enough to make the small rocky planets of our solar system, including Earth. On Earth, some of these elements became the raw ingredients of life, which ultimately blossomed into the great diversity of life on Earth today.

In summary, most of the material from which we and our planet are made was created inside stars that lived and died before the birth of our Sun. As astronomer Carl Sagan (1934–1996) said, we are "star stuff."

Throughout this book we will see that human life is intimately connected with the development of the universe as a whole. This illustration presents an overview of our cosmic origins, showing some of the crucial steps that made our existence possible.

1 Birth of the Universe: The expansion of the universe began with the hot and dense Big Bang. The cubes show how one region of the universe has expanded with time. The universe continues to expand, but on smaller scales gravity has pulled matter together to make galaxies.

4 Earth and Life: By the time our solar system was born, 4½ billion years ago, about 2% of the original hydrogen and helium had been converted into heavier elements. We are therefore "star stuff," because we and our planet are made from elements manufactured in stars that lived and died long ago.

② **Galaxies as Cosmic Recycling Plants:** The early universe contained only two chemical elements: hydrogen and helium. All other elements were made by stars and recycled from one stellar generation to the next within galaxies like our Milky Way.

Stars are born in clouds of gas and dust; planets may form in surrounding disks.

Massive stars explode when they die, scattering the elements they've produced into space.

Stars shine with energy released by nuclear fusion, which ultimately manufactures all elements heavier than hydrogen and helium.

③ **Life Cycles of Stars:** Many generations of stars have lived and died in the Milky Way.

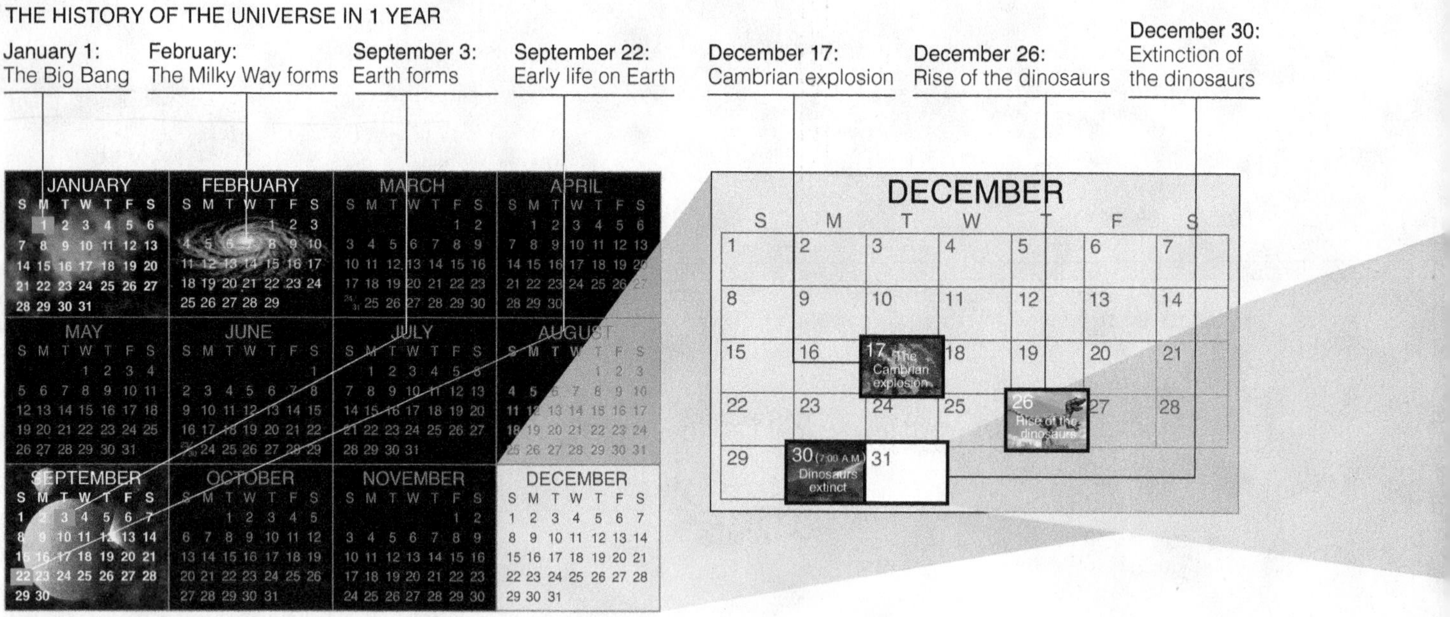

January 1:	February:	September 3:	September 22:	December 17:	December 26:	December 30:
The Big Bang	The Milky Way forms	Earth forms	Early life on Earth	Cambrian explosion	Rise of the dinosaurs	Extinction of the dinosaurs

FIGURE 1.11 The cosmic calendar compresses the 14-billion-year history of the universe into 1 year, so each month represents a little more than 1 billion years. This cosmic calendar is adapted from a version created by Carl Sagan. (For a more detailed version, see the "You Are Here in Time" foldout diagram in the front of the book.)

How do our lifetimes compare to the age of the universe?

We can put the 14-billion-year age of the universe into perspective by imagining this time compressed into a single year, so each month represents a little more than 1 billion years. On this *cosmic calendar*, the Big Bang occurred at the first instant of January 1 and the present is the stroke of midnight on December 31 (**FIGURE 1.11**).

On this time scale, the Milky Way Galaxy probably formed in February. Many generations of stars lived and died in the subsequent cosmic months, enriching the galaxy with the "star stuff" from which we and our planet are made.

Our solar system and our planet did not form until early September on this scale ($4\frac{1}{2}$ billion years ago in real time). By late September, life on Earth was flourishing. However, for most of Earth's history, living organisms remained relatively primitive and microscopic. On the scale of the cosmic calendar, recognizable animals became prominent only in mid-December. Early dinosaurs appeared on the day after Christmas. Then, in a cosmic instant, the dinosaurs disappeared forever—probably because of the impact of an asteroid or a comet [**Section 12.4**]. In real time the death of the dinosaurs occurred some 65 million years ago, but on the cosmic calendar it was only yesterday. With the dinosaurs gone, small furry mammals inherited Earth. Some 60 million years later, or around 9 p.m. on December 31 of the cosmic calendar, early hominids (human ancestors) began to walk upright.

Perhaps the most astonishing fact about the cosmic calendar is that the entire history of human civilization falls into just the last half-minute. The ancient Egyptians built the pyramids only about 11 seconds ago on this scale. About 1 second ago, Kepler and Galileo proved that Earth orbits the Sun rather than vice versa. The average college student

was born about 0.05 second ago, around 11:59:59.95 p.m. on the cosmic calendar. On the scale of cosmic time, the human species is the youngest of infants, and a human lifetime is a mere blink of an eye.

> **THINK ABOUT IT**
>
> Study the backside of the foldout in the front of this book, which shows a more detailed version of the cosmic calendar. How does an understanding of the scale of time affect your view of human civilization? Explain.

1.3 SPACESHIP EARTH

Wherever you are as you read this book, you probably have the feeling that you're "just sitting here." Nothing could be further from the truth. As we'll discuss in this section, all of us are moving through space in so many ways that noted inventor and philosopher R. Buckminster Fuller (1895–1983) described us as travelers on *spaceship Earth*.

How is Earth moving through space?

As you "sit" on spaceship Earth, you are in fact being spun in circles as Earth rotates, you are racing around the Sun in Earth's orbit, you are circling the galactic center with our Sun, and you are careening through the cosmos in the Milky Way Galaxy. Let's explore each of these motions in a little more detail.

Rotation and Orbit The most basic motions of Earth are its daily **rotation** (spin) and its yearly **orbit** (or *revolution*) around the Sun.

Earth rotates once each day around its axis, which is the imaginary line connecting the North Pole to the South Pole. Earth rotates from west to east—counterclockwise as

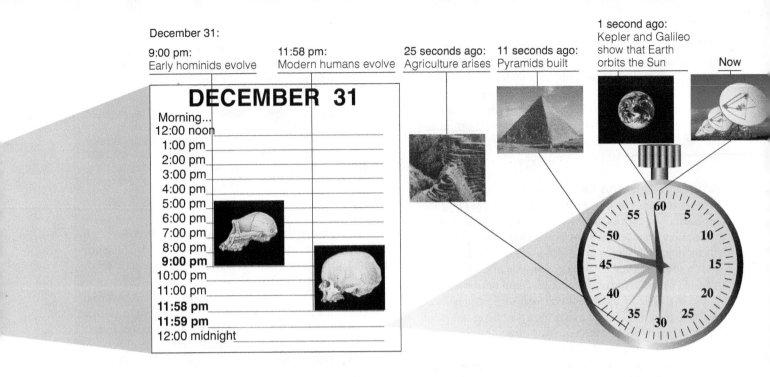

December 31:

9:00 pm:
Early hominids evolve

11:58 pm:
Modern humans evolve

25 seconds ago:
Agriculture arises

11 seconds ago:
Pyramids built

1 second ago:
Kepler and Galileo show that Earth orbits the Sun

Now

DECEMBER 31

Morning...
12:00 noon
1:00 pm
2:00 pm
3:00 pm
4:00 pm
5:00 pm
6:00 pm
7:00 pm
8:00 pm
9:00 pm
10:00 pm
11:00 pm
11:58 pm
11:59 pm
12:00 midnight

viewed from above the North Pole—which is why the Sun and stars appear to rise in the east and set in the west each day. Although the physical effects of rotation are so subtle that our ancestors assumed the heavens revolved around us, the rotation speed is substantial (**FIGURE 1.12**): Unless you live very near the North or South Pole, you are whirling around Earth's axis at a speed of more than 1000 kilometers per hour (600 miles per hour)—faster than most airplanes travel.

At the same time as it is rotating, Earth also orbits the Sun, completing one orbit each year (**FIGURE 1.13**). Earth's orbital distance varies slightly over the course of each year, but as we discussed earlier, the average distance is one astronomical unit (AU), which is about 150 million kilometers. Again, even though we don't feel this motion, the speed is impressive: We are racing around the Sun at a speed in excess of

100,000 kilometers per hour (60,000 miles per hour), which is faster than any spacecraft yet launched.

As you study Figure 1.13, notice that Earth's orbital path defines a flat plane that we call the **ecliptic plane**. Earth's axis is tilted by $23\frac{1}{2}°$ from a line *perpendicular* to the ecliptic plane. This **axis tilt** happens to be oriented so that the axis points almost directly at a star called *Polaris*, or the *North Star*. Keep in mind that the idea of axis tilt makes sense only in relation to the ecliptic plane. That is, the idea of "tilt" by itself has no meaning in space, where there is no absolute up or down. In space, "up" and "down" mean only "away from the center of Earth" (or another planet) and "toward the center of Earth," respectively.

THINK ABOUT IT

If there is no up or down in space, why do you think that most globes and maps have the North Pole on top? Would it be equally correct to have the South Pole on top or to turn a globe sideways? Explain.

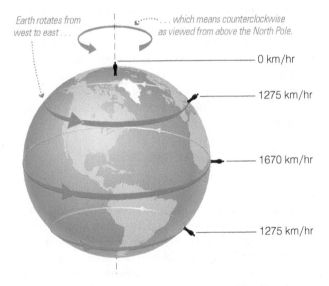

Earth rotates from west to east . . .

. . . which means counterclockwise as viewed from above the North Pole.

0 km/hr

1275 km/hr

1670 km/hr

1275 km/hr

FIGURE 1.12 As Earth rotates, your speed around Earth's axis depends on your location: The closer you are to the equator, the faster you travel with rotation.

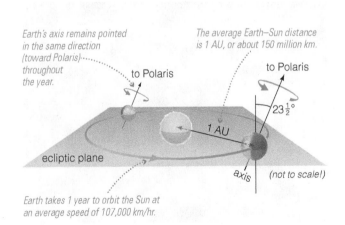

Earth's axis remains pointed in the same direction (toward Polaris) throughout the year.

to Polaris

The average Earth–Sun distance is 1 AU, or about 150 million km.

to Polaris

$23\frac{1}{2}°$

1 AU

ecliptic plane

axis

(not to scale!)

Earth takes 1 year to orbit the Sun at an average speed of 107,000 km/hr.

FIGURE 1.13 Earth orbits the Sun at a surprisingly high speed. Notice that Earth both rotates and orbits counterclockwise as viewed from above the North Pole.

Notice also that Earth orbits the Sun in the same direction that it rotates on its axis: counterclockwise as viewed from above the North Pole. This is not a coincidence but a consequence of the way our planet was born. As we'll discuss in Chapter 8, strong evidence indicates that Earth and the other planets were born in a spinning disk of gas that surrounded our Sun when it was young, and Earth rotates and orbits in the same direction that the disk was spinning.

Motion Within the Local Solar Neighborhood

Rotation and orbit are only a small part of the travels of spaceship Earth. Our entire solar system is on a great journey within the Milky Way Galaxy. There are two major components to this motion, both shown in FIGURE 1.14. Let's begin with our motion relative to other stars in our *local solar neighborhood,* by which we mean the region of the Sun and nearby stars.

To get a sense of the size of our local solar neighborhood relative to the galaxy, imagine drawing a tiny dot on the painting of the galaxy. Because the galaxy contains at least 100 billion stars, even a dot that is 10,000 times smaller than the whole painting will cover a region representing more than 10 million stars (because 100 billion ÷ 10,000 = 10 million). We usually think of our local solar neighborhood as a region containing just a few thousand to a few million of the nearest stars.

The arrows in the box in Figure 1.14 indicate that stars in our local solar neighborhood move essentially at random relative to one another. The speeds are quite fast: On average, our Sun is moving relative to nearby stars at a speed of about 70,000 kilometers per hour (40,000 miles per hour), almost three times as fast as the Space Station orbits Earth.

Given these high speeds, you might wonder why we don't see stars racing around our sky. The answer lies in their vast distances from us. You've probably noticed that a distant airplane appears to move through your sky more slowly than one flying close overhead. Stars are so far away that even at speeds of 70,000 kilometers per hour, their motions would be noticeable to the naked eye only if we watched them for thousands of years. That is why the patterns in the constellations seem to remain fixed. Nevertheless, in 10,000 years the constellations will be noticeably different from those we see today.

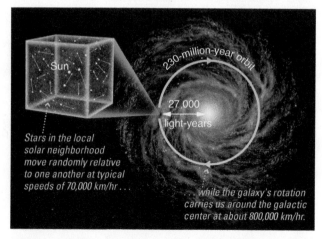

Stars in the local solar neighborhood move randomly relative to one another at typical speeds of 70,000 km/hr . . .

. . . while the galaxy's rotation carries us around the galactic center at about 800,000 km/hr.

FIGURE 1.14 This painting illustrates the motion of the Sun both within the local solar neighborhood and around the center of the galaxy.

In 500,000 years they will be unrecognizable. If you could watch a time-lapse movie made over millions of years, you *would* see stars racing across our sky.

THINK ABOUT IT

Despite the chaos of motion in the local solar neighborhood over millions and billions of years, collisions between star systems are extremely rare. Explain why. (*Hint*: Consider the sizes of star systems, such as the solar system, relative to the distances between them.)

Galactic Rotation If you look closely at leaves floating in a stream, their motions relative to one another might appear random, just like the motions of stars in the local solar neighborhood. As you widen your view, you see that all the leaves are being carried in the same general direction by the downstream current. In the same way, as we widen our view beyond the local solar neighborhood, the seemingly random motions of its stars give way to a simpler and even faster motion: rotation of the Milky Way Galaxy. Our solar system, located about 27,000 light-years from the galactic center, completes one orbit of the galaxy in about 230 million years. Even if you could watch from outside our galaxy, this motion would be unnoticeable to your naked eye. However, if you calculate the speed of our solar system as we orbit the center of the galaxy, you will find that it is close to 800,000 kilometers (500,000 miles) per hour.

Careful study of the galaxy's rotation reveals one of the greatest mysteries in science. Stars at different distances from the galactic center orbit at different speeds, and we can learn how mass is distributed in the galaxy by measuring these speeds. Such studies indicate that the stars in the disk of the galaxy represent only the "tip of the iceberg" compared to the mass of the entire galaxy (FIGURE 1.15). Most of the mass of the galaxy seems to be located outside the visible disk (occupying the galactic *halo* that surrounds and encompasses the disk), but the matter that makes up this mass is completely invisible to our telescopes. We therefore know very little about the nature of this matter, which we refer to as *dark matter* (because of the lack of light from it). Studies of other galaxies suggest that they also are made mostly of dark matter, which means this mysterious matter must significantly outweigh the ordinary matter that makes up planets and stars. We know even less about the mysterious *dark energy* that seems to make up much of the total energy content of the universe. We'll discuss the mysteries of dark matter and dark energy in Chapter 23.

How do galaxies move within the universe?

The billions of galaxies in the universe also move relative to one another. Within the Local Group (see Figure 1.1), some of the galaxies move toward us, some move away from us, and at least two small galaxies (known as the Large and Small Magellanic Clouds) apparently orbit our Milky Way Galaxy. Again, the speeds are enormous by earthly standards. For example, the Milky Way is moving toward the Andromeda Galaxy at about 300,000 kilometers per hour (180,000 miles per hour). Despite this high speed, we needn't worry about a

Most of the galaxy's light comes from stars and gas in the galactic disk and central bulge . . .

. . . but measurements suggest that most of the mass lies unseen in the spherical halo that surrounds the entire disk.

FIGURE 1.15 This painting shows an edge-on view of the Milky Way Galaxy. Study of galactic rotation shows that although most visible stars lie in the central bulge or thin disk, most of the mass lies in the halo that surrounds and encompasses the disk. Because this mass emits no light that we have detected, we call it *dark matter.*

MATHEMATICAL INSIGHT 1.4
Speeds of Rotation and Orbit

 Math Review Video: Problem Solving, Part 3

Building upon prior Mathematical Insights, we will now see how simple formulas—such as the formula for the circumference of a circle—expand the range of astronomical problems we can solve.

EXAMPLE 1: How fast is a person on Earth's equator moving with Earth's rotation?

SOLUTION:

Step 1 Understand: The question *how fast* tells us we are looking for a *speed*. If you remember that highway speeds are posted in miles (or kilometers) per hour, you'll realize that speed is a distance (such as miles) divided by a time (such as hours). In this case, the distance is Earth's equatorial circumference, because that is how far a person at the equator travels with each rotation (see Figure 1.12); we'll therefore use the formula for the circumference of a circle, $C = 2 \times \pi \times radius$. The time is 24 hours, because that is how long each rotation takes.

Step 2 Solve: From Appendix E.1, Earth's equatorial radius is 6378 km, so its circumference is $2 \times \pi \times 6378$ km $= 40{,}074$ km. We divide this distance by the time of 24 hours:

$$\text{rotation speed at equator} = \frac{\text{equatorial circumference}}{\text{length of day}}$$
$$= \frac{40{,}074 \text{ km}}{24 \text{ hr}} = 1670 \frac{\text{km}}{\text{hr}}$$

Step 3 Explain: A person at the equator is moving with Earth's rotation at a speed of about 1670 kilometers per hour, which is a little over 1000 miles per hour, or about twice the flying speed of a commercial jet.

EXAMPLE 2: How fast is Earth orbiting the Sun?

SOLUTION:

Step 1 Understand: We are again asked *how fast* and therefore need to divide a distance by a time. In this case, the distance is the circumference of Earth's orbit, and the time is the 1 year that Earth takes to complete each orbit.

Step 2 Solve: Earth's average distance from the Sun is 1 AU, or about 150 million (1.5×10^8) km, so the orbit circumference is about $2 \times \pi \times 1.5 \times 10^8$ km $\approx 9.40 \times 10^8$ km. The orbital speed is this distance divided by the time of 1 year, which we convert to hours so that we end up with units of km/hr:

$$\text{orbital speed} = \frac{\text{orbital circumference}}{1 \text{ yr}}$$
$$= \frac{9.40 \times 10^8 \text{ km}}{1 \text{ yr} \times \frac{365 \text{ day}}{\text{yr}} \times \frac{24 \text{ hr}}{\text{day}}} \approx 107{,}000 \frac{\text{km}}{\text{hr}}$$

Step 3 Explain: Earth orbits the Sun at an average speed of about 107,000 km/hr (66,000 mi/hr). Most "speeding bullets" travel between about 500 and 1000 km/hr, so Earth's orbital speed is more than 100 times as fast as a speeding bullet.

collision anytime soon. Even if the Milky Way and Andromeda Galaxies are approaching each other head-on, it will be billions of years before any collision begins.

When we look outside the Local Group, however, we find two astonishing facts recognized in the 1920s by Edwin Hubble, for whom the Hubble Space Telescope was named:

1. Virtually every galaxy outside the Local Group is moving *away* from us.

2. The more distant the galaxy, the faster it appears to be racing away.

These facts might make it sound as if we suffered from a cosmic case of chicken pox, but there is a much more natural explanation: *The entire universe is expanding.* We'll save the details for later in the book, but you can understand the basic idea by thinking about a raisin cake baking in an oven.

The Raisin Cake Analogy Imagine that you make a raisin cake in which the distance between adjacent raisins is 1 centimeter. You place the cake into the oven, where it expands as it bakes. After 1 hour, you remove the cake, which has expanded so that the distance between adjacent raisins has increased to 3 centimeters (FIGURE 1.16). The expansion of the cake seems fairly obvious. But what would you see if you lived *in* the cake, as we live in the universe?

Pick any raisin (it doesn't matter which one) and call it the Local Raisin. Figure 1.16 shows one possible choice, with three nearby raisins also labeled. The accompanying table summarizes what you would see if you lived within the Local Raisin. Notice, for example, that Raisin 1 starts out at a distance of 1 centimeter before baking and ends up

at a distance of 3 centimeters after baking, which means it moves a distance of 2 centimeters away from the Local Raisin during the hour of baking. Hence, its speed as seen from the Local Raisin is 2 centimeters per hour. Raisin 2 moves from a distance of 2 centimeters before baking to a distance of 6 centimeters after baking, which means it moves a distance of 4 centimeters away from the Local Raisin during the hour. Hence, its speed is 4 centimeters per hour, or twice the speed of Raisin 1. Generalizing, the fact that the cake is expanding means that all the raisins are moving away from the Local Raisin, with more distant raisins moving away faster.

THINK ABOUT IT

Suppose a raisin started out 10 centimeters from the Local Raisin. How far away would it be after one hour, and how fast would it be moving away from the Local Raisin?

Hubble's discovery that galaxies are moving in much the same way as the raisins in the cake, with most moving away from us and more distant ones moving away faster, implies that the universe is expanding much like the raisin cake. If you now imagine the Local Raisin as representing our Local Group of galaxies and the other raisins as representing more distant galaxies or clusters of galaxies, you have a basic picture of the expansion of the universe. Like the expanding dough between the raisins in the cake, *space* itself is growing between galaxies. More distant galaxies move away from us faster because they are carried along with this expansion like the raisins in the expanding cake. Many billions of light-years away, we see galaxies moving away from us at speeds approaching the speed of light.

The Real Universe There's at least one important distinction between the raisin cake and the universe: A cake has a center and edges, but we do not think the same is true

From an outside perspective, the cake expands uniformly as it bakes . . .

Before baking: raisins are all 1 cm apart.

Local Raisin

1 hr

After baking: raisins are all 3 cm apart.

Local Raisin

. . . but from the point of view of the Local Raisin, all other raisins move farther away during baking, with more distant raisins moving faster.

Distances and Speeds as Seen from the Local Raisin

Raisin Number	Distance Before Baking	Distance After Baking (1 hour later)	Speed
1	1 cm	3 cm	2 cm/hr
2	2 cm	6 cm	4 cm/hr
3	3 cm	9 cm	6 cm/hr
⋮	⋮	⋮	⋮

FIGURE 1.16 interactive figure An expanding raisin cake offers an analogy to the expanding universe. Someone living in one of the raisins inside the cake could figure out that the cake is expanding by noticing that all other raisins are moving away, with more distant raisins moving away faster. In the same way, we know that we live in an expanding universe because all galaxies outside our Local Group are moving away from us, with more distant ones moving faster.

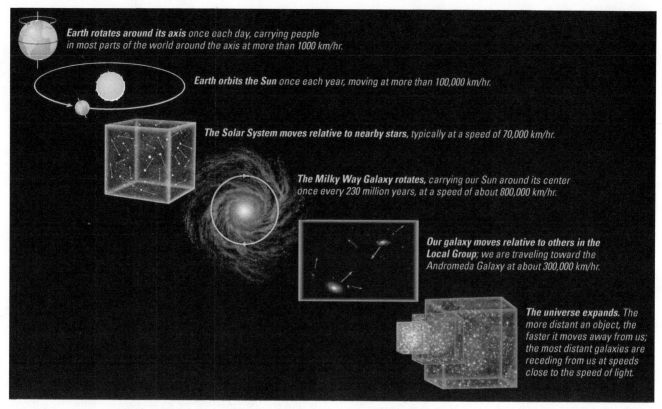

FIGURE 1.17 This figure summarizes the basic motions of Earth in the universe, along with their associated speeds.

of the entire universe. Anyone living in any galaxy in an expanding universe sees just what we see—other galaxies moving away, with more distant ones moving away faster. Because the view from each point in the universe is about the same, no place can claim to be more "central" than any other place.

It's also important to realize that, unlike the case with a raisin cake, we can't actually *see* galaxies moving apart with time—the distances are too vast for any motion to be noticeable on the time scale of a human life. Instead, we measure the speeds of galaxies by spreading their light into spectra and observing what we call *Doppler shifts* [**Section 5.4**]. This illustrates how modern astronomy depends both on careful observations and on using current understanding of the laws of nature to explain what we see.

Motion Summary FIGURE 1.17 summarizes the motions we have discussed. As we have seen, we are never truly sitting still. We spin around Earth's axis at more than 1000 kilometers per hour, while our planet orbits the Sun at more than 100,000 kilometers per hour. Our solar system moves among the stars of the local solar neighborhood at typical speeds of 70,000 kilometers per hour, while also orbiting the center of the Milky Way Galaxy at a speed of about 800,000 kilometers per hour. Our galaxy moves among the other galaxies of the Local Group, while all other galaxies move away from us at speeds that grow greater with distance in our expanding universe. Spaceship Earth is carrying us on a remarkable journey.

1.4 THE HUMAN ADVENTURE OF ASTRONOMY

In relatively few pages, we've laid out a fairly complete overview of modern scientific ideas about the universe. But our goal in this book is not simply for you to be able to recite these ideas. Rather, it is to help you understand the evidence that supports them and the extraordinary story of how they developed.

How has the study of astronomy affected human history?

Astronomy is a human adventure in the sense that it affects everyone—even those who have never looked at the sky—because the history of astronomy has been so deeply intertwined with the development of civilization. Revolutions in astronomy have gone hand in hand with the revolutions in science and technology that have shaped modern life.

Witness the repercussions of the *Copernican revolution*, which showed us that Earth is not the center of the universe but rather just one planet orbiting the Sun. This revolution, which we will discuss further in Chapter 3, began when Copernicus published his idea of a Sun-centered solar system in 1543. Three later figures—Tycho Brahe, Johannes Kepler, and Galileo—provided the key evidence that eventually led to wide acceptance of the Copernican idea. The revolution culminated with Isaac Newton's uncovering of the laws of motion and gravity. Newton's work, in turn, became the foundation of physics that helped fuel the industrial revolution.

More recently, the development of space travel and the computer revolution have helped fuel tremendous progress in astronomy. We've sent probes to all the planets in our solar system, and many of our most powerful observatories, including the Hubble Space Telescope, reside in space. On the ground, computer design and control have led to tremendous growth in the size and power of telescopes.

Many of these efforts, and the achievements they spawned, led to profound social change. The most famous example is the fate of Galileo, whom the Vatican put under house arrest in 1633 for his claims that Earth orbits the Sun. Although the Church soon recognized that Galileo was right, he was formally vindicated only in 1992 with a statement by Pope John Paul II. In the meantime, his case spurred great debate in religious circles and profoundly influenced both theological and scientific thinking.

As you progress through this book and learn about astronomical discovery, try to keep in mind the context of the human adventure. You will then be learning not just about a science, but also about one of the great forces that has shaped our modern world.

These forces will continue to play a role in our future. What will it mean to us when we learn the nature of dark matter and dark energy? How will our view of Earth change when we learn whether life is common or rare in the universe? Only time may answer these questions, but the chapters ahead will give you the foundation you need to understand how we changed from a primitive people looking at patterns in the night sky to a civilization capable of asking deep questions about our existence.

The Big Picture

Putting Chapter 1 into Context

In this first chapter, we developed a broad overview of our place in the universe. As we consider the universe in more depth in the rest of the book, remember the following "big picture" ideas:

- Earth is not the center of the universe but instead is a planet orbiting a rather ordinary star in the Milky Way Galaxy. The Milky Way Galaxy, in turn, is one of billions of galaxies in our observable universe.

- Cosmic distances are literally astronomical, but we can put them in perspective with the aid of scale models and other scaling techniques. When you think about these enormous scales, don't forget that every star is a sun and every planet is a unique world.

- We are "star stuff." The atoms from which we are made began as hydrogen and helium in the Big Bang and were later fused into heavier elements by massive stars. Stellar deaths released these atoms into space, where our galaxy recycled them into new stars and planets. Our solar system formed from such recycled matter some $4\frac{1}{2}$ billion years ago.

- We are latecomers on the scale of cosmic time. The universe was already more than half its current age when our solar system formed, and it took billions of years more before humans arrived on the scene.

- All of us are being carried through the cosmos on spaceship Earth. Although we cannot feel this motion in our everyday lives, the associated speeds are surprisingly high. Learning about the motions of spaceship Earth gives us a new perspective on the cosmos and helps us understand its nature and history.

SUMMARY OF KEY CONCEPTS

1.1 THE SCALE OF THE UNIVERSE

- **What is our place in the universe?** Earth is a planet orbit-

ing the Sun. Our Sun is one of more than 100 billion stars in the **Milky Way Galaxy.** Our galaxy is one of about 40 galaxies in the **Local Group.** The Local Group is one small part of the **Local Supercluster,** which is one small part of the **universe.**

- **How big is the universe?** If we imagine our Sun as a large

grapefruit, Earth is a ball point that orbits 15 meters away; the nearest stars are thousands of kilometers away on the same scale. Our galaxy contains more than 100 billion stars—so many that it would take thousands of years just to count them out loud.
The observable universe contains roughly 100 billion galaxies, and the total number of stars is comparable to the number of grains of dry sand on all the beaches on Earth.

1.2 THE HISTORY OF THE UNIVERSE

- **How did we come to be?** The universe began in the **Big**
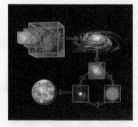
Bang and has been expanding ever since, except in localized regions where gravity has caused matter to collapse into galaxies and stars. The Big Bang essentially produced only two chemical elements: hydrogen and helium. The rest have been produced by stars and recycled within galaxies from one generation of stars to the next, which is why we are "star stuff."

- **How do our lifetimes compare to the age of the universe?** On a cosmic calendar that compresses the history of

the universe into 1 year, human civilization is just a few seconds old, and a human lifetime lasts only a fraction of a second.

1.3 SPACESHIP EARTH

■ **How is Earth moving through space?** Earth **rotates** on its
axis once each day and **orbits**
the Sun once each year. At
the same time, we move with
our Sun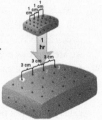
in random directions relative to other stars
in our local solar neighborhood, while the
galaxy's rotation carries us around the center
of the galaxy every 230 million years.

■ **How do galaxies move within the
universe?** Galaxies move essentially at
random within the Local Group, but all
galaxies beyond the Local Group are moving away from us.
More distant galaxies are moving faster, which tells us that we
live in an expanding universe.

1.4 THE HUMAN ADVENTURE OF ASTRONOMY

■ **How has the study of astronomy affected human history?**
Throughout history, astronomy has developed hand in hand
with social and technological development. Astronomy thereby
touches all of us and is a human adventure that all can enjoy.

VISUAL SKILLS CHECK

*Use the following questions to check your understanding of some of the many types of visual information used
in astronomy. Answers are provided in Appendix J. For additional practice, try the Chapter 1 Visual Quiz at
MasteringAstronomy®.*

Useful Data:

Earth-Sun distance = 150,000,000 km

Diameter of Sun = 1,400,000 km

Earth-Moon distance = 384,000 km

Diameter of Earth = 12,800 km

*The figure above shows the sizes of Earth and the Moon to scale; the scale used is 1 cm = 4000 km. Using what you've
learned about astronomical scale in this chapter, answer the following questions. Hint: If you are unsure of the answers,
you can calculate them using the data given above.*

1. If you wanted to show the *distance* between Earth and the Moon
   on the same scale, about how far apart would you need to place
   the two photos?
   a. 10 centimeters (about the width of your hand)
   b. 1 meter (about the length of your arm)
   c. 100 meters (about the length of a football field)
   d. 1 kilometer (a little more than a half mile)
2. Suppose you wanted to show the Sun on the same scale. About
   how big would it need to be?
   a. 2.5 centimeters in diameter (the size of a golf ball)
   b. 25 centimeters in diameter (the size of a basketball)
   c. 2.5 meters in diameter (about 8 feet across)
   d. 2.5 kilometers in diameter (the size of a small town)
3. About how far away from Earth would the Sun be located on
   this scale?
   a. 3.75 meters (about 12 feet)
   b. 37.5 meters (about the height of a 12-story building)
   c. 375 meters (about the length of four football fields)
   d. 37.5 kilometers (the size of a large city)
4. Could you use the same scale to represent the distances to
   nearby stars? Why or why not?

EXERCISES AND PROBLEMS

MasteringAstronomy®

For instructor-assigned homework go to MasteringAstronomy®.

REVIEW QUESTIONS

Short-Answer Questions Based on the Reading

1. Briefly describe the major levels of structure (such as planet, star,
   galaxy) in the universe.
2. Define *astronomical unit* and *light-year*.
3. Explain the statement *The farther away we look in distance, the
   further back we look in time.*
4. What do we mean by the *observable universe*? Is it the same thing
   as the entire universe?
5. Using techniques described in the chapter, put the following into
   perspective: the size of our solar system; the distance to nearby
   stars; the size and number of stars in the Milky Way Galaxy; the
   number of stars in the observable universe.
6. What do we mean when we say that the universe is *expanding*,
   and how does expansion lead to the idea of the *Big Bang* and our
   current estimate of the age of the universe?
7. In what sense are we "star stuff"?

8. Use the cosmic calendar to describe how the human race fits into the scale of time.

9. Briefly explain Earth's daily rotation and annual orbit, defining the terms *ecliptic plane* and *axis tilt*.

10. Briefly describe our solar system's location and motion within the Milky Way Galaxy.

11. Where does *dark matter* seem to reside in our galaxy? What makes dark matter and *dark energy* so mysterious?

12. What key observations lead us to conclude that the universe is expanding? Use the raisin cake model to explain how these observations imply expansion.

TEST YOUR UNDERSTANDING

Does It Make Sense?

Decide whether the statement makes sense (or is clearly true) or does not make sense (or is clearly false). Explain clearly; not all of these have definitive answers, so your explanation is more important than your chosen answer.

Example: I walked east from our base camp at the North Pole.

Solution: The statement does not make sense because east has no meaning at the North Pole—all directions are south from the North Pole.

13. Our solar system is bigger than some galaxies.

14. The universe is billions of light-years in age.

15. It will take me light-years to complete this homework assignment!

16. Someday we may build spaceships capable of traveling a light-year in only a decade.

17. Astronomers recently discovered a moon that does not orbit a planet.

18. NASA plans soon to launch a spaceship that will photograph our Milky Way Galaxy from beyond its halo.

19. The observable universe is the same size today as it was a few billion years ago.

20. Photographs of distant galaxies show them as they were when they were much younger than they are today.

21. At a nearby park, I built a scale model of our solar system in which I used a basketball to represent Earth.

22. Because nearly all galaxies are moving away from us, we must be located at the center of the universe.

Quick Quiz

Choose the best answer to each of the following. Explain your reasoning with one or more complete sentences.

23. Which of the following correctly lists our "cosmic address" from small to large? (a) Earth, solar system, Milky Way Galaxy, Local Group, Local Supercluster, universe (b) Earth, solar system, Local Group, Local Supercluster, Milky Way Galaxy, universe (c) Earth, Milky Way Galaxy, solar system, Local Group, Local Supercluster, universe.

24. An astronomical unit is (a) any planet's average distance from the Sun. (b) Earth's average distance from the Sun. (c) any large astronomical distance.

25. The star Betelgeuse is about 600 light-years away. If it explodes tonight, (a) we'll know because it will be brighter than the full Moon in the sky. (b) we'll know because debris from the explosion will rain down on us from space. (c) we won't know about it until about 600 years from now.

26. If we represent the solar system on a scale that allows us to walk from the Sun to Pluto in a few minutes, then (a) the planets are the size of basketballs and the nearest stars are a few miles away. (b) the planets are marble-size or smaller and the nearest stars are thousands of miles away. (c) the planets are microscopic and the stars are light-years away.

27. The total number of stars in the observable universe is roughly equivalent to (a) the number of grains of sand on all the beaches on Earth. (b) the number of grains of sand on Miami Beach. (c) infinity.

28. When we say the universe is *expanding*, we mean that (a) everything in the universe is growing in size. (b) the average distance between galaxies is growing with time. (c) the universe is getting older.

29. If stars existed but galaxies did not, (a) we would probably still exist anyway. (b) we would not exist because life on Earth depends on the light of galaxies. (c) we would not exist because we are made of material that was recycled in galaxies.

30. Could we see a galaxy that is 50 billion light-years away? (a) Yes, if we had a big enough telescope. (b) No, because it would be beyond the bounds of our observable universe. (c) No, because a galaxy could not possibly be that far away.

31. The age of our solar system is about (a) one-third of the age of the universe. (b) three-fourths of the age of the universe. (c) two billion years less than the age of the universe.

32. The fact that nearly all galaxies are moving away from us, with more distant ones moving faster, helped us to conclude that (a) the universe is expanding. (b) galaxies repel each other like magnets. (c) our galaxy lies near the center of the universe.

PROCESS OF SCIENCE

Examining How Science Works

33. *Earth as a Planet.* For most of human history, scholars assumed Earth was the center of the universe. Today, we know that our Sun is just one star in a vast universe. How did science make it possible for us to learn these facts about Earth?

34. *Thinking About Scale.* One key to success in science is finding simple ways to evaluate new ideas, and making a simple scale model is often helpful. Suppose someone tells you that the reason it is warmer during the day than at night is that the day side of Earth is closer to the Sun than the night side. Evaluate this idea by thinking about the size of Earth and its distance from the Sun in a scale model of the solar system.

35. *Looking for Evidence.* In this first chapter, we have discussed the scientific story of the universe but have not yet discussed most of the evidence that backs it up. Choose one idea presented in this chapter—such as the idea that there are billions of galaxies in the universe, or that the universe was born in the Big Bang, or that the galaxy contains more dark matter than ordinary matter—and briefly discuss the type of evidence you would want to see before accepting the idea. (*Hint:* It's okay to look ahead in the book to see the evidence presented in later chapters.)

GROUP WORK EXERCISE

36. *Counting the Milky Way's Stars.* In this exercise, you will first make an estimate of the number of stars in the Milky Way and then apply some scientific thinking to your estimation method. Before you begin, assign the following roles to the people in your group: *Scribe* (takes notes on the group's activities), *Proposer* (proposes explanations to the group), *Skeptic* (points out weaknesses in proposed explanations), and *Moderator* (leads group discussion and makes sure everyone contributes).

a. Estimate the number of stars in the Milky Way as follows. First, count the number of stars within 12 light-years of the Sun, which are listed in Appendix F. Assuming that the Milky Way's disk is 100,000 light-years across and 1000 light-years thick, its volume is about 1 billion times the volume of the region of your star count. You should therefore multiply your count by 1 billion to get an estimate of the total number of stars in the Milky Way. **b.** Your estimate from part a is based on the number of stars near the Sun. Compare it to the value given in this chapter and determine whether your estimate is an underestimate or an overestimate of the total number of stars in the Milky Way. Write down a list of possible reasons why your technique gave you an under/overestimate.

INVESTIGATE FURTHER

In-Depth Questions to Increase Your Understanding

Short-Answer/Essay Questions

37. *Alien Technology.* Some people believe that Earth is regularly visited by aliens who travel here from other star systems. For this to be true, how much more advanced than our own technology would the alien space travel technology have to be? Write one to two paragraphs to give a sense of the technological difference. (*Hint:* Use the scale model from this chapter to contrast the distance the aliens would have to travel easily with the distances we currently are capable of traveling.)

38. *Raisin Cake Universe.* Suppose that all the raisins in a cake are 1 centimeter apart before baking and 4 centimeters apart after baking.
   a. Draw diagrams to represent the cake before and after baking.
   b. Identify one raisin as the Local Raisin on your diagrams. Construct a table showing the distances and speeds of other raisins as seen from the Local Raisin. **c.** Briefly explain how your expanding cake is similar to the expansion of the universe.

39. *Scaling the Local Group of Galaxies.* Both the Milky Way Galaxy and the Andromeda Galaxy (M31) have a diameter of about 100,000 light-years. The distance between the two galaxies is about 2.5 million light-years.
   a. Using a scale on which 1 centimeter represents 100,000 light-years, draw a sketch showing both galaxies and the distance between them to scale. **b.** How does the separation between galaxies compare to the separation between stars? Based on your answer, discuss the likelihood of galactic collisions in comparison to the likelihood of stellar collisions.

40. *The Cosmic Perspective.* Write a short essay describing how the ideas presented in this chapter affect your perspectives on your own life and on human civilization.

Quantitative Problems

Be sure to show all calculations clearly and state your final answers in complete sentences.

41. *Distances by Light.* Just as a light-year is the distance that light can travel in 1 year, we define a light-second as the distance that light can travel in 1 second, a light-minute as the distance that light can travel in 1 minute, and so on. Calculate the distance in both kilometers and miles represented by each of the following:
   a. 1 light-second. **b.** 1 light-minute. **c.** 1 light-hour. **d.** 1 light-day.

42. *Spacecraft Communication.* We use radio waves, which travel at the speed of light, to communicate with robotic spacecraft. How long does it take a message to travel from Earth to a spacecraft at
   a. Mars at its closest to Earth (about 56 million km)? **b.** Mars at its farthest from Earth (about 400 million km)? **c.** Pluto at its average distance from Earth (about 5.9 billion km)?

43. *Saturn vs. the Milky Way.* Photos of Saturn and photos of galaxies can look so similar that children often think the photos show similar objects. In reality, a galaxy is far larger than any planet. About how many times larger is the diameter of the Milky Way Galaxy than the diameter of Saturn's rings? (Data: Saturn's rings are about 270,000 km in diameter; the Milky Way is 100,000 light-years in diameter.)

44. *Galaxy Scale.* Consider the 1-to-10^{19} scale on which the disk of the Milky Way Galaxy fits on a football field. On this scale, how far is it from the Sun to Alpha Centauri (real distance: 4.4 light-years)? How big is the Sun itself on this scale? Compare the Sun's size on this scale to the actual size of a typical atom (about 10^{-10} m in diameter).

45. *Universal Scale.* Suppose we wanted to make a scale model of the Local Group of galaxies, in which the Milky Way Galaxy was the size of a marble (about 1 cm in diameter).
   a. How far from the Milky Way Galaxy would the Andromeda Galaxy be on this scale? **b.** How far would the Sun be from Alpha Centauri on this scale? **c.** How far would it be from the Milky Way Galaxy to the most distant galaxies in the observable universe on this scale?

46. *Driving Trips.* Imagine that you could drive your car at a constant speed of 100 km/hr (62 mi/hr), even across oceans and in space. (In reality, the law of gravity would make driving through space at a constant speed all but impossible.) How long would it take to drive **a.** around Earth's equator? **b.** from the Sun to Earth? **c.** from the Sun to Pluto? **d.** to Alpha Centauri?

47. *Faster Trip.* Suppose you wanted to reach Alpha Centauri in 100 years.
   a. How fast would you have to go, in km/hr? **b.** How many times faster is the speed you found in part a than the speeds of our fastest current spacecraft (around 50,000 km/hr)?

48. *Galactic Rotation Speed.* We are located about 27,000 light-years from the galactic center and we orbit the center about once every 230 million years. How fast are we traveling around the galaxy, in km/hr?

49. *Earth Rotation Speed.* Mathematical Insight 1.3 shows how to find Earth's equatorial rotation speed. To find the rotation speed at any other latitude, you need the following fact: The radial distance from Earth's axis at any latitude is equal to the equatorial radius times the *cosine* of the latitude. Use this fact to find the rotation speed at the following latitudes. (*Hint:* When using the cosine (cos) function, be sure your calculator is set to recognize angles in degree mode, not in radian or gradient mode.)
   a. 30°N **b.** 60°N **c.** your latitude.

Discussion Questions

50. *Eliot Quote.* Think carefully about the chapter-opening quotation from T. S. Eliot. What do you think he means? Explain clearly.

51. *Infant Species.* In the last few tenths of a second before midnight on December 31 of the cosmic calendar, we have developed an incredible civilization and learned a great deal about the universe, but we also have developed technology with which we could destroy ourselves. The midnight bell is striking, and the choice for the future is ours. How far into the next cosmic year do you think our civilization will survive? Defend your opinion.

52. *A Human Adventure.* Astronomical discoveries clearly are important to science, but are they also important to our personal lives? Defend your opinion.

Web Projects

53. *Astronomy on the Web.* The Web contains a vast amount of astronomical information. Spend at least an hour exploring astronomy on the Web. Write two or three paragraphs summarizing what you learned from your research. What was your favorite astronomical website, and why?

54. *NASA Missions.* Visit the NASA website to learn about upcoming astronomy missions. Write a one-page summary of the mission you believe is most likely to give us new astronomical information before the end of your astronomy course.

55. *The Hubble Ultra Deep Field.* The photo that opens this chapter is called the Hubble Ultra Deep Field. Find this photo on the Hubble Space Telescope website. Learn how it was taken, what it shows, and what we've learned from it. Write a short summary of your findings.

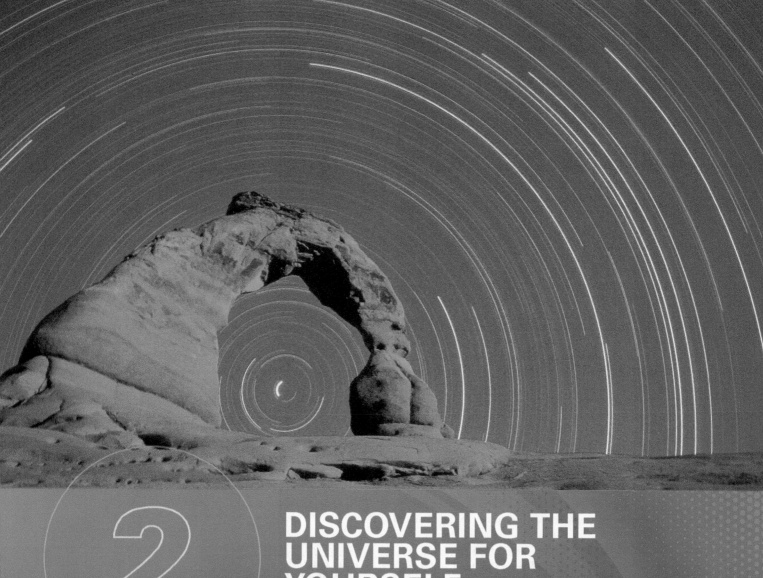

2 DISCOVERING THE UNIVERSE FOR YOURSELF

We had the sky, up there, all speckled with stars, and we used to lay on our backs and look up at them, and discuss about whether they was made, or only just happened.
　　　　　　　　　　—*Mark Twain, Huckleberry Finn*

This is an exciting time in the history of astronomy. A new generation of telescopes is scanning the depths of the universe. Increasingly sophisticated space probes are collecting new data about the planets and other objects in our solar system. Rapid advances in computing technology are allowing scientists to analyze the vast amount of new data and to model the processes that occur in planets, stars, galaxies, and the universe.

One goal of this book is to help *you* share in the ongoing adventure of astronomical discovery. One of the best ways to become a part of this adventure is to do what other humans have done for thousands of generations: Go outside, observe the sky around you, and contemplate the awe-inspiring universe of which you are a part. In this chapter, we'll discuss a few key ideas that will help you understand what you see in the sky.

2.1 PATTERNS IN THE NIGHT SKY

Today we take for granted that we live on a small planet orbiting an ordinary star in one of many galaxies in the universe. But this fact is not obvious from a casual glance at the night sky, and we've learned about our place in the cosmos only through a long history of careful observations. In this section, we'll discuss major features of the night sky and how we understand them in light of our current knowledge of the universe.

What does the universe look like from Earth?

Shortly after sunset, as daylight fades to darkness, the sky appears to slowly fill with stars. On clear, moonless nights far from city lights, more than 2000 stars may be visible to your naked eye, along with the whitish band of light that we call the Milky Way (**FIGURE 2.1**). As you look at the stars, your mind may group them into patterns that look like familiar shapes or objects. If you observe the sky night after night or year after year, you will recognize the same patterns of stars. These patterns have not changed noticeably in the past few thousand years.

Constellations People of nearly every culture gave names to patterns they saw in the sky. We usually refer to such patterns as constellations, but to astronomers the term has a more precise meaning: A **constellation** is a *region* of the sky with well-defined borders; the familiar patterns of stars merely help us locate the constellations. Just as every spot of land in the continental United States is part of some state, every point in the sky belongs to some constellation. **FIGURE 2.2** shows the borders of the constellation Orion and several of its neighbors.

FIGURE 2.1 This photo shows the Milky Way over Haleakala crater on the island of Maui, Hawaii. The bright spot just below (and slightly left of) the center of the band is the planet Jupiter.

The names and borders of the 88 official constellations (Appendix H) were chosen in 1928 by members of the International Astronomical Union (IAU). Most of the IAU members lived in Europe or the United States, so they chose names familiar in the western world. That is why the official names for constellations visible in the Northern Hemisphere can be traced back to civilizations of the ancient Middle East,

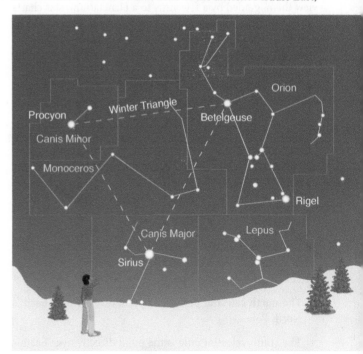

FIGURE 2.2 Red lines mark official borders of several constellations near Orion. Yellow lines connect recognizable patterns of stars within constellations. Sirius, Procyon, and Betelgeuse form a pattern that spans several constellations and is called the *Winter Triangle*. This view shows how it appears on winter evenings from the Northern Hemisphere.

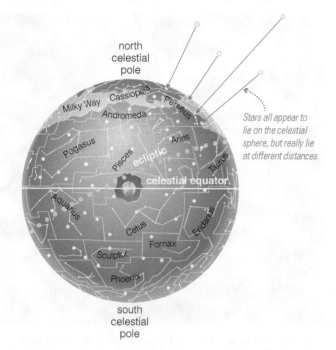

north celestial pole

Milky Way Cassiopeia Perseus
Andromeda
Pegasus Aries
Pisces ecliptic
Taurus
celestial equator
Aquarius
Cetus Eridanus
Fornax
Sculptor
Phoenix

south celestial pole

Stars all appear to lie on the celestial sphere, but really lie at different distances.

FIGURE 2.3 The stars and constellations appear to lie on a celestial sphere that surrounds Earth. This is an illusion created by our lack of depth perception in space, but it is useful for mapping the sky.

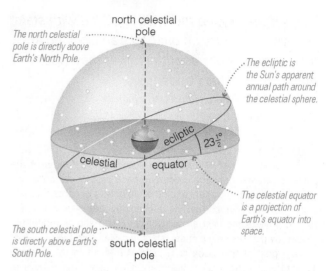

north celestial pole

The north celestial pole is directly above Earth's North Pole.

The ecliptic is the Sun's apparent annual path around the celestial sphere.

ecliptic
$23\frac{1}{2}°$
celestial equator

The celestial equator is a projection of Earth's equator into space.

The south celestial pole is directly above Earth's South Pole.

south celestial pole

FIGURE 2.4 This schematic diagram shows key features of the celestial sphere.

while Southern Hemisphere constellations carry names that originated with 17th-century European explorers.

Recognizing the patterns of just 20 or so constellations is enough to make the sky seem as familiar as your own neighborhood. The best way to learn the constellations is to go out and view them, guided by a few visits to a planetarium, star charts (Appendix I), or sky-viewing apps for smart phones and tablets.

The Celestial Sphere The stars in a particular constellation appear to lie close to one another but may be quite far apart in reality, because they may lie at very different distances from Earth. This illusion occurs because we lack depth perception when we look into space, a consequence of the fact that the stars are so far away [**Section 1.1**]. The ancient Greeks mistook this illusion for reality, imagining the stars and constellations to lie on a great **celestial sphere** that surrounds Earth (**FIGURE 2.3**).

We now know that Earth seems to be in the center of the celestial sphere only because it is where we are located as we look into space. Nevertheless, the celestial sphere is a useful illusion, because it allows us to map the sky as seen from Earth. For reference, we identify four special points and circles on the celestial sphere (**FIGURE 2.4**).

- The **north celestial pole** is the point directly over Earth's North Pole.

- The **south celestial pole** is the point directly over Earth's South Pole.

- The **celestial equator,** which is a projection of Earth's equator into space, makes a complete circle around the celestial sphere.

- The **ecliptic** is the path the Sun follows as it appears to circle around the celestial sphere once each year. It crosses the celestial equator at a $23\frac{1}{2}°$ angle, because that is the tilt of Earth's axis.

The Milky Way The band of light that we call the Milky Way circles all the way around the celestial sphere, passing through more than a dozen constellations. The widest and brightest parts of the Milky Way are most easily seen from the Southern Hemisphere, which probably explains why the Aborigines of Australia gave names to patterns within the Milky Way in the same way other cultures named patterns of stars.

Our Milky Way Galaxy gets its name from this band of light, and the two "Milky Ways" are closely related: *The Milky Way in the night sky traces our galaxy's disk of stars—the galactic plane—as it appears from our location within the Milky Way Galaxy.* **FIGURE 2.5** shows the idea. Our galaxy is shaped like a thin pancake with a bulge in the middle. We view the universe from our location a little more than halfway out from the center of this "pancake." In all directions that we look within the pancake, we see the countless stars and vast interstellar clouds that make up the Milky Way in the night sky; that is why the band of light makes a full circle around our sky. The Milky Way appears somewhat wider in the direction of the constellation Sagittarius, because that is the direction in which we are looking toward the galaxy's central bulge. We have a clear view to the distant universe only when we look *away* from the galactic plane, along directions that have relatively few stars and clouds to block our view.

The dark lanes that run down the center of the Milky Way contain the densest clouds, obscuring our view of stars behind them. In fact, these clouds generally prevent us from seeing more than a few thousand light-years into our galaxy's disk. As a result, much of our own galaxy remained hidden from view until just a few decades ago, when new technologies allowed us to peer through the clouds by observing forms of light that are invisible to our eyes (such as radio waves and X rays [**Section 5.2**]).

When we look out of the galactic plane (white arrows), we have a clear view to the distant universe.

Galactic plane

Location of our solar system

When we look in any direction into the galactic plane (blue arrows), we see the stars and interstellar clouds that make up the Milky Way in the night sky.

FIGURE 2.5 This painting shows how our galaxy's structure affects our view from Earth.

THINK ABOUT IT

Consider a distant galaxy located in the same direction from Earth as the center of our own galaxy (but much farther away). Could we see it with our eyes? Explain.

The Local Sky The celestial sphere provides a useful way of thinking about the appearance of the universe from Earth. But it is not what we actually see when we go outside. Instead, your **local sky**—the sky as seen from wherever you happen to be standing—appears to take the shape of a hemisphere or dome, which explains why people of many ancient cultures imagined that we lived on a flat Earth under a great dome encompassing the world. The dome shape arises from the fact that we see only half of the celestial sphere at any particular moment from any particular location, while the ground blocks the other half from view.

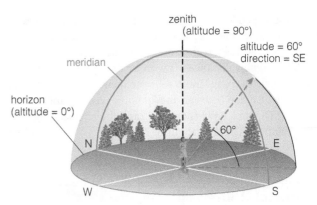

zenith
(altitude = 90°)

altitude = 60°
direction = SE

meridian

horizon
(altitude = 0°)

60°

N   E

W   S

FIGURE 2.6 From any place on Earth, the local sky looks like a dome (hemisphere). This diagram shows key reference points in the local sky. It also shows how we can describe any position in the local sky by its altitude and direction.

FIGURE 2.6 shows key reference features of the local sky. The boundary between Earth and sky defines the **horizon.** The point directly overhead is the **zenith.** The **meridian** is an imaginary half circle stretching from the horizon due south, through the zenith, to the horizon due north.

We can pinpoint the position of any object in the local sky by stating its **direction** along the horizon (sometimes stated as *azimuth*, which is degrees clockwise from due north) and its **altitude** above the horizon. For example, Figure 2.6 shows a person pointing to a star located in the direction of southeast at an altitude of 60°. Note that the zenith has altitude 90° but no direction, because it is straight overhead.

Angular Sizes and Distances Our lack of depth perception on the celestial sphere means we have no way to judge the true sizes or separations of the objects we see in the sky. However, we can describe the *angular* sizes or separations of objects without knowing how far away they are.

The **angular size** of an object is the angle it appears to span in your field of view. For example, the angular sizes of the Sun and Moon are each about $\frac{1}{2}$° (FIGURE 2.7a). Note that angular size does not by itself tell us an object's true size, because angular

a The angular sizes of the Sun and the Moon are about 1/2°.

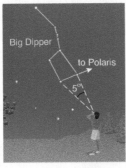

b The angular distance between the "pointer stars" of the Big Dipper is about 5°, and the angular length of the Southern Cross is about 6°.

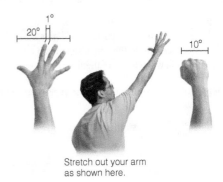

Stretch out your arm as shown here.

c You can estimate angular sizes or distances with your outstretched hand.

FIGURE 2.7 We measure *angular sizes* or *angular distances,* rather than actual sizes or distances, when we look at objects in the sky.

size also depends on distance. The Sun is about 400 times as large in diameter as the Moon, but it has the same angular size in our sky because it is also about 400 times as far away.

The **angular distance** between a pair of objects in the sky is the angle that appears to separate them. For example, the angular distance between the "pointer stars" at the end of the Big Dipper's bowl is about 5° and the angular length of the Southern Cross is about 6° (FIGURE 2.7b). You can use

your outstretched hand to make rough estimates of angles in the sky (FIGURE 2.7c).

For more precise astronomical measurements, we subdivide each degree into 60 **arcminutes** and subdivide each arcminute into 60 **arcseconds** (FIGURE 2.8). We abbreviate arcminutes with the symbol ′ and arcseconds with the symbol ″. For example, we read 35°27′15″ as "35 degrees, 27 arcminutes, 15 arcseconds."

MATHEMATICAL INSIGHT 2.1

Angular Size, Physical Size, and Distance

An object's angular size depends on its physical (actual) size and distance. FIGURE 1a shows the basic idea: An object's physical size does not change as you move it farther from your eye, but its *angular size* gets smaller, making it appear smaller against the background.

FIGURE 1b shows a simple approximation that we can use to find a formula relating angular size to physical size and distance. As long as an object's angular size is relatively small (less than a few degrees), its physical size (diameter) is similar to that of a small piece of a circle going all the way around your eye with a radius equal to the object's distance from your eye. The object's angular size (in degrees) is therefore the *same fraction* of the full 360° circle as its physical size is of the circle's full circumference (given by the formula $2\pi \times distance$). That is,

$$\frac{\text{angular size}}{360°} = \frac{\text{physical size}}{2\pi \times \text{distance}}$$

We solve for the angular size by multiplying both sides by 360°:

$$\text{angular size} = \text{physical size} \times \frac{360°}{2\pi \times \text{distance}}$$

This formula is often called the **small-angle formula**, because it is valid only when the angular size is small.

EXAMPLE 1: The two headlights on a car are separated by 1.5 meters. What is their angular separation when the car is 500 meters away?

SOLUTION:

Step 1 Understand: We can use the small-angle formula by thinking of the "separation" between the two lights as a "size." That is, if we set the physical size to the actual separation of 1.5 meters, the small-angle formula will tell us the angular separation.

Step 2 Solve: We simply plug in the given values and solve:

$$\begin{aligned} \text{angular separation} &= \text{physical separation} \times \frac{360°}{2\pi \times \text{distance}} \\ &= 1.5 \text{ m} \times \frac{360°}{2\pi \times 500 \text{ m}} \approx 0.17° \end{aligned}$$

Step 3 Explain: We have found that the angular separation of the two headlights is 0.17°. This small angle will be easier to interpret if we convert it to arcminutes. There are 60 arcminutes in 1°, so 0.17° is equivalent to 0.17 × 60 = 10.2 arcminutes. In other words, the

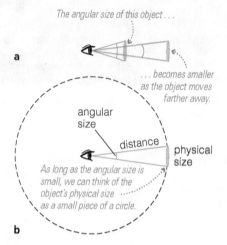

FIGURE 1 Angular size depends on physical size and distance.

angular separation of the headlights is about 10 arcminutes, or about a third of the 30 arcminute (0.5°) angular diameter of the Moon.

EXAMPLE 2: Estimate the Moon's actual diameter from its angular diameter of about 0.5° and its distance of about 380,000 km.

SOLUTION:

Step 1 Understand: We are seeking to find a physical size (diameter) from an angular size and distance. We therefore need to solve the small-angle formula for the *physical size*, which we do by switching its left and right sides and multiplying both sides by $(2\pi \times distance)/360°$:

$$\text{physical size} = \text{angular size} \times \frac{2\pi \times \text{distance}}{360°}$$

Step 2 Solve: We now plug in the given values of the Moon's angular size and distance:

$$\text{physical size} = 0.5° \times \frac{2\pi \times 380,000 \text{ km}}{360°} \approx 3300 \text{ km}$$

Step 3 Explain: We have used the Moon's approximate angular size and distance to find that its diameter is about 3300 kilometers. We could find a more exact value (3476 km) by using more precise values for the angular diameter and distance.

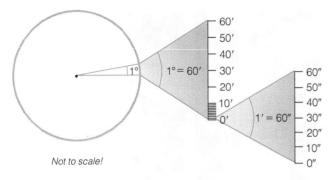

Not to scale!

FIGURE 2.8 We subdivide each degree into 60 arcminutes and each arcminute into 60 arcseconds.

Why do stars rise and set?

If you spend a few hours out under a starry sky, you'll notice that the universe seems to be circling around us, with stars moving gradually across the sky from east to west. Many ancient people took this appearance at face value, concluding that we lie at the center of a universe that rotates around us each day. Today we know that the ancients had it backward: It is Earth that rotates daily, not the rest of the universe.

We can picture the movement of the sky by imagining the celestial sphere rotating around Earth (FIGURE 2.9). From this perspective you can see how the universe seems to turn around us: Every object on the celestial sphere appears to make a simple daily circle around Earth. However, the motion can look a little more complex in the local sky, because the horizon cuts the celestial sphere in half. FIGURE 2.10 shows the idea for a location in the United States. If you study the figure carefully,

you'll notice the following key facts about the paths of various stars through the local sky:

- Stars near the north celestial pole are **circumpolar**, meaning that they remain perpetually above the horizon, circling (counterclockwise) around the north celestial pole each day.

- Stars near the south celestial pole never rise above the horizon at all.

- All other stars have daily circles that are partly above the horizon and partly below it, which means they appear to rise in the east and set in the west.

The time-exposure photograph that opens this chapter (page 24), taken at Arches National Park in Utah, shows a part of the daily paths of stars. Paths of circumpolar stars are visible within the arch; notice that the complete daily circles for these stars are above the horizon, although the photo shows only a portion of each circle. The north celestial pole lies at the center of these circles. The circles grow larger for stars farther from

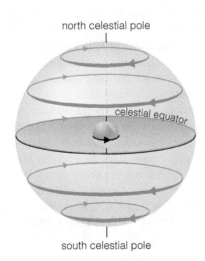

FIGURE 2.9 Earth rotates from west to east (black arrow), making the celestial sphere *appear* to rotate around us from east to west (red arrows).

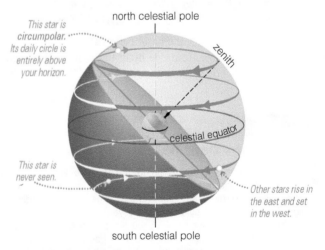

FIGURE 2.10 The local sky for a location in the United States (40°N). The horizon slices through the celestial sphere at an angle to the equator, causing the daily circles of stars to appear tilted in the local sky. Note: It may be easier to follow the star paths in the local sky if you rotate the page so that the zenith points up.

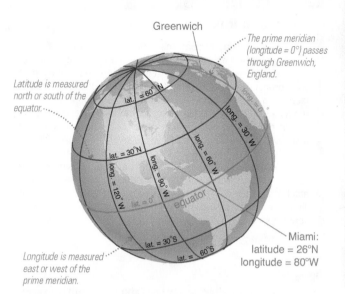

a We can locate any place on Earth's surface by its latitude and longitude.

b The entrance to the Old Royal Greenwich Observatory, near London. The line emerging from the door marks the prime meridian.

FIGURE 2.11 Definitions of latitude and longitude.

the north celestial pole. If they are large enough, the circles cross the horizon, so that the stars rise in the east and set in the west. The same ideas apply in the Southern Hemisphere, except that circumpolar stars are those near the south celestial pole and they circle clockwise rather than counterclockwise.

> ### THINK ABOUT IT
> Do distant galaxies also rise and set like the stars in our sky? Why or why not?

Why do the constellations we see depend on latitude and time of year?

If you stay in one place, the basic patterns of motion in the sky will stay the same from one night to the next. However, if you travel far north or south, you'll see a different set of

> ### COMMON MISCONCEPTIONS
> #### Stars in the Daytime
>
> Stars may appear to vanish in the daytime and "come out" at night, but in reality the stars are always present. The reason you don't see stars in the daytime is that their dim light is overwhelmed by the bright daytime sky. You *can* see bright stars in the daytime with the aid of a telescope, or if you are fortunate enough to observe a total eclipse of the Sun. Astronauts can also see stars in the daytime. Above Earth's atmosphere, where there is no air to scatter sunlight, the Sun is a bright disk against a dark sky filled with stars. (However, the Sun is so bright that astronauts must block its light if they wish to see the stars.)

constellations than you see at home. And even if you stay in one place, you'll see different constellations at different times of year. Let's explore why.

Variation with Latitude **Latitude** measures north-south position on Earth, and **longitude** measures east-west position (FIGURE 2.11). Latitude is defined to be 0° at the equator, increasing to 90°N at the North Pole and 90°S at the South Pole. By international treaty, longitude is defined to be 0° along the **prime meridian**, which passes through Greenwich, England. Stating a latitude and a longitude pinpoints a location on Earth. For example, Miami lies at about 26°N latitude and 80°W longitude.

Latitude affects the constellations we see because it affects the locations of the horizon and zenith relative to the celestial sphere. FIGURE 2.12 shows how this works for the latitudes of the North Pole (90°N) and Sydney, Australia (34°S). Note that although the sky varies with latitude, it does *not* vary with longitude. For example, Charleston (South Carolina) and San Diego (California) are at about the same latitude, so people in both cities see the same set of constellations at night.

You can learn more about how the sky varies with latitude by studying diagrams like those in Figures 2.10 and 2.12. For example, at the North Pole, you can see only objects that lie on the northern half of the celestial sphere, and they are all circumpolar. That is why the Sun remains above the horizon for 6 months at the North Pole: The Sun lies north of the celestial equator for half of each year (see Figure 2.3), so during these 6 months it circles the sky at the North Pole just like a circumpolar star.

The diagrams also show a fact that is very important to navigation:

The altitude of the celestial pole in your sky is equal to your latitude.

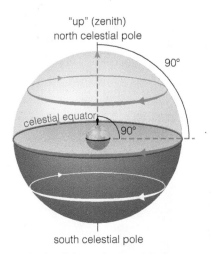

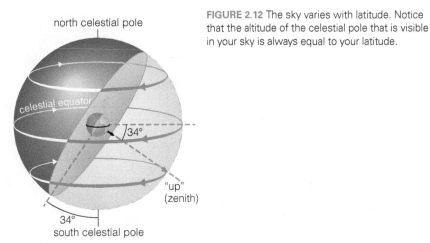

a The local sky at the North Pole (latitude 90°N).

b The local sky at latitude 34°S.

For example, if you see the north celestial pole at an altitude of 40° above your north horizon, your latitude is 40°N. Similarly, if you see the south celestial pole at an altitude of 34° above your south horizon, your latitude is 34°S. You can therefore determine your latitude simply by finding the celestial pole in your sky (FIGURE 2.13). Finding the north celestial pole is fairly easy, because it lies very close to the star Polaris, also known as the North Star (Figure 2.13a). In the Southern Hemisphere, you can find the south celestial pole with the aid of the Southern Cross (Figure 2.13b). We'll discuss celestial navigation and how the sky varies with latitude in more detail in Chapter S1.

SEE IT FOR YOURSELF

What is *your* latitude? Use Figure 2.13 to find the celestial pole in your sky, and estimate its altitude with your hand as shown in Figure 2.7c. Is its altitude what you expect?

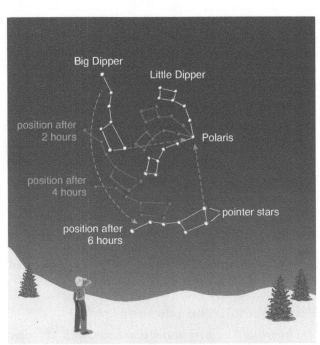

looking northward in the Northern Hemisphere

a The pointer stars of the Big Dipper point to the North Star, Polaris, which lies within 1° of the north celestial pole. The sky appears to turn *counterclockwise* around the north celestial pole.

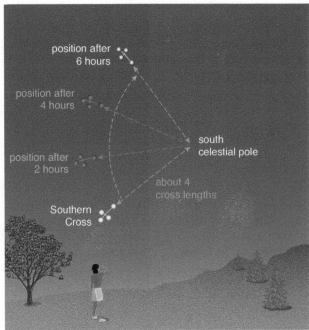

looking southward in the Southern Hemisphere

b The Southern Cross points to the south celestial pole, which is not marked by any bright star. The sky appears to turn *clockwise* around the south celestial pole.

FIGURE 2.13 **interactive figure** You can determine your latitude by measuring the altitude of the celestial pole in your sky.

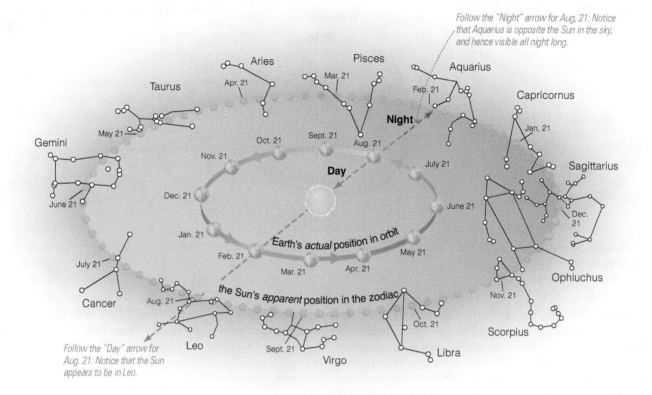

Follow the "Night" arrow for Aug, 21: Notice that Aquarius is opposite the Sun in the sky, and hence visible all night long.

Follow the "Day" arrow for Aug, 21: Notice that the Sun appears to be in Leo.

Earth's *actual* position in orbit

the Sun's *apparent* position in the zodiac

FIGURE 2.14 interactive figure The Sun appears to move steadily eastward along the ecliptic as Earth orbits the Sun, so we see the Sun against the background of different zodiac constellations at different times of year. For example, on August 21 the Sun appears to be in Leo, because it is between us and the much more distant stars that make up Leo.

Variation with Time of Year The night sky changes throughout the year because of Earth's changing position in its orbit around the Sun. **FIGURE 2.14** shows how this works. As Earth orbits, the Sun *appears* to move steadily eastward along the ecliptic, with the stars of different constellations in the background at different times of year. The constellations along the ecliptic make up what we call the **zodiac**; tradition places 12 constellations along the zodiac, but the official borders include a thirteenth constellation, Ophiuchus.

The Sun's apparent location along the ecliptic determines which constellations we see at night. For example, Figure 2.14 shows that the Sun appears to be in Leo in late August. We therefore cannot see Leo at this time (because it is in our daytime sky), but we can see Aquarius all night long because of its location opposite Leo on the celestial sphere. Six months later, in February, we see Leo at night while Aquarius is above the horizon only in the daytime.

(MA) **Seasons Tutorial, Lessons 1–3**

2.2 THE REASON FOR SEASONS

We have seen how Earth's rotation makes the sky appear to circle us daily and how the night sky changes as Earth orbits the Sun each year. The combination of Earth's rotation and orbit also leads to the progression of the seasons.

What causes the seasons?

You know that we have seasonal changes, such as longer and warmer days in summer and shorter and cooler days in winter. But why do the seasons occur? The answer is that the tilt of Earth's axis causes sunlight to fall differently on Earth at different times of year.

FIGURE 2.15 (pages 34–35) illustrates the key ideas. Step 1 illustrates the tilt of Earth's axis, which remains pointed in the same direction in space (toward Polaris) throughout the year.

As a result, the orientation of the axis *relative to the Sun* changes over the course of each orbit: The Northern Hemisphere is tipped toward the Sun in June and away from the Sun in December, while the reverse is true for the Southern Hemisphere. That is why the two hemispheres experience opposite seasons. The rest of the figure shows how the changing angle of sunlight on the two hemispheres leads directly to seasons.

Step 2 shows Earth in June, when axis tilt causes sunlight to strike the Northern Hemisphere at a steeper angle and the Southern Hemisphere at a shallower angle. The steeper sunlight angle makes it summer in the Northern Hemisphere for two reasons. First, as shown in the zoom-out, the steeper angle means more concentrated sunlight, which tends to make it warmer. Second, if you visualize what happens as Earth rotates each day, you'll see that the steeper angle also means the Sun follows a longer and higher path through the sky, giving the Northern Hemisphere more hours of daylight during which it is warmed by the Sun. The opposite is true for the Southern Hemisphere at this time: The shallower sunlight angle makes it winter there because sunlight is less concentrated and the Sun follows a shorter, lower path through the sky.

The sunlight angle gradually changes as Earth orbits the Sun. At the opposite side of Earth's orbit, Step 4 shows that it has become winter for the Northern Hemisphere and summer for the Southern Hemisphere. In between these two extremes, Step 3 shows that both hemispheres are illuminated equally in March and September. It is therefore spring for the hemisphere that is on the way from winter to summer, and fall for the hemisphere on the way from summer to winter.

Notice that the seasons on Earth are caused only by the axis tilt and *not* by any change in Earth's distance from the Sun. Although Earth's orbital distance varies over the course of each year, the variation is fairly small: Earth is only about 3% farther from the Sun at its farthest point than at its nearest. The difference in the strength of sunlight due to this small change in distance is easily overwhelmed by the effects caused by the axis tilt. If Earth did not have an axis tilt, we would not have seasons.

THINK ABOUT IT

Jupiter has an axis tilt of about 3°, small enough to be insignificant. Saturn has an axis tilt of about 27°, slightly greater than that of Earth. Both planets have nearly circular orbits around the Sun. Do you expect Jupiter to have seasons? Do you expect Saturn to have seasons? Explain.

Solstices and Equinoxes To help us mark the changing seasons, we define four special moments in the year, each of which corresponds to one of the four special positions in Earth's orbit shown in Figure 2.15.

- The **summer (June) solstice**, which occurs around June 21, is the moment when the Northern Hemisphere is tipped most directly toward the Sun and receives the most direct sunlight.

- The **winter (December) solstice**, which occurs around December 21, is the moment when the Northern Hemisphere receives the least direct sunlight.

- The **spring (March) equinox**, which occurs around March 21, is the moment when the Northern Hemisphere goes from being tipped slightly away from the Sun to being tipped slightly toward the Sun.

- The **fall (September) equinox**, which occurs around September 22, is the moment when the Northern Hemisphere first starts to be tipped away from the Sun.

The exact dates and times of the solstices and equinoxes vary from year to year, but stay within a couple of days of the dates given above. In fact, our modern calendar includes leap years in a pattern specifically designed to keep the solstices and equinoxes around the same dates [**Section S1.1**].

We can mark the dates of the equinoxes and solstices by observing changes in the Sun's path through our sky (**FIGURE 2.16**). The equinoxes occur on the only two days of the year on which the Sun rises precisely due east and sets precisely due west. The June solstice occurs on the day on which the Sun follows its longest and highest path through the Northern Hemisphere sky (and its shortest and lowest path through the Southern Hemisphere sky). It is therefore the day on which the Sun rises and sets farther to the north than on any other day of the year, and on which the noon Sun reaches its highest point in the Northern Hemisphere sky. The opposite is true on the day of the December solstice, when the Sun rises and sets farthest to the south and the noon Sun is lower in the Northern Hemisphere sky than on any other day of the year. **FIGURE 2.17** shows how the Sun's position in the sky varies over the course of the year.

First Days of Seasons We usually say that each equinox and solstice marks the first day of a season. For example, the day of the summer solstice is usually called the "first day of summer." Notice, however, that the summer (June) solstice occurs when the Northern Hemisphere has its *maximum* tilt toward the Sun. You might then wonder why we consider the solstice to be the beginning rather than the midpoint of summer.

The choice is somewhat arbitrary, but it makes sense in at least two ways. First, it was much easier for ancient people to identify the days on which the Sun reached extreme positions in the sky—such as when it reached its highest point on the summer solstice—than other days in between.

Earth's seasons are caused by the tilt of its rotation axis, which is why the seasons are opposite in the two hemispheres. The seasons do *not* depend on Earth's distance from the Sun, which varies only slightly throughout the year.

① Axis Tilt: Earth's axis points in the same direction throughout the year, which causes changes in Earth's orientation *relative to the Sun.*

② Northern Summer/Southern Winter: In June, sunlight falls more directly on the Northern Hemisphere, which makes it summer there because solar energy is more concentrated and the Sun follows a longer and higher path through the sky. The Southern Hemisphere receives less direct sunlight, making it winter.

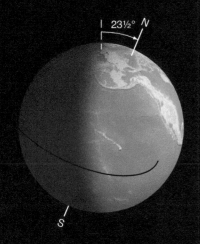

23½°   N

S

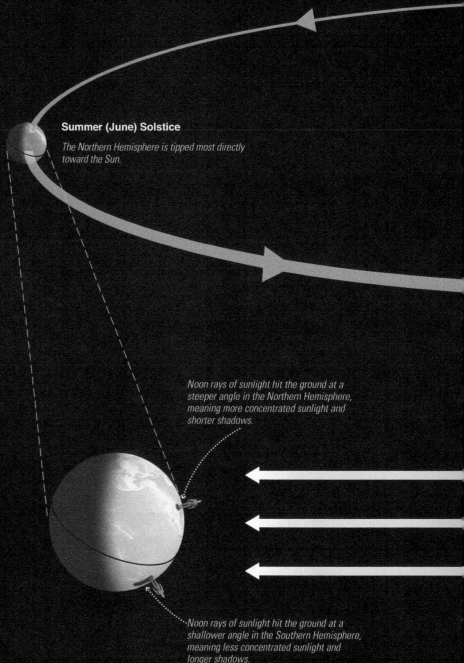

Summer (June) Solstice

The Northern Hemisphere is tipped most directly toward the Sun.

Noon rays of sunlight hit the ground at a steeper angle in the Northern Hemisphere, meaning more concentrated sunlight and shorter shadows.

Noon rays of sunlight hit the ground at a shallower angle in the Southern Hemisphere, meaning less concentrated sunlight and longer shadows.

Interpreting the Diagram

To interpret the seasons diagram properly, keep in mind:

1. Earth's size relative to its orbit would be microscopic on this scale, meaning that both hemispheres are at essentially the same distance from the Sun.

2. The diagram is a side view of Earth's orbit. A top-down view (below) shows that Earth orbits in a nearly perfect circle and comes closest to the Sun in January.

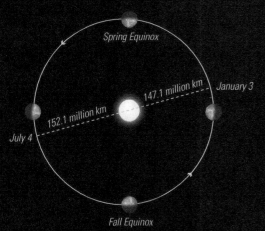

Spring Equinox

147.1 million km   January 3

152.1 million km

July 4

Fall Equinox

③ Spring/Fall: Spring and fall begin when sunlight falls equally on both hemispheres, which happens twice a year: In March, when spring begins in the Northern Hemisphere and fall in the Southern Hemisphere; and in September, when fall begins in the Northern Hemisphere and spring in the Southern Hemisphere.

④ Northern Winter/Southern Summer: In December, sunlight falls less directly on the Northern Hemisphere, which makes it winter because solar energy is less concentrated and the Sun follows a shorter and lower path through the sky. The Southern Hemisphere receives more direct sunlight, making it summer.

Spring (March) Equinox

The Sun shines equally on both hemispheres.

The variation in Earth's orientation relative to the Sun means that the seasons are linked to four special points in Earth's orbit:

Solstices *are the two points at which sunlight becomes most extreme for the two hemispheres.*

Equinoxes *are the two points at which the hemispheres are equally illuminated.*

Winter (December) Solstice

The Southern Hemisphere is tipped most directly toward the Sun.

Fall (September) Equinox

The Sun shines equally on both hemispheres.

Noon rays of sunlight hit the ground at a shallower angle in the Northern Hemisphere, meaning less concentrated sunlight and longer shadows.

Noon rays of sunlight hit the ground at a steeper angle in the Southern Hemisphere, meaning more concentrated sunlight and shorter shadows.

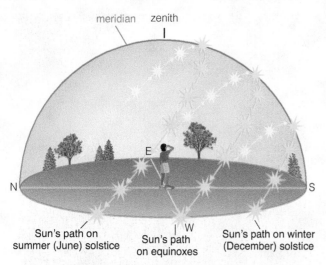

FIGURE 2.16 **interactive figure** This diagram shows the Sun's path on the solstices and equinoxes for a Northern Hemisphere sky (latitude 40°N). The precise paths are different for other latitudes; for example, at latitude 40°S, the paths look similar except tilted to the north rather than to the south. Notice that the Sun rises exactly due east and sets exactly due west only on the equinoxes.

Second, we usually think of the seasons in terms of weather, and the solstices and equinoxes correspond well with the beginnings of seasonal weather patterns. For example, although the Sun's path through the Northern Hemisphere sky is longest and highest around the time of the summer solstice, the warmest days tend to come 1 to 2 months later. To understand why, think about what happens when you heat a pot of cold soup. Even though you may have the stove turned on high from the start, it takes a while for the soup to warm up. In the same way, it takes some time for sunlight to heat the ground and oceans from the cold of winter to the warmth of summer. "Midsummer" in terms of weather therefore comes in late July and early August, which makes the summer solstice a pretty good choice for the "first day of summer." For similar reasons, the winter solstice is a good choice for the first day of winter, and the spring and fall equinoxes are good choices for the first days of those seasons.

Seasons Around the World Notice that the names of the solstices and equinoxes reflect the northern seasons, and therefore sound backward to people who live in the Southern Hemisphere. For example, Southern Hemisphere

FIGURE 2.17 This composite photograph shows images of the Sun taken at the same time of morning (technically, at the same "mean solar time") and from the same spot (over a large sundial in Carefree, Arizona) at 7- to 11-day intervals over the course of a year; the photo looks eastward, so north is to the left and south is to the right. Because this location is in the Northern Hemisphere, the Sun images that are high and to the north represent times near the summer solstice and the images that are low and to the south represent times near the winter solstice. The "figure 8" shape (called an *analemma*) arises from a combination of Earth's axis tilt and Earth's varying speed as it orbits the Sun (see the Special Topic on page 91).

winter begins when Earth is at the orbital point usually called the *summer* solstice. This apparent injustice to people in the Southern Hemisphere arose because the solstices and equinoxes were named long ago by people living in the Northern Hemisphere. A similar injustice is inflicted on people living in equatorial regions. If you study Figure 2.15 carefully, you'll see that Earth's equator gets its most direct sunlight on the two equinoxes and its least direct sunlight on the solstices. People living near the equator therefore don't experience four seasons in the same way as people living at mid-latitudes. Instead, equatorial regions generally have rainy and dry seasons, with the rainy seasons coming when the Sun is higher in the sky.

In addition, seasonal variations around the times of the solstices are more extreme at high latitudes. For example, Vermont has much longer summer days and much longer winter nights than Florida. At the Arctic Circle (latitude $66\frac{1}{2}°$), the Sun remains above the horizon all day long on the summer solstice (FIGURE 2.18), and never rises on the winter solstice. The most extreme cases occur at the North and South Poles, where the Sun remains above the horizon for 6 months in summer and below the horizon for 6 months in winter.*

Why Orbital Distance Doesn't Affect Our Seasons

We've seen that the seasons are caused by Earth's axis tilt, not by Earth's slightly varying distance from the Sun. Still, we might expect the varying orbital distance to play at least some role. For example, the Northern Hemisphere has winter when

*These statements are true for the Sun's *real* position, but the bending of light by Earth's atmosphere makes the Sun *appear* to be about 0.6° higher than it really is when it is near the horizon.

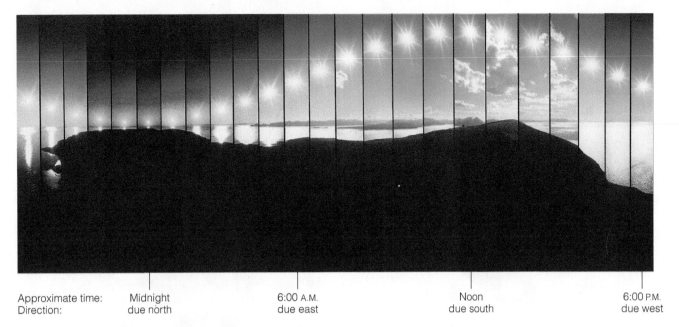

Approximate time:	Midnight	6:00 A.M.	Noon	6:00 P.M.
Direction:	due north	due east	due south	due west

FIGURE 2.18 This sequence of photos shows the progression of the Sun around the horizon on the summer solstice at the Arctic Circle. Notice that the Sun skims the northern horizon at midnight, then gradually rises higher, reaching its highest point when it is due South at noon.

Earth is closer to the Sun and summer when Earth is farther away (see the lower left diagram in Figure 2.15), so we might expect the Northern Hemisphere to have more moderate seasons than the Southern Hemisphere. In fact, weather records show that the opposite is true: Northern Hemisphere seasons are slightly more extreme than those of the Southern Hemisphere.

The main reason for this surprising fact becomes clear when you look at a map of Earth (FIGURE 2.19). Most of Earth's land lies in the Northern Hemisphere, with far more ocean in the Southern Hemisphere. As you'll notice at any beach, lake, or pool, water takes longer to heat or cool than soil or rock (largely because sunlight heats bodies of water to a depth of many meters while heating only the very top layer of land). The water temperature therefore remains fairly steady both day and night, while the ground can heat up and cool down dramatically. The Southern Hemisphere's larger amount of ocean moderates its climate. The Northern Hemisphere, with more land and less ocean, heats up and cools down more easily, which is why it has the more extreme seasons.

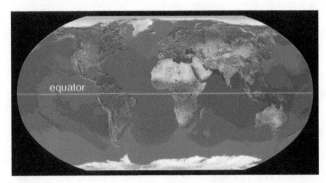

FIGURE 2.19 Most land lies in the Northern Hemisphere while most ocean lies in the Southern Hemisphere. The climate-moderating effects of water make Southern Hemisphere seasons less extreme than Northern Hemisphere seasons.

Although distance from the Sun plays no role in Earth's seasons, the same is not true for planets that have much greater distance variations. For example, Mars has about the same axis tilt as Earth and therefore has similar seasonal patterns. However, because Mars is more than 20% closer to the Sun during its Southern Hemisphere summer than during its Northern Hemisphere summer, its Southern Hemisphere experiences much more extreme seasonal changes.

How does the orientation of Earth's axis change with time?

We have now discussed both daily and seasonal changes in the sky, but there are other changes that occur over longer periods of time. One of the most important of these slow changes is **precession,** a gradual wobble that alters the orientation of Earth's axis in space.

Precession occurs with many rotating objects. You can see it easily by spinning a top (FIGURE 2.20a). As the top spins rapidly, you'll notice that its axis also sweeps out a circle at a slower rate. We say that the top's axis *precesses.* Earth's axis precesses in much the same way, but far more slowly (FIGURE 2.20b). Each cycle of Earth's precession takes about 26,000 years, gradually changing where the axis points in space. Today, the axis points toward Polaris, making it our North Star. Some 13,000 years from now, Vega will be the bright star closest to true north. At most other times, the axis does not point near any bright star.

Notice that precession does not change the *amount* of the axis tilt (which stays close to $23\frac{1}{2}°$) and therefore does not affect the pattern of the seasons. However, because the solstices and equinoxes correspond to points in Earth's orbit that depend on the direction the axis points in space, their positions in the orbit gradually shift with the cycle of precession. As a result, the constellations associated with the solstices and equinoxes

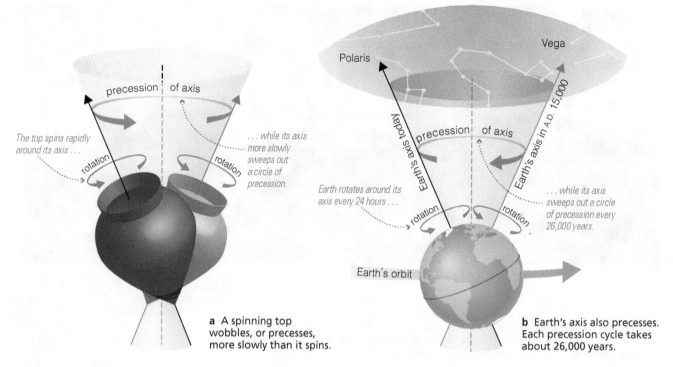

a A spinning top wobbles, or precesses, more slowly than it spins.

b Earth's axis also precesses. Each precession cycle takes about 26,000 years.

FIGURE 2.20 interactive figure Precession affects the orientation of a spinning object's axis but not the amount of its tilt.

change over time. For example, a couple thousand years ago the Sun appeared in the constellation Cancer on the day of the summer solstice, but now it appears in Gemini on that day. This explains something you can see on any world map: The latitude at which the Sun is directly overhead on the summer solstice ($23\frac{1}{2}°$N) is called the *Tropic of Cancer*, telling us that it got its name back when the Sun used to appear in Cancer on the summer solstice.

THINK ABOUT IT

What constellation will the Sun be in on the summer solstice about 2000 years from now? (*Hint:* Figure 2.14 shows the names and order of the zodiac constellations.)

Precession is caused by gravity's effect on a tilted, rotating object that is *not* a perfect sphere. You have probably seen how gravity affects a top. If you try to balance a nonspinning top on its point, it will fall over almost immediately. This happens because a top that is not spherical will inevitably lean a little to one side. No matter how slight this lean, gravity will quickly tip the nonspinning top over. However, if you spin the top rapidly, it does not fall over so easily. The spinning top stays upright because rotating objects tend to keep spinning around the same rotation axis (a consequence of the *law of conservation of angular momentum* [**Section 4.3**]). This tendency prevents gravity from immediately pulling the spinning top over, since falling over would mean a change in the spin axis from near-vertical to horizontal. Instead, gravity succeeds only in making the axis trace circles of precession. As friction slows the top's spin, the circles of precession get

wider and wider, and ultimately the top falls over. If there were no friction to slow its spin, the top would spin and precess forever.

The spinning (rotating) Earth precesses because of gravitational tugs from the Sun and Moon. Earth is not quite a perfect sphere, because it bulges at its equator. Because the equator is tilted $23\frac{1}{2}°$ to the ecliptic plane, the gravitational attractions of the Sun and Moon try to pull the equatorial bulge into the ecliptic plane, effectively trying to "straighten out" Earth's axis tilt. However, like the spinning top, Earth tends to keep rotating around the same axis. Gravity therefore does not succeed in changing Earth's axis tilt and instead only makes the axis precess. To gain a better understanding of precession and how it works, you might wish to experiment with a simple toy gyroscope. *Gyroscopes* are essentially

COMMON MISCONCEPTIONS

Sun Signs

You probably know your astrological "Sun sign." When astrology began a few thousand years ago, your Sun sign was supposed to represent the constellation in which the Sun appeared on your birth date. However, because of precession, this is no longer the case for most people. For example, if your birthday is March 21, your Sun sign is Aries even though the Sun now appears in Pisces on that date. The problem is that astrological Sun signs are based on the positions of the Sun among the stars as they were almost 2000 years ago. Because Earth's axis has moved about 1/13 of the way through its 26,000-year precession cycle since that time, the Sun signs are off by nearly a month from the actual positions of the Sun among the constellations today.

rotating wheels mounted in a way that allows them to move freely, which makes it easy to see how their spin rate affects their motion. (The fact that gyroscopes tend to keep the same rotation axis makes them very useful in aircraft and spacecraft navigation.)

MA Phases of the Moon Tutorial, Lessons 1–3

2.3 THE MOON, OUR CONSTANT COMPANION

Aside from the seasons and the daily circling of the sky, the most familiar pattern of change in the sky is that of the changing phases of the Moon. We will explore these changes in this section—along with the rarer changes that occur with eclipses—and see that they are consequences of the Moon's orbit around Earth.

Why do we see phases of the Moon?

As the Moon orbits Earth, it returns to the same position relative to the Sun in our sky (such as along the Earth-Sun line) about every $29\frac{1}{2}$ days. This time period marks the cycle of **lunar phases**, in which the Moon's appearance in our sky changes as its position relative to the Sun changes. This $29\frac{1}{2}$-day period is also the origin of the word *month* (think "moonth").

The Moon's Orbit to Scale FIGURE 2.21 shows the Moon's orbit on the 1-to-10-billion scale model of the solar system that we discussed in Chapter 1. Recall that on this scale, the Sun is about the size of a large grapefruit, which means the entire orbit of the Moon could fit inside it. When you then consider the fact that the Sun is located 15 meters away on this scale, you'll realize that for practical purposes the Sun's rays all hit Earth and the Moon from the same direction. This fact is helpful to understanding the Moon's phases, because it means we can think of sunlight coming from a single direction at both Earth and the Moon, an effect shown clearly in the inset photo. The figure also shows the elliptical shape of the Moon's orbit, which causes the Earth-Moon distance to vary between about 356,000 and 407,000 kilometers.

Like the Sun, the Moon appears to move gradually eastward through the constellations of the zodiac. However, while the Sun takes a year for each circuit, the Moon takes only about a month, which means it moves at a rate of about 360° per month, or $\frac{1}{2}$°—its own angular size—each hour. If the Moon is visible tonight, go out and note its location relative to a few bright stars. Then go out again a couple hours later. Can you notice the Moon's change in position relative to the stars?

Understanding Phases The easiest way to understand the lunar phases is with the simple demonstration illustrated in FIGURE 2.22. Take a ball outside on a sunny day. (If it's dark

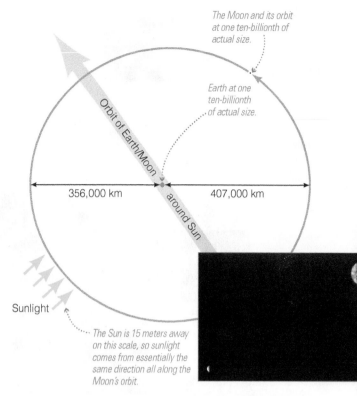

FIGURE 2.21 The Moon's orbit on the 1-to-10-billion scale introduced in Chapter 1 (see Figure 1.6); black labels indicate the Moon's actual distance at its nearest to and farthest from Earth. The orbit is so small compared to the distance to the Sun that sunlight strikes the entire orbit from the same direction. You can see this in the inset photo, which shows the Moon and Earth photographed from Mars by the Mars Reconnaissance Orbiter.

or cloudy, you can use a flashlight instead of the Sun; put the flashlight on a table a few meters away and shine it toward you.) Hold the ball at arm's length to represent the Moon while your head represents Earth. Slowly spin counterclockwise so that the ball goes around you the way the Moon orbits Earth. (If you live in the Southern Hemisphere, spin clockwise because you view the sky "upside down" compared to the Northern Hemisphere.) As you turn, you'll see the ball go through phases just like the Moon's. If you think about what's happening, you'll realize that the phases of the ball result from just two basic facts:

1. Half the ball always faces the Sun (or flashlight) and therefore is bright, while the other half faces away from the Sun and therefore is dark.

2. As you look at the ball at different positions in its "orbit" around your head, you see different combinations of its bright and dark faces.

For example, when you hold the ball directly opposite the Sun, you see only the bright portion of the ball, which represents the "full" phase. When you hold the ball at its "first-quarter" position, half the face you see is dark and the other half is bright.

We see lunar phases for the same reason. Half the Moon is always illuminated by the Sun, but the amount of this illuminated half that we see from Earth depends on the Moon's position in its orbit. The photographs in Figure 2.22 show how the phases look.

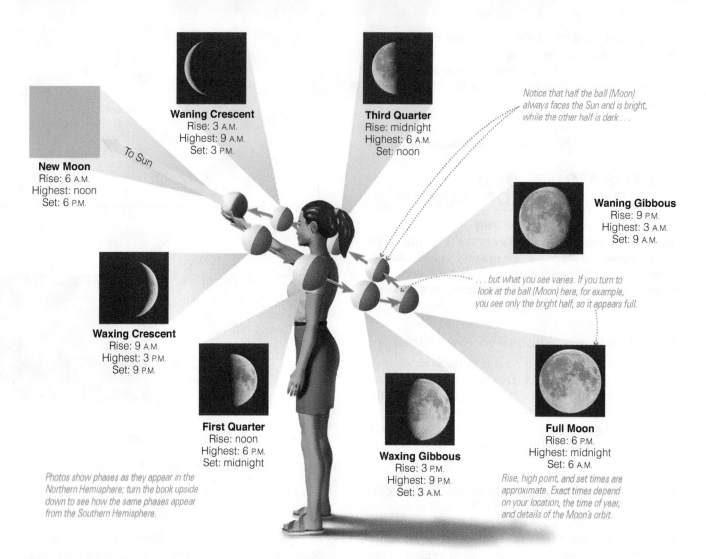

Waning Crescent
Rise: 3 A.M.
Highest: 9 A.M.
Set: 3 P.M.

Third Quarter
Rise: midnight
Highest: 6 A.M.
Set: noon

New Moon
Rise: 6 A.M.
Highest: noon
Set: 6 P.M.

To Sun

Notice that half the ball (Moon) always faces the Sun and is bright, while the other half is dark . . .

Waning Gibbous
Rise: 9 P.M.
Highest: 3 A.M.
Set: 9 A.M.

Waxing Crescent
Rise: 9 A.M.
Highest: 3 P.M.
Set: 9 P.M.

. . . but what you see varies. If you turn to look at the ball (Moon) here, for example, you see only the bright half, so it appears full.

First Quarter
Rise: noon
Highest: 6 P.M.
Set: midnight

Waxing Gibbous
Rise: 3 P.M.
Highest: 9 P.M.
Set: 3 A.M.

Full Moon
Rise: 6 P.M.
Highest: midnight
Set: 6 A.M.

Photos show phases as they appear in the Northern Hemisphere; turn the book upside down to see how the same phases appear from the Southern Hemisphere.

Rise, high point, and set times are approximate. Exact times depend on your location, the time of year, and details of the Moon's orbit.

FIGURE 2.22 interactive figure A simple demonstration illustrates the phases of the Moon. The half of the ball (Moon) facing the Sun is always illuminated while the half facing away is always dark, but you see the ball go through phases as it orbits around your head (Earth). (The new moon photo shows blue sky, because a new moon is always close to the Sun in the sky and hence hidden from view by the bright light of the Sun.)

The Moon's phase is directly related to the time it rises, reaches its highest point in the sky, and sets. For example, the full moon must rise around sunset, because it occurs when the Moon is opposite the Sun in the sky. It therefore reaches its highest point in the sky at midnight and sets around sunrise. Similarly, a first-quarter moon must rise around noon, reach its highest point around 6 p.m., and set around midnight, because it occurs when the Moon is about 90° east of the Sun in our sky. Figure 2.22 lists the approximate rise, highest point, and set times for each phase.

THINK ABOUT IT

Suppose you go outside in the morning and notice that the visible face of the Moon is half light and half dark. Is this a first-quarter or third-quarter moon? How do you know?

Notice that the phases from new to full are said to be *waxing*, which means "increasing." Phases from full to new

are *waning*, or "decreasing." Also notice that no phase is called a "half moon." Instead, we see half the Moon's face at first-quarter and third-quarter phases; these phases mark the times when the Moon is one quarter or three quarters of the way through its monthly cycle (which begins at new moon). The phases just before and after new moon are called *crescent*, while those just before and after full moon are called *gibbous* (pronounced with a hard *g* as in "gift"). A gibbous moon is

COMMON MISCONCEPTIONS

Shadows and the Moon

Many people guess that the Moon's phases are caused by Earth's shadow falling on its surface, but this is not the case. As we've seen, the Moon's phases are caused by the fact that we see different portions of its day and night sides at different times as it orbits around Earth. The only time Earth's shadow falls on the Moon is during the relatively rare event of a lunar eclipse.

essentially the opposite of a crescent moon—a crescent moon has a small sliver of light while a gibbous moon has a small sliver of dark. The term *gibbous* literally means "humpbacked," so you can see how the gibbous moon got its name.

The Moon's Synchronous Rotation Although we see many *phases* of the Moon, we do not see many *faces*. From Earth we always see (nearly*) the same face of the Moon. This happens because the Moon rotates on its axis in the same amount of time it takes to orbit Earth, a trait called **synchronous rotation**. A simple demonstration shows the idea. Place a ball on a table to represent Earth while you represent the Moon. Start by facing the ball. If you do not rotate as you walk around the ball, you'll be looking away from it by the time you are halfway around your orbit (**FIGURE 2.23a**). The only way you can face the ball at all times is by completing exactly one rotation while you complete one orbit (**FIGURE 2.23b**). Note that the Moon's synchronous rotation is *not* a coincidence; rather, it is a consequence of Earth's gravity affecting the Moon in much the same way the Moon's gravity causes tides on Earth [**Section 4.5**].

The View from the Moon A good way to solidify your understanding of the lunar phases is to imagine that you live on the side of the Moon that faces Earth. For example, what would you see if you looked at Earth when people on Earth saw a new moon? By remembering that a new moon occurs when the Moon is between the Sun and Earth, you'll realize that from the Moon you'd be looking at Earth's daytime side and hence would see a *full earth*. Similarly, at full moon you would be facing the night side of Earth and would see a *new earth*. In general, you'd always see Earth in a phase opposite the phase of the Moon seen by people on

---

*Because the Moon's orbital speed varies (in accord with Kepler's second law [**Section 3.3**]) while its rotation rate is steady, the visible face appears to wobble slightly back and forth as the Moon orbits Earth. This effect, called *libration*, allows us to see a total of about 59% of the Moon's surface over the course of a month, even though we see only 50% of the Moon at any single time.

Earth at the same time. Moreover, because the Moon always shows nearly the same face to Earth, Earth would appear to hang nearly stationary in your sky as it went through its cycle of phases.

Thinking about the view from the Moon clarifies another interesting feature of the lunar phases: The dark portion of the lunar face is not *totally* dark. Just as we can see at night by the light of the Moon, if you were in the dark area of the Moon during crescent phase your moonscape would be illuminated by a nearly full (gibbous) Earth. In fact, because Earth is much larger than the Moon, the illumination would be much greater than what the full moon provides on Earth. In other words, sunlight reflected by Earth faintly illuminates the "dark" portion of the Moon's face. We call this illumination the *ashen light*, or *earthshine*, and it enables us to see the outline of the full face of the Moon even when the Moon is not full.

a If you do not rotate while walking around the model, you will not always face it.

b You will face the model at all times only if you rotate exactly once during each orbit.

FIGURE 2.23 The fact that we always see the same face of the Moon means that the Moon must rotate once in the same amount of time it takes to orbit Earth once. You can see why by walking around a model of Earth while imagining that you are the Moon.

What causes eclipses?

Occasionally, the Moon's orbit around Earth causes events much more dramatic than lunar phases. The Moon and Earth both cast shadows in sunlight, and these shadows can create **eclipses** when the Sun, Earth, and Moon fall into a straight line. Eclipses come in two basic types:

- A **lunar eclipse** occurs when Earth lies directly between the Sun and Moon, so Earth's shadow falls on the Moon.

- A **solar eclipse** occurs when the Moon lies directly between the Sun and Earth, so the Moon's shadow falls on Earth.

Note that, because Earth is much larger than the Moon, Earth's shadow can cover the entire Moon during a lunar eclipse. Therefore, a lunar eclipse can be seen by anyone on the night side of Earth when it occurs. In contrast, the Moon's shadow can cover only a small portion of Earth at any one moment, so you must be living within the relatively small pathway through which the shadow moves to see a solar eclipse. That is why you see lunar eclipses more often than solar eclipses, even though both types occur about equally often.

Conditions for Eclipses Look once more at Figure 2.22. The figure makes it look as if the Sun, Earth, and Moon line up with every new and full moon. If this figure told the whole story of the Moon's orbit, we would have both a lunar and a solar eclipse every month—but we don't.

The missing piece of the story in Figure 2.22 is that the Moon's orbit is slightly inclined (by about 5°) to the ecliptic

COMMON MISCONCEPTIONS

Moon in the Daytime and Stars on the Moon

Night is so closely associated with the Moon in traditions and stories that many people mistakenly believe that the Moon is visible only in the nighttime sky. In fact, the Moon is above the horizon as often in the daytime as at night, though it is easily visible only when its light is not drowned out by sunlight. For example, a first-quarter moon is easy to spot in the late afternoon as it rises through the eastern sky, and a third-quarter moon is visible in the morning as it heads toward the western horizon.

Another misconception appears in illustrations that show a star in the dark portion of the crescent moon. The star in the dark portion appears to be in front of the Moon, which is impossible because the Moon is much closer to us than is any star.

plane (the plane of Earth's orbit around the Sun). To visualize this inclination, imagine the ecliptic plane as the surface of a pond, as shown in **FIGURE 2.24**. Because of the inclination of its orbit, the Moon spends most of its time either above or below this surface. It crosses *through* this surface only twice during each orbit: once coming out and once going back in. The two points in each orbit at which the Moon crosses the surface are called the **nodes** of the Moon's orbit.

Notice that the nodes are aligned approximately the same way (diagonally on the page in Figure 2.24) throughout the year, which means they lie along a nearly straight line with

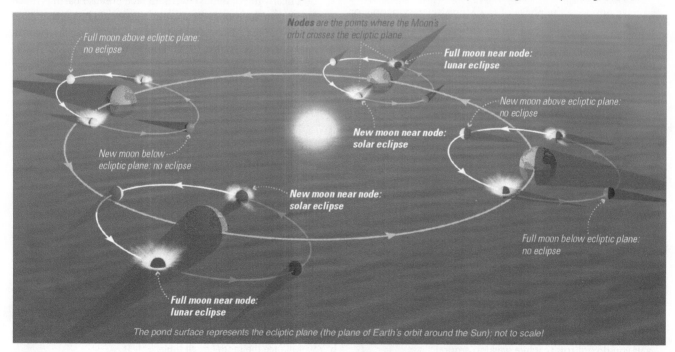

Nodes are the points where the Moon's orbit crosses the ecliptic plane.

Full moon above ecliptic plane: no eclipse

Full moon near node: lunar eclipse

New moon above ecliptic plane: no eclipse

New moon below ecliptic plane: no eclipse

New moon near node: solar eclipse

New moon near node: solar eclipse

Full moon below ecliptic plane: no eclipse

Full moon near node: lunar eclipse

The pond surface represents the ecliptic plane (the plane of Earth's orbit around the Sun); not to scale!

FIGURE 2.24 This illustration represents the ecliptic plane as the surface of a pond. The Moon's orbit is tilted by about 5° to the ecliptic plane, so the Moon spends half of each orbit above the plane (the pond surface) and half below it. Eclipses occur only when the Moon is at both a node (passing through the pond surface) and a phase of either new moon (for a solar eclipse) or full moon (for a lunar eclipse)—as is the case with the lower left and top right orbits shown.

the Sun and Earth about twice each year. We therefore find the following conditions for an eclipse to occur:

1. The phase of the Moon must be full (for a lunar eclipse) or new (for a solar eclipse).

2. The new or full moon must occur during one of the periods when the nodes of the Moon's orbit are aligned with the Sun and Earth.

Inner and Outer Shadows Figure 2.24 shows the Moon and Earth each casting only a simple "shadow cone" (extending away from the Sun) at each position shown. However, a closer look at the geometry shows that the shadow of the Moon or Earth actually consists of two distinct regions: a central **umbra,** where sunlight is completely blocked, and a surrounding **penumbra,** where sunlight is only partially blocked (**FIGURE 2.25**). The shadow cones in Figure 2.24 represent only the umbra, but both shadow regions are important to understanding eclipses.

Lunar Eclipses A lunar eclipse begins at the moment when the Moon's orbit first carries it into Earth's penumbra. After that, we will see one of three types of lunar eclipse (**FIGURE 2.26**). If the Sun, Earth, and Moon are nearly perfectly aligned, the

FIGURE 2.27 This multiple-exposure photograph shows the progression (left to right) of a total lunar eclipse observed from Tenerife, Canary Islands (Spain). Totality began (far right) just before the Moon set in the west. Notice Earth's curved shadow advancing across the Moon during the partial phases, and the redness of the full moon during totality.

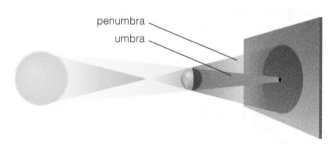

penumbra
umbra

FIGURE 2.25 The shadow cast by an object in sunlight. Sunlight is fully blocked in the umbra and partially blocked in the penumbra.

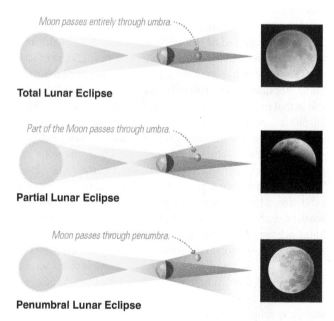

Moon passes entirely through umbra.

Total Lunar Eclipse

Part of the Moon passes through umbra.

Partial Lunar Eclipse

Moon passes through penumbra.

Penumbral Lunar Eclipse

FIGURE 2.26 **Interactive figure** The three types of lunar eclipse.

Moon passes through Earth's umbra and we see a **total lunar eclipse.** If the alignment is somewhat less perfect, only part of the full moon passes through the umbra (with the rest in the penumbra) and we see a **partial lunar eclipse.** If the Moon passes through *only* Earth's penumbra, we see a **penumbral lunar eclipse.** Penumbral eclipses are the most common type of lunar eclipse, but they are the least visually impressive because the full moon darkens only slightly.

Total lunar eclipses are the most spectacular. The Moon becomes dark and eerily red during **totality,** when the Moon is entirely engulfed in the umbra. Totality usually lasts about an hour, with partial phases both before and after. The curvature of Earth's shadow during partial phases shows that Earth is round (**FIGURE 2.27**). To understand the redness during totality, consider the view of an observer on the eclipsed Moon, who would see Earth's night side surrounded by the reddish glow of all the sunrises and sunsets occurring on the Earth at that moment. It is this reddish light that illuminates the Moon during total eclipse.

Solar Eclipses We can also see three types of solar eclipse (**FIGURE 2.28**). If a solar eclipse occurs when the Moon is in a part of its orbit where it is relatively close to Earth (see Figure 2.21), the Moon's umbra can cover a small area of Earth's surface (up to about 270 kilometers in diameter). Within this area you will see a **total solar eclipse.** If the eclipse occurs when the Moon is in a part of its orbit that puts it farther from Earth, the umbra may not reach Earth's surface at all. In that case, you will see an **annular eclipse**—a ring of sunlight surrounding the Moon—in the small region of Earth directly behind the umbra. In either case, the region of totality or annularity will be surrounded by a much larger region (typically about 7000 kilometers in diameter) that falls within the Moon's penumbral shadow. Here you will see a **partial solar eclipse,** in which only part of the Sun is blocked from view. The combination of Earth's rotation and the Moon's orbital motion causes the Moon's shadows to race across the

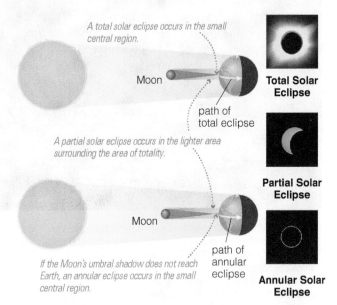

A total solar eclipse occurs in the small central region.

Moon

path of total eclipse

A partial solar eclipse occurs in the lighter area surrounding the area of totality.

Moon

If the Moon's umbral shadow does not reach Earth, an annular eclipse occurs in the small central region.

path of annular eclipse

Total Solar Eclipse

Partial Solar Eclipse

Annular Solar Eclipse

a The three types of solar eclipse. The diagrams show the Moon's shadow falling on Earth; note the dark central umbra surrounded by the much lighter penumbra.

b This photo from Earth orbit shows the Moon's shadow (umbra) on Earth during a total solar elipse. Notice that only a small region of Earth experiences totality at any one time.

FIGURE 2.28 **Interactive figure** During a solar eclipse, the Moon's small shadow moves rapidly across the face of Earth.

face of Earth at a typical speed of about 1700 kilometers per hour. As a result, the umbral shadow traces a narrow path across Earth, and totality never lasts more than a few minutes in any particular place.

A total solar eclipse is a spectacular sight. It begins when the disk of the Moon first appears to touch the Sun. Over the next couple of hours, the Moon appears to take a larger and larger "bite" out of the Sun. As totality approaches, the sky darkens and temperatures fall. Birds head back to their nests, and crickets begin their nighttime chirping. During the few minutes of totality, the Moon completely blocks the normally visible disk of the Sun, allowing the faint *corona* to be seen (FIGURE 2.29). The surrounding sky takes on a twilight glow,

FIGURE 2.29 This multiple-exposure photograph shows the progression of a total solar eclipse over La Paz, Mexico. Totality (central image) lasts only a few minutes, during which time we can see the faint corona around the outline of the Sun. The foreground church was photographed at a different time of day.

and planets and bright stars become visible in the daytime. As totality ends, the Sun slowly emerges from behind the Moon over the next couple of hours. However, because your eyes have adapted to the darkness, totality appears to end far more abruptly than it began.

Predicting Eclipses Few phenomena have so inspired and humbled humans throughout the ages as eclipses. For many cultures, eclipses were mystical events associated with fate or the gods, and countless stories and legends surround them. One legend holds that the Greek philosopher Thales (c. 624–546 B.C.) successfully predicted the year (but presumably not the precise time) that a total eclipse of the Sun would be visible in the area where he lived, which is now part of Turkey. The eclipse occurred as two opposing armies (the Medes and the Lydians) were massing for battle, and it so frightened them that they put down their weapons, signed a treaty, and returned home. Because modern research shows that the only eclipse visible in that part of the world at about that time occurred on May 28, 585 B.C., we know the precise date on which the treaty was signed—the earliest historical event that can be dated precisely.

Much of the mystery of eclipses probably stems from the relative difficulty of predicting them. Look again at Figure 2.24. The two periods each year when the nodes of the Moon's orbit are nearly aligned with the Sun are called **eclipse seasons.** Each eclipse season lasts a few weeks. Some type of lunar eclipse occurs during each eclipse season's full moon, and some type of solar eclipse occurs during its new moon.

If Figure 2.24 told the whole story, eclipse seasons would occur every 6 months and predicting eclipses would be easy. For example, if eclipse seasons always occurred in January and July, eclipses would always occur on the dates of new and full moons in those months. Actual eclipse prediction is

TABLE 2.1 Lunar Eclipses 2013–2016*

Date	Type	Where You Can See It
April 25, 2013	partial	Europe, Africa, Asia, Australia
May 25, 2013	penumbral	Americas, Africa
Oct. 18, 2013	penumbral	Americas, Europe, Africa, Asia
April 15, 2014	total	Australia, Pacific, Americas
Oct. 8, 2014	total	Asia, Australia, Pacific, Americas
April 4, 2015	total	Asia, Australia, Pacific, Americas
Sept. 28, 2015	total	Americas, Europe, Africa
March 23, 2016	penumbral	Asia, Australia, Pacific, western Americas
Sept. 16, 2016	penumbral	Europe, Africa, Asia, Australia

*Dates are based on Universal Time and hence are those in Greenwich, England, at the time of the eclipse; check a news source for the local time and date. Eclipse predictions by Fred Espenak, NASA GSFC.

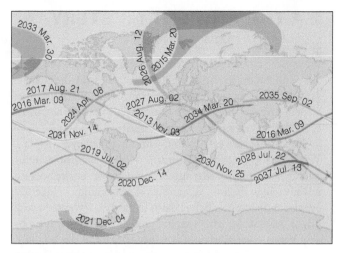

FIGURE 2.30 This map shows the paths of totality for solar eclipses from 2013 through 2037. Paths of the same color represent eclipses occurring in successive saros cycles, separated by 18 years 11 days. For example, the 2034 eclipse occurs 18 years 11 days after the 2016 eclipse (both shown in red). Eclipse predictions by Fred Espenak, NASA GSFC.

more difficult than this because of something the figure does not show: The nodes slowly move around the Moon's orbit, so the eclipse seasons occur slightly less than 6 months apart (about 173 days apart).

The combination of the changing dates of eclipse seasons and the $29\frac{1}{2}$-day cycle of lunar phases makes eclipses recur in a cycle of about 18 years, $11\frac{1}{3}$ days, called the **saros cycle.** Astronomers in many ancient cultures identified the saros cycle and used it to make eclipse predictions. For example, in the Middle East the Babylonians achieved remarkable success at predicting eclipses more than 2500 years ago, and the Mayans achieved similar success in Central America; in fact, the Mayan calendar includes a cycle (the *sacred round*) of 260 days—almost exactly $1\frac{1}{2}$ times the 173.32 days between successive eclipse seasons.

However, while the saros cycle allows you to predict when an eclipse will occur, it does not allow you to predict exactly where or the precise type of eclipse. For example, if a total solar eclipse occurred today, another would occur 18 years $11\frac{1}{3}$ days from now, but it would not be visible from the same places on Earth and might be annular or partial rather than total. No ancient culture achieved the ability to predict eclipses in every detail.

Today, we can predict eclipses because we know the precise details of the orbits of Earth and the Moon. TABLE 2.1 lists upcoming lunar eclipses; notice that, as we expect, eclipses generally come a little less than 6 months apart. FIGURE 2.30 shows paths of totality for upcoming total solar eclipses (but not for partial or annular eclipses), using color coding to show eclipses that repeat with the saros cycle.

THINK ABOUT IT

In Table 2.1, notice that there's one exception to the "rule" of eclipses coming a little less than 6 months apart: the 2013 lunar eclipses of April 25 and May 25. How can eclipses occur just a month apart? Explain.

SPECIAL TOPIC

Does the Moon Influence Human Behavior?

From myths of werewolves to stories of romance under the full moon, human culture is filled with claims that the Moon influences our behavior. Can we say anything scientific about such claims?

The Moon clearly has important influences on Earth, perhaps most notably through its role in creating tides [**Section 4.5**]. Although the Moon's tidal force cannot directly affect objects as small as people, the ocean tides have indirect effects. For example, fishermen, boaters, and surfers all adjust at least some of their activities to the cycle of the tides.

Another potential influence might come from the lunar phases. Physiological patterns in many species appear to follow the lunar phases; for example, some crabs and turtles lay eggs only at full moon.

No human trait is so closely linked to lunar phases, but the average human menstrual cycle is so close in length to a lunar month that it is difficult to believe the similarity is mere coincidence.

Nevertheless, aside from the physiological cycles and the influence of tides on people who live near the oceans, claims that the lunar phase affects human behavior are difficult to verify scientifically. For example, although it is possible that the full moon brings out certain behaviors, it may also simply be that some behaviors are easier to engage in when the sky is bright. A beautiful full moon may bring out your desire to walk on the beach under the moonlight, but there is no scientific evidence to suggest that the full moon would affect you the same way if you were confined to a deep cave.

2.4 THE ANCIENT MYSTERY OF THE PLANETS

We've now covered the appearance and motion of the stars, Sun, and Moon in the sky. That leaves us with the planets yet to discuss. As you'll soon see, planetary motion posed an ancient mystery that played a critical role in the development of modern civilization.

Five planets are easy to find with the naked eye: Mercury, Venus, Mars, Jupiter, and Saturn. Mercury is visible infrequently, and only just after sunset or just before sunrise because it is so close to the Sun. Venus often shines brightly in the early evening in the west or before dawn in the east. If you see a very bright "star" in the early evening or early morning, it is probably Venus. Jupiter, when it is visible at night, is the brightest object in the sky besides the Moon and Venus. Mars is often recognizable by its reddish color, though you should check a star chart to make sure you aren't looking at a bright red star. Saturn is also easy to see with the naked eye, but because many stars are just as bright as Saturn, it helps to know where to look. (It also helps to know that planets tend not to twinkle as much as stars.) Sometimes several planets may appear close together in the sky, offering a particularly beautiful sight (FIGURE 2.31).

FIGURE 2.31 This photograph shows a grouping in our sky of all five planets that are easily visible to the naked eye. It was taken near Chatsworth, New Jersey, on April 23, 2002. The next such close grouping of these five planets in our sky will occur in September 2040.

Why was planetary motion so hard to explain?

Over the course of a single night, planets behave like all other objects in the sky: Earth's rotation makes them appear to rise in the east and set in the west. But if you continue to watch the planets night after night, you will notice that their movements among the constellations are quite complex. Instead of moving steadily eastward relative to the stars, like the Sun and Moon, the planets vary substantially in both speed and brightness; in fact, the word *planet* comes from the Greek for "wandering star." Moreover, while the planets *usually* move eastward through the constellations, they occasionally reverse course, moving westward through the zodiac (FIGURE 2.32). These periods of **apparent retrograde motion** (*retrograde* means "backward") last from a few weeks to a few months, depending on the planet.

For ancient people who believed in an Earth-centered universe, apparent retrograde motion was very difficult to explain; after all, what could make planets sometimes turn around and go backward if everything moves in circles around Earth? The ancient Greeks came up with some very clever ways to explain it, but their explanations (which we'll study in Chapter 3) were quite complex.

In contrast, apparent retrograde motion has a simple explanation in a Sun-centered solar system. You can demonstrate it for yourself with the help of a friend (FIGURE 2.33a). Pick a spot in an open area to represent the Sun. You can represent Earth by walking counterclockwise around the Sun, while your friend represents a more distant planet (such as Mars or Jupiter) by walking in the same direction around the Sun at a greater distance. Your friend should walk more slowly than you, because more distant planets orbit the Sun more slowly. As you walk, watch how your friend appears to

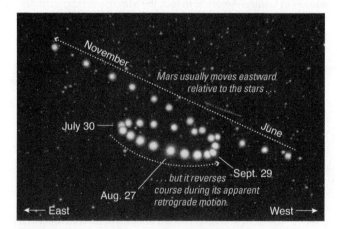

FIGURE 2.32 This composite of 29 individual photos (taken at 5- to 8-day intervals in 2003) shows a retrograde loop of Mars. Note that Mars is biggest and brightest in the middle of the retrograde loop, because that is where it is closest to Earth in its orbit. (The faint dots just right of center are images of the planet Uranus, which by coincidence was in the same part of the sky.)

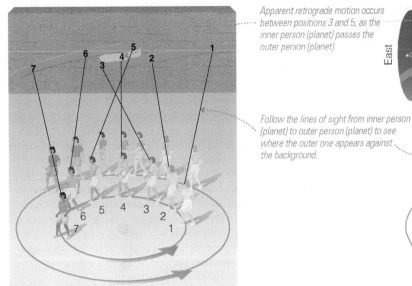

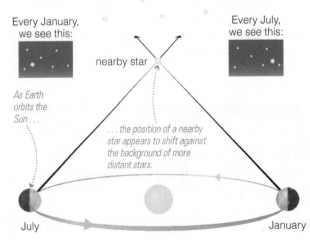

Apparent retrograde motion occurs between positions 3 and 5, as the inner person (planet) passes the outer person (planet).

Follow the lines of sight from inner person (planet) to outer person (planet) to see where the outer one appears against the background.

Earth orbit

Mars orbit

a The retrograde motion demonstration: Watch how your friend (in red) usually appears to move forward against the background of the building in the distance but appears to move backward as you (in blue) catch up to and pass her in your "orbit."

b This diagram shows how the same idea applies to a planet. Follow the lines of sight from Earth to Mars in numerical order. Notice that Mars appears to move westward relative to the distant stars as Earth passes it by in its orbit (roughly from points 3 to 5).

FIGURE 2.33 interactive figure Apparent retrograde motion—the occasional "backward" motion of the planets relative to the stars—has a simple explanation in a Sun-centered solar system.

move relative to buildings or trees in the distance. Although both of you always walk the same way around the Sun, your friend will appear to move backward against the background during the part of your "orbit" in which you catch up to and pass him or her. **FIGURE 2.33b** shows how the same idea applies to Mars. Note that Mars never actually changes direction; it only *appears* to go backward as Earth passes Mars in its orbit. (To understand the apparent retrograde motions of Mercury and Venus, which are closer to the Sun than is Earth, simply switch places with your friend and repeat the demonstration.)

Why did the ancient Greeks reject the real explanation for planetary motion?

If the apparent retrograde motion of the planets is so readily explained by recognizing that Earth orbits the Sun, why wasn't this idea accepted in ancient times? In fact, the idea that Earth goes around the Sun was suggested as early as 260 B.C. by the Greek astronomer Aristarchus (see Special Topic, page 48). Nevertheless, Aristarchus's contemporaries rejected his idea, and the Sun-centered solar system did not gain wide acceptance until almost 2000 years later.

Although there were many reasons the Greeks were reluctant to abandon the idea of an Earth-centered universe, one of the most important was their inability to detect what we call **stellar parallax.** Extend your arm and hold up one finger. If you keep your finger still and alternately close your left eye and right eye, your finger will appear to jump back and forth against the background. This apparent shifting, called *parallax,* occurs because your two eyes view your finger from opposite sides of your nose. If you move your finger closer to your face, the parallax increases. If you look at a distant tree or

flagpole instead of your finger, you may not notice any parallax at all. In other words, parallax depends on distance, with nearer objects exhibiting greater parallax than more distant objects.

If you now imagine that your two eyes represent Earth at opposite sides of its orbit around the Sun and that the tip of your finger represents a relatively nearby star, you have the idea of stellar parallax. That is, because we view the stars from different places in our orbit at different times of year, nearby stars should *appear* to shift back and forth against the background of more distant stars (**FIGURE 2.34**).

distant stars

Every January, we see this:

Every July, we see this:

nearby star

As Earth orbits the Sun . . .

. . . the position of a nearby star appears to shift against the background of more distant stars.

July

January

FIGURE 2.34 Stellar parallax is an apparent shift in the position of a nearby star as we look at it from different places in Earth's orbit. This figure is greatly exaggerated; in reality, the amount of shift is far too small to detect with the naked eye.

Who First Proposed a Sun-Centered Solar System?

You've probably heard of Copernicus, whose work in the 16th century started the revolution that ultimately overturned the ancient belief in an Earth-centered universe [**Section 3.3**]. However, the idea that Earth goes around the Sun was proposed much earlier by the Greek scientist Aristarchus (c. 310–230 B.C.).

Little of Aristarchus's work survives to the present day, so we cannot know what motivated him to suggest an idea so contrary to the prevailing view of an Earth-centered universe. However, it's likely that he was motivated by the fact that a Sun-centered system offers a much more natural explanation for the apparent retrograde motion of the planets. To account for the lack of detectable stellar parallax, Aristarchus suggested that the stars were extremely far away.

Aristarchus further strengthened his argument by estimating the sizes of the Moon and the Sun. By observing the shadow of Earth on the Moon during a lunar eclipse, he estimated the Moon's diameter to be about one-third of Earth's diameter—only slightly more than the actual value. He then used a geometric argument, based on measuring the angle between the Moon and the Sun at first- and third-quarter phases, to conclude that the Sun must be larger than

Earth. (Aristarchus's measurements were imprecise, so he estimated the Sun's diameter to be about 7 times Earth's rather than the correct value of about 100 times.) His conclusion that the Sun is larger than Earth may have been another reason he believed that Earth should orbit the Sun, rather than vice versa.

Although Aristarchus was probably the first to suggest that Earth orbits the Sun, his ideas built on the work of earlier scholars. For example, Heracleides (c. 388–315 B.C.) had previously suggested that Earth rotates, which offered Aristarchus a way to explain the daily circling of the sky in a Sun-centered system. Heracleides also suggested that not all heavenly bodies circle Earth: Based on the fact that Mercury and Venus always stay fairly close to the Sun in the sky, he argued that these two planets must orbit the Sun. In suggesting that *all* the planets orbit the Sun, Aristarchus was extending the ideas of Heracleides and others before him.

Aristarchus gained little support among his contemporaries, but his ideas never died, and Copernicus was aware of them when he proposed his own version of the Sun-centered system. Thus, our modern understanding of the universe owes at least some debt to the remarkable vision of a man born more than 2300 years ago.

Because the Greeks believed that all stars lie on the same celestial sphere, they expected to see stellar parallax in a slightly different way. If Earth orbited the Sun, they reasoned, at different times of year we would be closer to different parts of the celestial sphere and would notice changes in the angular separation of stars. However, no matter how hard they searched, they could find no sign of stellar parallax. They concluded that one of the following must be true:

1. Earth orbits the Sun, but the stars are so far away that stellar parallax is undetectable to the naked eye.

2. There is no stellar parallax because Earth remains stationary at the center of the universe.

Aside from a few notable exceptions such as Aristarchus, the Greeks rejected the correct answer (the first one) because they could not imagine that the stars could be *that* far away. Today, we can detect stellar parallax with the aid of telescopes,

providing direct proof that Earth really does orbit the Sun. Careful measurements of stellar parallax also provide the most reliable means of measuring distances to nearby stars [**Section 15.1**].

THINK ABOUT IT

How far apart are opposite sides of Earth's orbit? How far away are the nearest stars? Using the 1-to-10-billion scale from Chapter 1, describe the challenge of detecting stellar parallax.

The ancient mystery of the planets drove much of the historical debate over Earth's place in the universe. In many ways, the modern technological society we take for granted today can be traced directly to the scientific revolution that began in the quest to explain the strange wanderings of the planets among the stars in our sky. We will turn our attention to this revolution in the next chapter.

The Big Picture

Putting Chapter 2 into Context

In this chapter, we surveyed the phenomena of our sky. Keep the following "big picture" ideas in mind as you continue your study of astronomy:

■ You can enhance your enjoyment of astronomy by observing the sky. The more you learn about the appearance and apparent motions of the sky, the more you will appreciate what you can see in the universe.

■ From our vantage point on Earth, it is convenient to imagine that we are at the center of a great celestial sphere—even though

we really are on a planet orbiting a star in a vast universe. We can then understand what we see in the local sky by thinking about how the celestial sphere appears from our latitude.

■ Most of the phenomena of the sky are relatively easy to observe and understand. The more complex phenomena—particularly eclipses and apparent retrograde motion of the planets—challenged our ancestors for thousands of years. The desire to understand these phenomena helped drive the development of science and technology.

2.1 PATTERNS IN THE NIGHT SKY

- **What does the universe look like from Earth?** Stars and other celestial objects appear to lie on a great **celestial**  **sphere** surrounding Earth. We divide the celestial sphere into **constellations** with well-defined borders. From any location on Earth, we see half the celestial sphere at any one time as the dome of our **local sky,** in which the **horizon** is the boundary between Earth and sky, the **zenith** is the point directly overhead, and the **meridian** runs from due south to due north through the zenith.

- **Why do stars rise and set?** Earth's rotation makes stars  appear to circle around Earth each day. A star whose complete circle lies above our horizon is said to be **circumpolar.** Other stars have circles that cross the horizon, making them rise in the east and set in the west each day.

- **Why do the constellations we see depend on latitude and time of year?** The visible constellations vary with time of year because our night sky lies in different directions in space as we orbit the Sun. The constellations vary with **latitude** because your latitude determines the orientation of your horizon relative to the celestial sphere. The sky does not vary with **longitude.**

2.2 THE REASON FOR SEASONS

- **What causes the seasons?** The tilt of Earth's axis causes the seasons. The axis points in the same direction throughout  the year, so as Earth orbits the Sun, sunlight hits different parts of Earth more directly at different times of year.

- **How does the orientation of Earth's axis change**  **with time?** Earth's 26,000-year cycle of **precession** changes the orientation of the axis in space, although the tilt remains about $23\frac{1}{2}°$. The changing orientation of the axis does not affect the pattern of seasons, but it changes the identity of the North Star and shifts the locations of the solstices and equinoxes in Earth's orbit.

2.3 THE MOON, OUR CONSTANT COMPANION

- **Why do we see phases of the Moon?** The **phase** of the  Moon depends on its position relative to the Sun as it orbits Earth. The half of the Moon facing the Sun is always illuminated while the other half is dark, but from Earth we see varying combinations of the illuminated and dark faces.

- **What causes eclipses?** We see a **lunar eclipse** when Earth's shadow falls on the Moon and a **solar eclipse** when the Moon 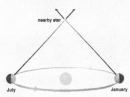 blocks our view of the Sun. We do not see an eclipse at every new and full moon because the Moon's orbit is slightly inclined to the ecliptic plane.

2.4 THE ANCIENT MYSTERY OF THE PLANETS

- **Why was planetary motion so hard to explain?** Planets  generally move eastward relative to the stars over the course of the year, but for weeks or months they reverse course during periods of **apparent retrograde motion.** This motion occurs when Earth passes by (or is passed by) another planet in its orbit, but it posed a major mystery to ancient people who assumed Earth to be at the center of the universe.

- **Why did the ancient Greeks reject the real explanation for planetary motion?** The Greeks rejected the idea that Earth goes around the Sun in part because they could not detect **stellar parallax**—slight apparent shifts in stellar positions  over the course of the year. To most Greeks, it seemed unlikely that the stars could be so far away as to make parallax undetectable to the naked eye, even though that is, in fact, the case.

Use the following questions to check your understanding of some of the many types of visual information used in astronomy. Answers are provided in Appendix J. For additional practice, try the Chapter 2 Visual Quiz at MasteringAstronomy®.

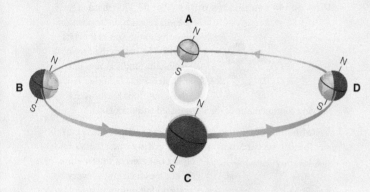

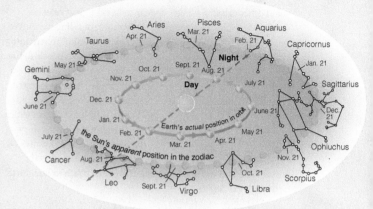

The figure above is a typical diagram used to describe Earth's seasons.

1. Which of the four labeled points (A through D) represents the beginning of summer for the Northern Hemisphere?
2. Which of the four labeled points represents the beginning of summer for the Southern Hemisphere?
3. Which of the four labeled points represents the beginning of spring for the Southern Hemisphere?
4. The diagram exaggerates the sizes of Earth and the Sun relative to the orbit. If Earth were correctly scaled relative to the orbit in the figure, how big would it be?
   a. about half the size shown   b. about 2 millimeters across
   c. about 0.1 millimeter across   d. microscopic
5. Given that Earth's actual distance from the Sun varies by less than 3% over the course of a year, why does the diagram look so elliptical?
   a. It correctly shows that Earth is closest to the Sun at points A and C and farthest at points B and D.
   b. The elliptical shape is an effect of perspective, since the diagram shows an almost edge-on view of a nearly circular orbit.
   c. The shape of the diagram is meaningless and is done only for artistic effect.

The figure above (based on Figure 2.14) shows the Sun's path through the constellations of the zodiac.

6. As viewed from Earth, in which zodiac constellation does the Sun appear to be located on April 21?
   a. Leo   b. Aquarius   c. Libra   d. Aries
7. If the date is April 21, what zodiac constellation will be visible on your meridian at midnight?
   a. Leo   b. Aquarius   c. Libra   d. Aries
8. If the date is April 21, what zodiac constellation will you see setting in the west shortly after sunset?
   a. Scorpius   b. Pisces   c. Taurus   d. Virgo

MasteringAstronomy®

For instructor-assigned homework go to MasteringAstronomy®.

REVIEW QUESTIONS

Short-Answer Questions Based on the Reading

1. What are *constellations*? How did they get their names?
2. Suppose you were making a model of the celestial sphere with a ball. Briefly describe all the things you would need to mark on your celestial sphere.
3. On a clear, dark night, the sky may appear to be "full" of stars. Does this appearance accurately reflect the way stars are distributed in space? Explain.
4. Why does the *local sky* look like a dome? Define *horizon, zenith,* and *meridian*. How do we describe the location of an object in the local sky?
5. Explain why we can measure only *angular sizes* and *angular distances* for objects in the sky. What are *arcminutes* and *arcseconds*?
6. What are *circumpolar stars*? Are more stars circumpolar at the North Pole or in the United States? Explain.

7. What are *latitude* and *longitude*? Does the sky vary with latitude? Does it vary with longitude? Explain.
8. What is the *zodiac*, and why do we see different parts of it at different times of year?
9. Suppose Earth's axis had no tilt. Would we still have seasons? Why or why not?
10. Briefly describe key facts about the solstices and equinoxes.
11. What is *precession*, and how does it affect what we see in our sky?
12. Briefly describe the Moon's cycle of *phases*. Can you ever see a full moon at noon? Explain.
13. Why do we always see the same face of the Moon?
14. Why don't we see an *eclipse* at every new and full moon? Describe the conditions needed for a *solar* or *lunar eclipse*.
15. What do we mean by the *apparent retrograde motion* of the planets? Why was this motion difficult for ancient astronomers to explain? How do we explain it today?

16. What is *stellar parallax*? How did an inability to detect it support the ancient belief in an Earth-centered universe?

TEST YOUR UNDERSTANDING

Does It Make Sense?

Decide whether the statement makes sense (or is clearly true) or does not make sense (or is clearly false). Explain clearly; not all of these have definitive answers, so your explanation is more important than your chosen answer.

17. The constellation Orion didn't exist when my grandfather was a child.
18. When I looked into the dark lanes of the Milky Way with my binoculars, I saw what must have been a cluster of distant galaxies.
19. Last night the Moon was so big that it stretched for a mile across the sky.
20. I live in the United States, and during my first trip to Argentina I saw many constellations that I'd never seen before.
21. Last night I saw Jupiter right in the middle of the Big Dipper. (*Hint*: Is the Big Dipper part of the zodiac?)
22. Last night I saw Mars move westward through the sky in its apparent retrograde motion.
23. Although all the known stars rise in the east and set in the west, we might someday discover a star that will rise in the west and set in the east.
24. If Earth's orbit were a perfect circle, we would not have seasons.
25. Because of precession, someday it will be summer everywhere on Earth at the same time.
26. This morning I saw the full moon setting at about the same time the Sun was rising.

Quick Quiz

Choose the best answer to each of the following. Explain your reasoning with one or more complete sentences.

27. Two stars that are in the same constellation (a) must both be part of the same cluster of stars in space. (b) must both have been discovered at about the same time. (c) may actually be very far away from each other.
28. The north celestial pole is 35° above your northern horizon. This tells you that (a) you are at latitude 35°N. (b) you are at longitude 35°E. (c) you are at latitude 35°S.
29. Beijing and Philadelphia have about the same latitude but very different longitudes. Therefore, tonight's night sky in these two places (a) will look about the same. (b) will have completely different sets of constellations. (c) will have partially different sets of constellations.
30. In winter, Earth's axis points toward the star Polaris. In spring, (a) the axis also points toward Polaris. (b) the axis points toward Vega. (c) the axis points toward the Sun.
31. When it is summer in Australia, the season in the United States is (a) winter. (b) summer. (c) spring.
32. If the Sun rises precisely due east, (a) you must be located at Earth's equator. (b) it must be the day of either the spring or the fall equinox. (c) it must be the day of the summer solstice.
33. A week after full moon, the Moon's phase is (a) first quarter. (b) third quarter. (c) new.
34. The fact that we always see the same face of the Moon tells us that (a) the Moon does not rotate. (b) the Moon's rotation period is the same as its orbital period. (c) the Moon looks the same on both sides.
35. If there is going to be a total lunar eclipse tonight, then you know that (a) the Moon's phase is full. (b) the Moon's phase is new. (c) the Moon is unusually close to Earth.

36. When we see Saturn going through a period of apparent retrograde motion, it means (a) Saturn is temporarily moving backward in its orbit of the Sun. (b) Earth is passing Saturn in its orbit, with both planets on the same side of the Sun. (c) Saturn and Earth must be on opposite sides of the Sun.

PROCESS OF SCIENCE

Examining How Science Works

37. *Earth-Centered or Sun-Centered?* Decide whether each of the following phenomena is consistent or inconsistent with a belief in an Earth-centered system. If consistent, describe how. If inconsistent, explain why, and also explain why the inconsistency did not immediately lead people to abandon the Earth-centered model.
    a. The daily paths of stars through the sky **b.** Seasons **c.** Phases of the Moon **d.** Eclipses **e.** Apparent retrograde motion of the planets
38. *Shadow Phases.* Many people incorrectly guess that the phases of the Moon are caused by Earth's shadow falling on the Moon. How would you convince a friend that the phases of the Moon have nothing to do with Earth's shadow? Describe the observations you would use to show that Earth's shadow can't be the cause of phases.

GROUP WORK EXERCISE

39. *Lunar Phases and Time of Day.* Before you begin, assign the following roles to the people in your group: *Scribe* (takes notes on the group's activities), *Proposer* (proposes explanations to the group), *Skeptic* (points out weaknesses in proposed explanations), and *Moderator* (leads group discussion and makes sure everyone contributes). Then each member of the group should draw a copy of the following diagram, which represents the Moon's orbit as seen from above Earth's North Pole (not to scale):

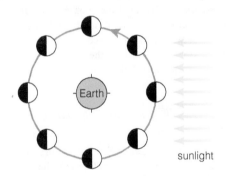

Discuss and answer the following questions as a group:
a. How would the Moon appear from Earth at each of the eight Moon positions? Label each one with the corresponding phase. **b.** What time of day corresponds to each of the four tick marks on Earth? Label each tick mark accordingly. **c.** Why doesn't the Moon's phase change during the course of one night? Explain your reasoning. **d.** At what times of day would a full moon be visible to someone standing on Earth? Write down when a full moon rises and explain why it appears to rise at that time. **e.** At what times of day would a third-quarter moon be visible to someone standing on Earth? Write down when a third-quarter moon sets and explain why it appears to set at that time. **f.** At what times of day would a waxing crescent moon be visible to someone standing on Earth? Write down when a waxing crescent moon rises and explain why it appears to rise at that time.

INVESTIGATE FURTHER

In-Depth Questions to Increase Your Understanding

40. *New Planet.* A planet in another solar system has a circular orbit and an axis tilt of 35°. Would you expect this planet to have seasons? If so, would you expect them to be more extreme than the seasons on Earth? If not, why not?

41. *Your View of the Sky.*
    a. What are your latitude and longitude? **b.** Where does the north (or south) celestial pole appear in your sky? **c.** Is Polaris a circumpolar star in your sky? Explain.

42. *View from the Moon.* Assume you live on the Moon, near the center of the face that looks toward Earth.
    a. Suppose you see a full earth in your sky. What phase of the Moon would people on Earth see? Explain. **b.** Suppose people on Earth see a full moon. What phase would you see for Earth? Explain. **c.** Suppose people on Earth see a waxing gibbous moon. What phase would you see for Earth? Explain. **d.** Suppose people on Earth are viewing a total lunar eclipse. What would you see from your home on the Moon? Explain.

43. *View from the Sun.* Suppose you lived on the Sun (and could ignore the heat). Would you still see the Moon go through phases as it orbits Earth? Why or why not?

44. *A Farther Moon.* Suppose the distance to the Moon were twice its actual value. Would it still be possible to have a total solar eclipse? Why or why not?

45. *A Smaller Earth.* Suppose Earth were smaller. Would solar eclipses be any different? If so, how? What about lunar eclipses?

46. *Observing Planetary Motion.* Find out which planets are currently visible in your evening sky. At least once a week, observe the planets and draw a diagram showing the position of each visible planet relative to stars in a zodiac constellation. From week to week, note how the planets are moving relative to the stars. Can you see any of the apparently wandering features of planetary motion? Explain.

47. *A Connecticut Yankee.* Find the book *A Connecticut Yankee in King Arthur's Court* by Mark Twain. Read the portion that deals with the Connecticut Yankee's prediction of an eclipse. In a one- to two-page essay, summarize the episode and explain how it helped the Connecticut Yankee gain power.

Be sure to show all calculations clearly and state your final answers in complete sentences.

48. *Arcminutes and Arcseconds.* There are 360° in a full circle.
    a. How many arcminutes are in a full circle? **b.** How many arcseconds are in a full circle? **c.** The Moon's angular size is about $\frac{1}{2}°$. What is this in arcminutes? In arcseconds?

49. *Latitude Distance.* Earth's radius is approximately 6370 km.
    a. What is Earth's circumference? **b.** What distance is represented by each degree of latitude? **c.** What distance is represented by each arcminute of latitude? **d.** Can you give similar answers for the distances represented by a degree or arcminute of longitude? Why or why not?

50. *Angular Conversions I.* The following angles are given in degrees and fractions of degrees. Rewrite them in degrees, arcminutes, and arcseconds.
    a. 24.3° **b.** 1.59° **c.** 0.1° **d.** 0.01° **e.** 0.001°

51. *Angular Conversions II.* The following angles are given in degrees, arcminutes, and arcseconds. Rewrite them in degrees and fractions of degrees.
    a. 7°38′42″ **b.** 12′54″ **c.** 1°59′59″ **d.** 1′ **e.** 1″

52. *Angular Size of Your Finger.* Measure the width of your index finger and the length of your arm. Based on your measurements, calculate the angular width of your index finger at arm's length. Does your result agree with the approximations shown in Figure 2.7c? Explain.

53. *Find the Sun's Diameter.* The Sun has an angular diameter of about 0.5° and an average distance of about 150 million km. What is the Sun's approximate physical diameter? Compare your answer to the actual value of 1,390,000 km.

54. *Find a Star's Diameter.* Estimate the diameter of the supergiant star Betelgeuse, using its angular diameter of about 0.05 arcsecond and distance of about 600 light-years. Compare your answer to the size of our Sun and the Earth-Sun distance.

55. *Eclipse Conditions.* The Moon's precise equatorial diameter is 3476 km, and its orbital distance from Earth varies between 356,400 and 406,700 km. The Sun's diameter is 1,390,000 km, and its distance from Earth ranges between 147.5 and 152.6 million km.
    a. Find the Moon's angular size at its minimum and maximum distances from Earth. **b.** Find the Sun's angular size at its minimum and maximum distances from Earth. **c.** Based on your answers to parts a and b, is it possible to have a total solar eclipse when the Moon and Sun are both at their maximum distance? Explain.

56. *Earth-Centered Language.* Many common phrases reflect the ancient Earth-centered view of our universe. For example, the phrase "the Sun rises each day" implies that the Sun is really moving over Earth. We know that the Sun only *appears* to rise as the rotation of Earth carries us to a place where we can see the Sun in our sky. Identify other common phrases that imply an Earth-centered viewpoint.

57. *Flat Earth Society.* Believe it or not, there is an organization called the Flat Earth Society. Its members hold that Earth is flat and that all indications to the contrary (such as pictures of Earth from space) are fabrications made as part of a conspiracy to hide the truth from the public. Discuss the evidence for a round Earth and how you can check it for yourself. In light of the evidence, is it possible that the Flat Earth Society is correct? Defend your opinion.

58. *Sky Information.* Search the Web for sources of daily information about sky phenomena (such as lunar phases, times of sunrise and sunset, or dates of equinoxes and solstices). Identify and briefly describe your favorite source.

59. *Constellations.* Search the Web for information about the constellations and their mythology. Write a short report about one or more constellations.

60. *Upcoming Eclipse.* Find information about an upcoming solar or lunar eclipse. Write a short report about how you could best observe the eclipse, including any necessary travel to a viewing site, and what you could expect to see. Bonus: Describe how you could photograph the eclipse.

3

THE SCIENCE OF ASTRONOMY

LEARNING GOALS

3.1 THE ANCIENT ROOTS OF SCIENCE

- In what ways do all humans use scientific thinking?
- How is modern science rooted in ancient astronomy?

3.2 ANCIENT GREEK SCIENCE

- Why does modern science trace its roots to the Greeks?
- How did the Greeks explain planetary motion?

3.3 THE COPERNICAN REVOLUTION

- How did Copernicus, Tycho, and Kepler challenge the Earth-centered model?

- What are Kepler's three laws of planetary motion?
- How did Galileo solidify the Copernican revolution?

3.4 THE NATURE OF SCIENCE

- How can we distinguish science from nonscience?
- What is a scientific theory?

3.5 ASTROLOGY

- How is astrology different from astronomy?
- Does astrology have any scientific validity?

We especially need imagination in science. It is not all mathematics, nor all logic, but is somewhat beauty and poetry.

—Maria Mitchell (1818–1889), astronomer and the first woman elected to the American Academy of Arts and Sciences

Today we know that Earth is a planet orbiting a rather ordinary star, in a galaxy of more than a hundred billion stars, in an incredibly vast universe. We know that Earth, along with the entire cosmos, is in constant motion. We know that, on the scale of cosmic time, human civilization has existed for only the briefest moment. How did we manage to learn these things?

It wasn't easy. In this chapter, we will trace how modern astronomy grew from its roots in ancient observations, including those of the Greeks. We'll pay special attention to the unfolding of the Copernican revolution, which overturned the ancient belief in an Earth-centered universe and laid the foundation for the rise of our technological civilization. Finally, we'll explore the nature of modern science and how science can be distinguished from nonscience.

3.1 THE ANCIENT ROOTS OF SCIENCE

The rigorous methods of modern science have proven to be among the most valuable inventions in human history. These methods have enabled us to discover almost everything we now know about nature and the universe, and they also have made our modern technology possible. In this section, we will explore the ancient roots of science, which grew out of experiences common to nearly all people and all cultures.

In what ways do all humans use scientific thinking?

Scientific thinking comes naturally to us. By about a year of age, a baby notices that objects fall to the ground when she drops them. She lets go of a ball—it falls. She pushes a plate of food from her high chair—it falls, too. She continues to drop all kinds of objects, and they all plummet to Earth. Through her powers of observation, the baby learns about the physical world, finding that things fall when they are unsupported. Eventually, she becomes so certain of this fact that, to her parents' delight, she no longer needs to test it continually.

One day someone gives the baby a helium balloon. She releases it, and to her surprise it rises to the ceiling! Her understanding of nature must be revised. She now knows that the principle "all things fall" does not represent the whole truth, although it still serves her quite well in most situations. It will be years before she learns enough about the atmosphere, the force of gravity, and the concept of density to understand *why* the balloon rises when most other objects fall. For now, she is delighted to observe something new and unexpected.

The baby's experience with falling objects and balloons exemplifies scientific thinking. In essence, science is a way of learning about nature through careful observation and trial-and-error experiments. Rather than thinking differently than other people, modern scientists simply are trained to organize everyday thinking in a way that makes it easier for them to share their discoveries and use their collective wisdom.

THINK ABOUT IT

Describe a few cases where you have learned by trial and error while cooking, participating in sports, fixing something, or working at a job.

Just as learning to communicate through language, art, or music is a gradual process for a child, the development of science has been a gradual process for humanity. Science in its modern form requires painstaking attention to detail, relentless testing of each piece of information to ensure its reliability, and a willingness to give up old beliefs that are not consistent with observed facts about the physical world. For professional scientists, these demands are the "hard work" part of the job. At heart, professional scientists are like the baby with the balloon, delighted by the unexpected and motivated by those rare moments when they—and all of us—learn something new about the universe.

How is modern science rooted in ancient astronomy?

Astronomy has been called the oldest of the sciences, because its roots stretch deepest into antiquity. Ancient civilizations did not always practice astronomy in the same ways or for the same reasons that we study it today, but they nonetheless had some amazing achievements. Understanding this ancient astronomy can give us a greater appreciation of how and why science developed through time.

Practical Benefits of Astronomy No one knows exactly how or when humans first began making careful observations of the sky, but we know observation has been going on for many thousands of years. This interest in astronomy probably comes in part from our inherent curiosity as humans, but ancient cultures also discovered that astronomy had practical benefits for timekeeping, keeping track of seasonal changes, and navigation.

One amazing example comes from people of central Africa. Although we do not know exactly when they developed the skill, people in some regions learned to predict rainfall patterns by making careful observations of the Moon. FIGURE 3.1 shows how the method works. The orientation of the "horns" of a waxing crescent moon (relative to the horizon) varies over the course of the year, primarily because the angle at which the ecliptic intersects the horizon changes during the year. (The orientation also depends on latitude.) In tropical regions in which there are distinct rainy and dry seasons—rather than the four seasons familiar at temperate latitudes—the orientation of the crescent moon can be used to predict how much rainfall should be expected over coming days and weeks.

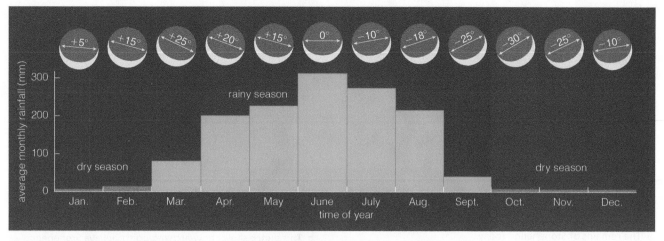

FIGURE 3.1 In central Nigeria, the orientation of the "horns" of a waxing crescent moon (shown along the top) correlates with the average amount of rainfall at different times of year. Local people could use this fact to predict the weather with reasonable accuracy. (Adapted from *Ancient Astronomers* by Anthony F. Aveni.)

Astronomy and Measures of Time The impact of ancient astronomical observations is still with us in our modern measures of time. The length of our day is the time it takes the Sun to make one full circuit of the sky. The length of a month comes from the Moon's cycle of phases [**Section 2.3**], and our year is based on the cycle of the seasons [**Section 2.2**]. The seven days of the week were named after the seven "planets" of ancient times (**TABLE 3.1**), which were the Sun, the Moon, and the five planets that are easily visible to the naked eye: Mercury, Venus, Mars, Jupiter, Saturn. Note that the ancient definition of *planet*, which comes from a Greek word meaning "wanderer," applied to any object that appeared to wander among the fixed stars. That is why the Sun and Moon were on the list while Earth was not, because we don't see our own planet moving in the sky.

THINK ABOUT IT
Uranus is faintly visible to the naked eye, but it was not recognized as a planet in ancient times. If Uranus had been brighter, would we now have eight days in a week? Defend your opinion.

TABLE 3.1 **The Seven Days of the Week and the Astronomical Objects They Honor**

The seven days were originally linked directly to the seven objects. The correspondence is no longer perfect, but the overall pattern is clear in many languages; some English names come from Germanic gods.

Object	Germanic God	English	French	Spanish
Sun	—	Sunday	dimanche	domingo
Moon	—	Monday	lundi	lunes
Mars	Tiw	Tuesday	mardi	martes
Mercury	Woden	Wednesday	mercredi	miércoles
Jupiter	Thor	Thursday	jeudi	jueves
Venus	Fria	Friday	vendredi	viernes
Saturn	—	Saturday	samedi	sábado

Because timekeeping was so important and required precise observations, many ancient cultures built structures or created special devices to help with it. Let's briefly investigate a few of the ways in which ancient cultures kept track of time.

Determining the Time of Day In the daytime, ancient peoples could tell time by observing the Sun's path through the sky. Many cultures probably used sticks and the shadows they cast as simple sundials [**Section S1.3**]. The ancient Egyptians built huge obelisks, often decorated in homage to the Sun, which probably also served as simple clocks (**FIGURE 3.2**).

At night, ancient people could estimate the time from the position and phase of the Moon (see Figure 2.22) or by observing the constellations visible at a particular time (see Figure 2.14). For example, ancient Egyptian star clocks, often

FIGURE 3.2 This ancient Egyptian obelisk, which stands 83 feet tall and weighs 331 tons, resides in St. Peter's Square at the Vatican in Rome. It is one of 21 surviving obelisks from ancient Egypt, most of which are now scattered around the world. Shadows cast by the obelisks may have been used to tell time.

a The remains of Stonehenge today.

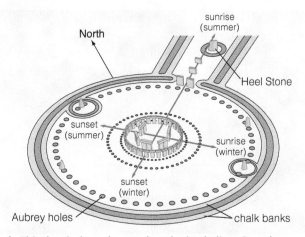

b This sketch shows how archaeologists believe Stonehenge looked upon its completion in about 1550 B.C. Several astronomical alignments are shown as they appear from the center. For example, the Sun rises directly over the Heel Stone on the summer solstice.

FIGURE 3.3 Stonehenge, in southern England, was built in stages from about 2750 B.C. to about 1550 B.C.

found painted on the coffin lids of Egyptian pharaohs, cataloged where particular stars appeared in the sky at various times of night throughout the year. By knowing the date from their calendar and observing the positions of the cataloged stars in the sky, the Egyptians could use the star clocks to estimate the time of night.

In fact, we can trace the origins of our modern clock to ancient Egypt, some 4000 years ago. The Egyptians divided daytime and nighttime into 12 equal parts each, which is how we got our 12 hours each of a.m. and p.m. The abbreviations *a.m.* and *p.m.* stand for the Latin terms *ante meridiem* and *post meridiem,* respectively, which mean "before the middle of the day" and "after the middle of the day."

By about 1500 B.C., Egyptians had abandoned star clocks in favor of clocks that measure time by the flow of water through an opening of a particular size, just as hourglasses measure time by the flow of sand through a narrow neck.* These *water clocks* had the advantage of working even when the sky was cloudy. They eventually became the primary timekeeping instruments for many cultures, including the Greeks, Romans, and Chinese. Water clocks, in turn, were replaced by mechanical clocks in the 17th century and by electronic clocks in the 20th century. Despite the availability of other types of clocks, sundials were common throughout ancient times and remain popular today both for their decorative value and as reminders that the Sun and stars once were our only guides to time.

Marking the Seasons Many ancient cultures built structures to help them mark the seasons. Stonehenge (FIGURE 3.3) is a well-known example that served both as an astronomical device and as a social and religious gathering place. In the

Americas, one of the most spectacular structures was the Templo Mayor (FIGURE 3.4) in the Aztec city of Tenochtitlán (in modern-day Mexico City), which featured twin temples on a flat-topped pyramid. From the vantage point of a royal observer watching from the opposite side of the plaza, the Sun rose through the notch between the temples on the equinoxes. Before the Conquistadors destroyed it, Spanish visitors reported elaborate rituals at the Templo Mayor, sometimes including human sacrifice, that were held at times determined by astronomical observations. After its destruction, stones from the Templo Mayor were used to build a cathedral in the great plaza of Mexico City.

Many cultures aligned their buildings and streets with the cardinal directions (north, south, east, and west), which made it easier to keep track of the changing rise and set positions of the Sun over the course of the year. This type of alignment is

FIGURE 3.4 This scale model shows the Templo Mayor and the surrounding plaza as they are thought to have looked before the Spanish Conquistadors destroyed them. The structure was used to help mark the seasons.

---

*Hourglasses using sand were not invented until about the 8th century A.D., long after the advent of water clocks. Natural sand grains vary in size, so making accurate hourglasses required technology for making uniform grains of sand.

FIGURE 3.5 This large structure, more than 20 meters in diameter, is a kiva in Chaco Canyon, New Mexico. It was built by Ancestral Pueblo People approximately 1000 years ago. Its main axis is aligned almost precisely north-south.

found at such diverse sites as the Egyptian pyramids and the Forbidden City in China and among ceremonial kivas built by the Ancestral Pueblo People of the American southwest (FIGURE 3.5). Many modern cities retain this layout, which is why you'll find so many streets that run directly north-south or east-west.

Other structures were used to mark the Sun's position on special dates such as the winter or summer solstice. Many such structures can be found around the world, but one of the most amazing is the *Sun Dagger*, made by the Ancestral Pueblo People in Chaco Canyon, New Mexico (FIGURE 3.6). Three large slabs of rock lie in front of a carved spiral in such a way that they produced special patterns of light and shadow at different times of year. For example, a single dagger of sunlight pierced the center of the spiral only at noon on the summer solstice, while two daggers of light bracketed the spiral at the winter solstice.

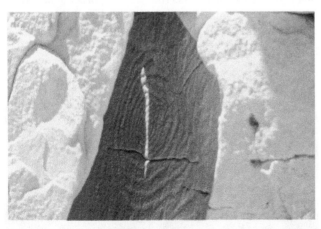

FIGURE 3.6 The Sun Dagger. Three large slabs of rock in front of the carved spiral produced patterns of light and shadow that varied throughout the year. Here, we see the single dagger of sunlight that pierced the center of the spiral only at noon on the summer solstice. (Unfortunately, within just 12 years of the site's 1977 discovery, the rocks shifted so that the effect no longer occurs; the shifts probably were due to erosion of the trail below the rocks caused by large numbers of visitors.)

The Sun Dagger may also have been used to mark a special cycle of the Moon that had ritual significance to the Ancestral Pueblo People. The rise and set positions of the full moon vary in an 18.6-year cycle (the cycle of precession of the Moon's orbit), so the full moon rises at its most southerly point along the eastern horizon only once every 18.6 years. At this time, known as a "major lunar standstill," the shadow of the full moon passes through the slabs of rock to lie tangent to the edge of the spiral in the Sun Dagger; then, 9.3 years later, the lunar shadow cuts through the center of the spiral. The major lunar standstill can also be observed with structures at nearby Chimney Rock and in cliff dwellings at Colorado's Mesa Verde National Park.

Solar and Lunar Calendars The tracking of the seasons eventually led to the advent of written calendars. Today, we use a *solar calendar*, meaning a calendar that is synchronized with the seasons so that seasonal events such as the solstices and equinoxes occur on approximately the same dates each year. The origins of our modern solar calendar go back to ancient Egypt, though many details (such as the timing of leap years) have been refined throughout history to keep the calendar well synchronized to the seasons [**Section S1.1**].

Solar calendars are not the only option. Many cultures created *lunar calendars* that aimed to stay synchronized with the Moon's $29\frac{1}{2}$-day cycle of phases, so that the Moon's phase was always the same on the first day of each month. A basic lunar calendar has 12 months, with some months lasting 29 days and others lasting 30 days; the lengths are chosen to make the average agree with the approximately $29\frac{1}{2}$-day lunar cycle. A 12-month lunar calendar therefore has only 354 or 355 days, or about 11 days fewer than a calendar based on the Sun. Such a calendar is still used in the Muslim religion. That is why the month-long fast of Ramadan (the ninth month) begins about 11 days earlier with each subsequent year.

Some cultures that used lunar calendars apparently did not like the idea of having their months cycle through the seasons over time, so they modified their calendars to take advantage of an interesting coincidence: 19 years on a solar calendar is almost precisely 235 months on a lunar calendar. As a result, the lunar phases repeat on the same dates about every 19 years (a pattern known as the *Metonic cycle*, so named because it was recognized by the Greek astronomer Meton in 432 B.C.). For example, there was a full moon on December 28, 2012, and there will be a full moon 19 years later, on December 28, 2031. Because an ordinary lunar calendar has only 19 × 12 = 228 months in a 19-year period, adding 7 extra months (to make 235) can keep the lunar calendar roughly synchronized to the seasons. One way of adding the 7 months is used in the Jewish calendar, which adds a thirteenth month in the third, sixth, eighth, eleventh, fourteenth, seventeenth, and nineteenth years of each 19-year cycle. This scheme keeps the dates of Jewish holidays within about a 1-month range on a solar calendar, with precise dates repeating every 19 years. It also explains why the date of Easter changes from year to year: The New Testament ties the date of Easter to the Jewish festival of Passover. In a slight modification of the original scheme, most Western Christians now celebrate Easter on the

FIGURE 3.7 This photo shows a model of the celestial sphere and other instruments on the roof of the ancient astronomical observatory in Beijing. The observatory was built in the 15th century; the instruments shown here were built later and show a European influence brought by Jesuit missionaries.

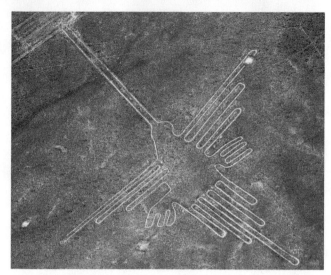

FIGURE 3.8 Hundreds of lines and patterns are etched in the sand of the Nazca desert in Peru. This aerial photo shows a large figure of a hummingbird.

first Sunday after the first full moon after March 21. If the full moon falls on Sunday, Easter is the following Sunday. (Eastern Orthodox churches calculate the date of Easter differently, because they base the date on the Julian rather than the Gregorian calendar [**Section S1.1**].)

Learning About Ancient Achievements The study of ancient astronomical achievements is a rich field of research. Many ancient cultures made careful observations of planets and stars, and some left remarkably detailed records. The Chinese, for example, began recording astronomical observations at least 5000 years ago, allowing ancient Chinese astronomers to make many important discoveries. By the 15th century, the Chinese had built a great observatory in Beijing, which still stands today (FIGURE 3.7). We can also study written records from ancient Middle Eastern civilizations such as those of Egypt and Babylonia.

Other cultures either did not leave clear written records or had records that were lost or destroyed, so we must piece together their astronomical achievements by studying the physical evidence they left behind. This type of study is usually called *archaeoastronomy*, a word that combines archaeology and astronomy. The astronomical uses of most of the structures we've discussed so far were discovered by researchers working in archaeoastronomy.

The cases we've discussed to this point have been fairly straightforward for archaeoastronomers to interpret, but many other cases are more ambiguous. For example, ancient people in what is now Peru etched hundreds of lines and patterns in the sand of the Nazca desert. Many of the lines point to places where the Sun or bright stars rise at particular times of year, but that doesn't prove anything: With hundreds of lines, random chance ensures that many will have astronomical alignments no matter how or why they were made. The patterns, many of which are large figures of animals (FIGURE 3.8), have evoked even more debate. Some people think they may be representations of constellations recognized by the people who lived in the region, but we do not know for sure.

THINK ABOUT IT
Animal figures like that in Figure 3.8 show up clearly only when seen from above. As a result, some UFO enthusiasts argue that the patterns must have been created by aliens. What do you think of this argument? Defend your opinion.

In some cases, scientists studying archaeoastronomy can use other clues to establish the intentions of ancient builders. For example, lodges built by the Pawnee people in Kansas feature strategically placed holes for observing the passage of constellations that figure prominently in Pawnee folklore. The correspondence between the folklore and the structural features provides a strong case for deliberate intent rather than coincidence. Similarly, traditions of the Inca Empire of South America held that its rulers were descendents of the Sun and therefore demanded close watch of the movements of the Sun and stars. This fact supports the idea that astronomical alignments in Inca cities and ceremonial centers, such as the World Heritage Site of Machu Picchu (FIGURE 3.9), were deliberate rather than accidental.

FIGURE 3.9 The World Heritage Site of Machu Picchu has structures aligned with sunrise at the winter and summer solstices.

FIGURE 3.10 A Micronesian stick chart, an instrument used by Polynesian Navigators to represent swell patterns around islands.

A different type of evidence makes a convincing case for the astronomical sophistication of ancient Polynesians, who lived and traveled among the islands of the mid- and South Pacific. Navigation was crucial to their survival because the next island in a journey usually was too distant to be seen. The most esteemed position in Polynesian culture was that of the Navigator, a person who had acquired the knowledge necessary to navigate great distances among the islands. Navigators used a combination of detailed knowledge of astronomy and an understanding of the patterns of waves and swells around different islands (FIGURE 3.10). The stars provided the broad navigational sense, while wave and swell patterns guided them to a precise landing point. A Navigator memorized all his knowledge and passed it to the next generation through a well-developed training program. Unfortunately, with the advent of modern navigational technology, many of the skills of the Navigators have been lost.

3.2 ANCIENT GREEK SCIENCE

Before a structure such as Stonehenge or the Templo Mayor could be built, careful observations had to be made and repeated over and over to ensure their accuracy. Careful, repeatable observations also underlie modern science. Elements of modern science were therefore present in many early human cultures. If the circumstances of history had been different, almost any culture might have been the first to develop what we consider to be modern science. In the end, however, history takes only one of countless possible paths. The path that led to modern science emerged from the ancient civilizations of the Mediterranean and the Middle East—especially from ancient Greece.

Greece gradually rose as a power in the Middle East beginning around 800 B.C. and was well established by about 500 B.C. Its geographical location placed it at a crossroads for travelers, merchants, and armies from northern Africa, Asia, and Europe. Building on the diverse ideas brought forth by the meeting of these many cultures, ancient Greek philosophers soon began their efforts to move human understanding of nature from the mythological to the rational.

Why does modern science trace its roots to the Greeks?

Greek philosophers developed at least three major innovations that helped pave the way for modern science. First, they developed a tradition of trying to understand nature without relying on supernatural explanations and of working communally to debate and challenge each other's ideas. Second, the Greeks used mathematics to give precision to their ideas, which allowed them to explore the implications of new ideas in much greater depth than would have otherwise been possible. Third, while much of their philosophical activity consisted of subtle debates grounded only in thought and was not scientific in the modern sense, the Greeks also saw the power of reasoning from observations. They understood that an explanation could not be right if it disagreed with observed facts.

Models of Nature Perhaps the greatest Greek contribution to science came from the way they synthesized all three innovations into the idea of creating models of nature, a practice that is central to modern science. Scientific models differ somewhat from the models you may be familiar with in everyday life. In our daily lives, we tend to think of models as miniature physical representations, such as model cars or airplanes. In contrast, a scientific **model** is a conceptual representation created to explain and predict observed phenomena. For example, a model of Earth's climate uses logic and mathematics to represent what we know about how the climate works. Its purpose is to explain and predict climate changes, such as the changes that may occur with global warming. Just as a model airplane does not faithfully represent every aspect of a real airplane, a scientific model may not fully explain all our observations of nature. Nevertheless, even the failings of a scientific model can be useful, because they often point the way toward building a better model.

From Greece to the Renaissance The Greeks created models that sought to explain many aspects of nature, including the properties of matter and the principles of motion. For our purposes, the most important of the Greek models was their Earth-centered model of the universe. Before we turn to its details, however, it's worth briefly discussing how ancient Greek philosophy was passed to Europe, where it ultimately grew into the principles of modern science.

Greek philosophy first began to spread widely with the conquests of Alexander the Great (356–323 B.C.). Alexander had a deep interest in science, perhaps in part because Aristotle (see Special Topic, page 61) had been his personal tutor. Alexander founded the city of Alexandria in Egypt, and shortly after his death the city commenced work on a great research center and library. The Library of Alexandria (FIGURE 3.11) opened in about 300 B.C. and remained the world's preeminent center of research for some 700 years. At its peak, it may have held as many as a half million books, handwritten on papyrus scrolls. Most of these scrolls were ultimately burned when the library was destroyed, their contents lost forever.

a This rendering shows an artist's reconstruction of the Great Hall of the ancient Library of Alexandria.

b A rendering similar to part a, showing a scroll room in the ancient library.

c The New Library of Alexandria in Egypt, which opened in 2003.

FIGURE 3.11 The ancient Library of Alexandria thrived for some 700 years, starting in about 300 B.C.

Much of the Library of Alexandria's long history remains unknown today, in part because the books that recorded its history were destroyed along with the library. Nevertheless, historians are confident that the library's demise was intertwined with the life and death of a woman named Hypatia (A.D. 370–415), one of the few prominent female scholars of the ancient world. Hypatia was one of the last resident scholars of the library, as well as the director of the observatory in Alexandria and one of the leading mathematicians and astronomers of her time. Tragically, she became a scapegoat during a time of rising

sentiment against free inquiry and was murdered in A.D. 415. The final destruction of the library took place not long after her death. In commemoration of the ancient library, Egypt built a New Library of Alexandria (the *Bibliotheca Alexandrina*, which opened in 2003), with hopes that it will once again make Alexandria a global center for scientific research.

The relatively few books that survived the destruction of the Library of Alexandria were preserved primarily thanks to the rise of a new center of intellectual inquiry in Baghdad (in present-day Iraq). While European civilization fell into the period of intellectual decline known as the Dark Ages, scholars of the new religion of Islam sought knowledge of mathematics and astronomy in hopes of better understanding the wisdom of Allah. During the 8th and 9th centuries A.D., scholars working in the Muslim Empire translated and thereby saved many ancient Greek works.

Around A.D. 800, the Islamic leader Al-Mamun (A.D. 786–833) established a "House of Wisdom" in Baghdad with a mission

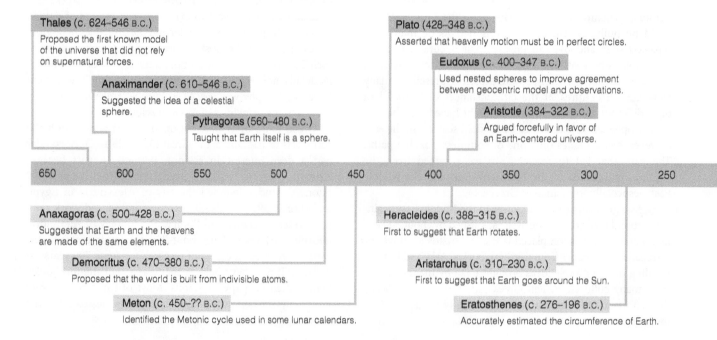

Thales (c. 624–546 B.C.)
Proposed the first known model of the universe that did not rely on supernatural forces.

Anaximander (c. 610–546 B.C.)
Suggested the idea of a celestial sphere.

Pythagoras (560–480 B.C.)
Taught that Earth itself is a sphere.

Plato (428–348 B.C.)
Asserted that heavenly motion must be in perfect circles.

Eudoxus (c. 400–347 B.C.)
Used nested spheres to improve agreement between geocentric model and observations.

Aristotle (384–322 B.C.)
Argued forcefully in favor of an Earth-centered universe.

650   600   550   500   450   400   350   300   250

Anaxagoras (c. 500–428 B.C.)
Suggested that Earth and the heavens are made of the same elements.

Democritus (c. 470–380 B.C.)
Proposed that the world is built from indivisible atoms.

Meton (c. 450–?? B.C.)
Identified the Metonic cycle used in some lunar calendars.

Heracleides (c. 388–315 B.C.)
First to suggest that Earth rotates.

Aristarchus (c. 310–230 B.C.)
First to suggest that Earth goes around the Sun.

Eratosthenes (c. 276–196 B.C.)
Accurately estimated the circumference of Earth.

Aristotle

Aristotle (384–322 B.C.) is among the best-known philosophers of the ancient world. Both his parents died when he was a child, and he was raised by a family friend. In his 20s and 30s, he studied under Plato (428–348 B.C.) at Plato's Academy. He later founded his own school, called the Lyceum, where he studied and lectured on virtually every subject. Historical records tell us that his lectures were collected and published in 150 volumes. About 50 of these volumes survive to the present day.

Many of Aristotle's scientific discoveries were about the nature of plants and animals. He studied more than 500 animal species in detail, dissecting specimens of nearly 50 species, and came up with a strikingly modern classification system. For example, he was the first person to recognize that dolphins should be classified with land

mammals rather than with fish. In mathematics, he is known for laying the foundations of mathematical logic. Unfortunately, he was far less successful in physics and astronomy, areas in which many of his claims turned out to be wrong.

Despite his wide-ranging discoveries and writings, Aristotle's philosophies were not particularly influential until many centuries after his death. His books were preserved and valued by Islamic scholars but were unknown in Europe until they were translated into Latin in the 12th and 13th centuries. Aristotle's work gained great influence only after his philosophy was integrated into Christian theology by St. Thomas Aquinas (1225–1274). In the ancient world, Aristotle's greatest influence came indirectly, through his role as the tutor of Alexander the Great.

much like that of the destroyed Library of Alexandria. Founded in a spirit of openness and tolerance, the House of Wisdom employed Jews, Christians, and Muslims, all working together in scholarly pursuits. Using the translated Greek scientific manuscripts as building blocks, these scholars developed the mathematics of algebra and many new instruments and techniques for astronomical observation. Most of the official names of constellations and stars come from Arabic because of the work of the scholars at Baghdad. If you look at a star chart, you will see that the names of many bright stars begin with *al* (e.g., Aldebaran, Algol), which means "the" in Arabic.

The Islamic world of the Middle Ages was in frequent contact with Hindu scholars from India, who in turn brought knowledge of ideas and discoveries from China. Hence, the intellectual center in Baghdad achieved a synthesis of the surviving work of the ancient Greeks and that of the Indians and the Chinese. The accumulated knowledge of the Baghdad scholars spread throughout the Byzantine empire (part of the former Roman Empire). When the Byzantine capital of

Constantinople (modern-day Istanbul) fell to the Turks in 1453, many Eastern scholars headed west to Europe, carrying with them the knowledge that helped ignite the European Renaissance.

How did the Greeks explain planetary motion?

The Greek **geocentric model** of the cosmos—so named because it placed a spherical Earth at the center of the universe—developed gradually over a period of several centuries. Because this model was so important in the history of science, let's briefly trace its development. FIGURE 3.12 will help you keep track of some of the personalities we will encounter.

Early Development of the Geocentric Model

We generally trace the origin of Greek science to the philosopher Thales (c. 624–546 B.C.; pronounced *thay-lees*). We encountered Thales earlier because of his legendary prediction

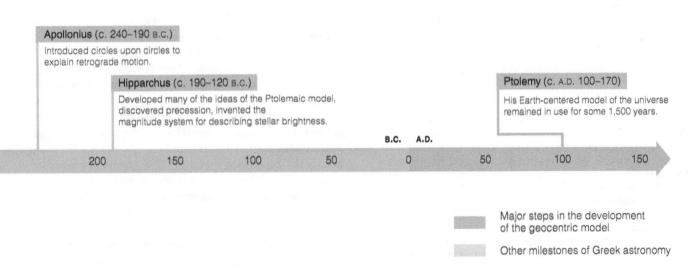

FIGURE 3.12 Timeline for major Greek figures in the development of astronomy. (All these individuals are discussed in this book, but not necessarily in this chapter.)

of a solar eclipse [**Section 2.3**]. Thales was the first person known to have addressed the question "What is the universe made of?" without resorting to supernatural explanations. His own guess—that the universe fundamentally consists of water and that Earth is a flat disk floating in an infinite ocean—was not widely accepted even in his own time. Nevertheless, just by asking the question he suggested that the world is inherently understandable and thereby inspired others to come up with better models for the structure of the universe.

A more sophisticated idea followed soon after, proposed by a student of Thales named Anaximander (c. 610–546 B.C.). Anaximander suggested that Earth floats in empty space surrounded by a sphere of stars and two separate rings along which the Sun and Moon travel. We therefore credit him with inventing the idea of a celestial sphere [**Section 2.1**]. Interestingly, Anaximander imagined Earth itself to be cylindrical rather than spherical in shape. He probably chose this shape because he knew Earth had to be curved in a north-south direction to explain changes in the constellations with latitude. Because the visible constellations do not change with longitude, he saw no need for curvature in the east-west direction.

We do not know precisely when the Greeks first began to think that Earth is round, but this idea was taught as early as about 500 B.C. by the famous mathematician Pythagoras (c. 560–480 B.C.). He and his followers envisioned Earth as a sphere floating at the center of the celestial sphere. Much of their motivation for adopting a spherical Earth probably was philosophical: The Pythagoreans had a mystical interest in mathematical perfection, and they considered a sphere to be geometrically perfect. More than a century later, Aristotle cited observations of Earth's curved shadow on the Moon during lunar eclipses as evidence for a spherical Earth.

The Pythagorean interest in "heavenly perfection" became deeply ingrained in most Greek philosophers. It took on even more significance after Plato (428–348 B.C.) asserted that all heavenly objects move in perfect circles at constant speeds and therefore must reside on huge spheres encircling Earth (FIGURE 3.13). The Platonic belief in perfection influenced astronomical models for the next 2000 years. Of course,

FIGURE 3.13 This model represents the Greek idea of the heavenly spheres (c. 400 B.C.). Earth is a sphere that rests in the center. The Moon, the Sun, and the planets all have their own spheres. The outermost sphere holds the stars.

those Greeks who made observations found Plato's model problematic: The apparent retrograde motion of the planets [**Section 2.4**], already well known by that time, clearly showed that planets do *not* move at constant speeds around Earth.

An ingenious solution came from Plato's colleague Eudoxus (c. 400–347 B.C.), who created a model in which the Sun, the Moon, and the planets each had their own spheres nested within several other spheres. Individually, the nested spheres turned in perfect circles. By carefully choosing the sizes, rotation axes, and rotation speeds for the invisible spheres, Eudoxus was able to make them work together in a way that reproduced many of the observed motions of the Sun, Moon, and planets in our sky. Other Greeks refined the model by comparing its predictions to observations and adding more spheres to improve the agreement.

This is how things stood when Aristotle (384–322 B.C.) arrived on the scene. Whether Eudoxus and his followers thought of the nested spheres as real physical objects is not clear, but Aristotle certainly did. In Aristotle's model, all the spheres responsible for celestial motion were transparent and interconnected like the gears of a giant machine. Earth's position at the center was explained as a natural consequence of gravity. Aristotle argued that gravity pulled heavy things toward the center of the universe (and allowed lighter things to float toward the heavens), thereby causing all the dirt, rock, and water of the universe to collect at the center and form the spherical Earth. We now know that Aristotle was wrong about both gravity and Earth's location. However, largely because of his persuasive arguments for an Earth-centered universe, the geocentric view dominated Western thought for almost 2000 years.

COMMON MISCONCEPTIONS

Columbus and a Flat Earth

A widespread myth gives credit to Columbus for learning that Earth is round, but knowledge of Earth's shape predated Columbus by nearly 2000 years. Not only were scholars of Columbus's time well aware that Earth is round, but they even knew its approximate size: Earth's circumference was first measured in about 240 B.C. by the Greek scientist Eratosthenes. In fact, a likely reason Columbus had so much difficulty finding a sponsor for his voyages was that he tried to argue a point on which he was wrong: He claimed the distance by sea from western Europe to eastern Asia to be much less than scholars knew it to be. When he finally found a patron in Spain and left on his journey, he was so woefully underprepared that the voyage would almost certainly have ended in disaster if the Americas hadn't stood in his way.

Ptolemy's Synthesis Greek modeling of the cosmos culminated in the work of Claudius Ptolemy (c. A.D. 100–170; pronounced *TOL-e-mee*). Ptolemy's model still placed Earth at the center of the universe, but it differed in significant ways from the nested spheres of Eudoxus and Aristotle. We refer to Ptolemy's geocentric model as the **Ptolemaic model** to distinguish it from earlier geocentric models.

To explain the apparent retrograde motion of the planets, the Ptolemaic model applied an idea first suggested by Apollonius (c. 240–190 B.C.). This idea held that each planet moved around Earth on a small circle that turned upon a larger circle (**FIGURE 3.14**). (The small circle is sometimes called an *epicycle,* and the larger circle is called a *deferent.*) A planet following this circle-upon-circle motion would trace a loop as seen from Earth, with the backward portion of the loop mimicking apparent retrograde motion.

Ptolemy also relied heavily on the work of Hipparchus (c. 190–120 B.C.), considered one of the greatest of the Greek astronomers. Among his many accomplishments, Hipparchus developed the circle-upon-circle idea of Apollonius into a model that could predict planetary positions. To do this, Hipparchus had to add several features to the basic idea; for example, he included even smaller circles that moved upon the original set of small circles, and he positioned the large circles slightly off-center from Earth.

Ptolemy's great accomplishment was to adapt and synthesize earlier ideas into a single system that agreed quite well with the astronomical observations available at the time. In the end, he created and published a model that could correctly forecast future planetary positions to within a few degrees of arc, which is about the angular size of your hand held at arm's length against the sky. This was sufficiently accurate to keep

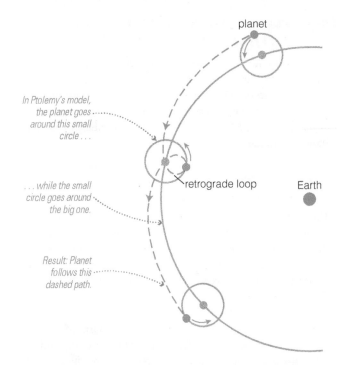

FIGURE 3.14 interactive figure This diagram shows how the Ptolemaic model accounted for apparent retrograde motion. Each planet is assumed to move around a small circle that turns upon a larger circle. The resulting path (dashed) includes a loop in which the planet goes backward as seen from Earth.

the model in use for the next 1500 years. When Ptolemy's book describing the model was translated by Arabic scholars around A.D. 800, they gave it the title *Almagest,* derived from words meaning "the greatest compilation."

SPECIAL TOPIC

Eratosthenes Measures Earth

In a remarkable feat, the Greek scientist Eratosthenes accurately estimated the size of Earth in about 240 B.C. He did it by comparing the altitude of the Sun on the summer solstice in the Egyptian cities of Syene (modern-day Aswan) and Alexandria.

Eratosthenes knew that the Sun passed directly overhead in Syene on the summer solstice. He also knew that in Alexandria, to the north, the Sun came within only 7° of the zenith on the summer solstice. He therefore reasoned that Alexandria must be 7° of latitude to the north of Syene (**FIGURE 1**). Because 7° is $\frac{7}{360}$ of a circle, he concluded that the north-south distance between Alexandria and Syene must be $\frac{7}{360}$ of the circumference of Earth.

Eratosthenes estimated the north-south distance between Syene and Alexandria to be 5000 stadia (the *stadium* was a Greek unit of distance). Thus, he concluded that

$$\frac{7}{360} \times \text{circumference of Earth} = 5000 \text{ stadia}$$

From this he found Earth's circumference to be about 250,000 stadia.

We don't know exactly what distance a stadium meant to Eratosthenes, but from sizes of actual Greek stadiums, it must have been about $\frac{1}{6}$ kilometer. Thus, Eratosthenes estimated the circumference of Earth to be about $\frac{250,000}{6} = 42,000$ kilometers—impressively close to the real value of just over 40,000 kilometers.

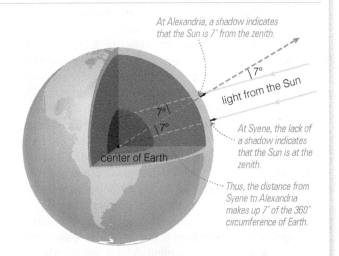

FIGURE 1 At noon on the summer solstice, the Sun appears at the zenith in Syene but 7° shy of the zenith in Alexandria. Thus, 7° of latitude, which corresponds to a distance of $\frac{7}{360}$ of Earth's circumference, must separate the two cities.

3.3 THE COPERNICAN REVOLUTION

The Greeks and other ancient peoples developed many important scientific ideas, but what we now think of as science arose during the European Renaissance. Within a half century after the fall of Constantinople, Polish scientist Nicholas Copernicus began the work that ultimately overturned the Earth-centered Ptolemaic model.

How did Copernicus, Tycho, and Kepler challenge the Earth-centered model?

The ideas introduced by Copernicus fundamentally changed the way we perceive our place in the universe. The story of this dramatic change, known as the **Copernican revolution**, is in many ways the story of the origin of modern science. It is also the story of several key personalities, beginning with Copernicus himself.

Copernicus Nicholas Copernicus was born in Toruń, Poland, on February 19, 1473. His family was wealthy and he received an education in mathematics, medicine, and law. He began studying astronomy in his late teens.

By that time, tables of planetary motion based on the Ptolemaic model had become noticeably inaccurate. But few people were willing to undertake the difficult calculations required to revise the tables. The best tables available had been compiled some two centuries earlier under the guidance of Spanish monarch Alphonso X (1221–1284). Commenting on the tedious nature of the work, the monarch is said to have complained, "If I had been present at the creation, I would have recommended a simpler design for the universe."

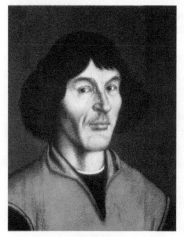

Copernicus (1473–1543)

In his quest for a better way to predict planetary positions, Copernicus decided to try Aristarchus's Sun-centered idea, first proposed more than 1700 years earlier [**Section 2.4**]. He had read of Aristarchus's work, and recognized the much simpler explanation for apparent retrograde motion offered by a Sun-centered system (see Figure 2.33). But he went far beyond Aristarchus in working out mathematical details of the model. Through this process, Copernicus discovered simple geometric relationships that allowed him to calculate each planet's orbital period around the Sun and its relative distance from the Sun in terms of the Earth-Sun distance (see Mathematical Insight S1.1). The model's success in providing a geometric layout for the solar system convinced him that the Sun-centered idea must be correct.

Despite his own confidence in the model, Copernicus was hesitant to publish his work, fearing that his suggestion that Earth moved would be considered absurd. However, he discussed his system with other scholars, including high-ranking officials of the Catholic Church, who urged him to publish a book. Copernicus saw the first printed copy of his book, *De Revolutionibus Orbium Coelestium* ("Concerning the Revolutions of the Heavenly Spheres"), on the day he died—May 24, 1543.

Publication of the book spread the Sun-centered idea widely, and many scholars were drawn to its aesthetic advantages. Nevertheless, the Copernican model gained relatively few converts over the next 50 years, for a good reason: It didn't work all that well. The primary problem was that while Copernicus had been willing to overturn Earth's central place in the cosmos, he had held fast to the ancient belief that heavenly motion must occur in perfect circles. This incorrect assumption forced him to add numerous complexities to his system (including circles on circles much like those used by Ptolemy) to get it to make decent predictions. In the end, his complete model was no more accurate and no less complex than the Ptolemaic model, and few people were willing to throw out thousands of years of tradition for a new model that worked just as poorly as the old one.

Tycho Part of the difficulty faced by astronomers who sought to improve either the Ptolemaic or the Copernican system was a lack of quality data. The telescope had not yet been invented, and existing naked-eye observations were not very accurate. Better data were needed, and they were provided by the Danish nobleman Tycho Brahe (1546–1601), usually known simply as Tycho (pronounced *tie-koe*).

Tycho became interested in astronomy as a young boy, but his family discouraged this interest. He therefore kept his passion secret, learning the constellations from a miniature model of a celestial sphere that he kept hidden. As he grew older, Tycho was often arrogant about both his noble birth and his intellectual abilities. At age 20, he fought a duel with another student over which of them was the better mathematician. Part of Tycho's nose was cut off, and he designed a replacement piece made of silver and gold.

Tycho Brahe (1546–1601)

In 1563, Tycho decided to observe a widely anticipated alignment of Jupiter and Saturn. To his surprise, the alignment occurred nearly 2 days later than the date Copernicus had predicted. Resolving to improve the state of astronomical prediction, he set about compiling careful observations of stellar and planetary positions in the sky.

Tycho's fame grew after he observed what he called a *nova*, meaning "new star," in 1572. By measuring its parallax and comparing it to the parallax of the Moon, he proved that the nova was much farther away than the Moon. (Today, we know that Tycho saw a *supernova*—the explosion of a distant star [**Section 17.3**].) In 1577, Tycho made similar observations of a comet and proved that it too lay in the realm of the heavens. Others, including Aristotle, had argued that comets were phenomena of Earth's atmosphere. King Frederick II of Denmark decided to sponsor Tycho's ongoing work, providing him with money to build an unparalleled observatory for naked-eye observations (**FIGURE 3.15**). After Frederick II died in 1588, Tycho moved to Prague, where his work was supported by German emperor Rudolf II.

Over a period of three decades, Tycho and his assistants compiled naked-eye observations accurate to within less than 1 arcminute—less than the thickness of a fingernail viewed at arm's length. Because the telescope was invented shortly after his death, Tycho's data remain the best set of naked-eye observations ever made. Despite the quality of his observations, Tycho never succeeded in coming up with a satisfying explanation for planetary motion. He was convinced that the

planets must orbit the Sun, but his inability to detect stellar parallax [**Section 2.4**] led him to conclude that Earth must remain stationary. He therefore advocated a model in which the Sun orbits Earth while all other planets orbit the Sun. Few people took this model seriously.

Kepler Tycho failed to explain the motions of the planets satisfactorily, but he succeeded in finding someone who could: In 1600, he hired the young German astronomer Johannes Kepler (1571–1630). Kepler and Tycho had a strained relationship, but Tycho recognized the talent of his young apprentice. In 1601, as he lay on his deathbed, Tycho begged Kepler to find a system that would make sense of his observations so "that it may not appear I have lived in vain."[*]

Johannes Kepler (1571–1630)

Kepler was deeply religious and believed that understanding the geometry of the heavens would bring him closer to God. Like Copernicus, he believed that planetary orbits should be perfect circles, so he worked diligently to match circular motions to Tycho's data.

Kepler labored with particular intensity to find an orbit for Mars, which posed the greatest difficulties in matching the data to a circular orbit. After years of calculation, Kepler found a circular orbit that matched all of Tycho's observations of Mars's position along the ecliptic (east-west) to within 2 arcminutes. However, the model did not correctly predict Mars's positions north or south of the ecliptic. Because Kepler sought a physically realistic orbit for Mars, he could not (as Ptolemy and Copernicus had done) tolerate one model for the east-west positions and another for the north-south positions. He attempted to find a unified model with a circular orbit. In doing so, he found that some of his predictions differed from Tycho's observations by as much as 8 arcminutes.

Kepler surely was tempted to ignore these discrepancies and attribute them to errors by Tycho. After all, 8 arcminutes is barely one-fourth the angular diameter of the full moon. But Kepler trusted Tycho's careful work. The small discrepancies finally led Kepler to abandon the idea of circular orbits—and to find the correct solution to the ancient riddle of planetary motion. About this event, Kepler wrote:

> *If I had believed that we could ignore these eight minutes [of arc], I would have patched up my hypothesis accordingly. But, since it was not permissible to ignore, those eight minutes pointed the road to a complete reformation in astronomy.*

FIGURE 3.15 Tycho Brahe in his naked-eye observatory, which worked much like a giant protractor. He could sit and observe a planet through the rectangular hole in the wall as an assistant used a sliding marker to measure the angle on the protractor.

---

[*]For a particularly moving version of the story of Tycho and Kepler, see Episode 3 of Carl Sagan's *Cosmos* video series.

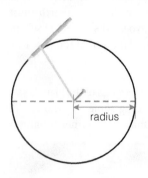

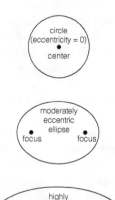

FIGURE 3.16

interactive figure An ellipse is a special type of oval. These diagrams show how an ellipse differs from a circle and how different ellipses vary in their eccentricity.

a Drawing a circle with a string of fixed length.

b Drawing an ellipse with a string of fixed length.

c Eccentricity describes how much an ellipse deviates from a perfect circle.

Kepler's key discovery was that planetary orbits are not circles but instead are a special type of oval called an **ellipse**. You can draw a circle by putting a pencil on the end of a string, tacking the string to a board, and pulling the pencil around (**FIGURE 3.16a**). Drawing an ellipse is similar, except that you must stretch the string around *two* tacks (**FIGURE 3.16b**). The locations of the two tacks are called the **foci** (singular, **focus**) of the ellipse. The long axis of the ellipse is called its *major axis*, each half of which is called a **semimajor axis**; as you'll see shortly, the length of the semimajor axis is particularly important in astronomy. The short axis is called the *minor axis*. By altering the distance between the two foci while keeping the length of string the same, you can draw ellipses of varying **eccentricity**, a quantity that describes how much an ellipse is stretched out compared to a perfect circle (**FIGURE 3.16c**). A circle is an ellipse with zero eccentricity, and greater eccentricity means a more elongated ellipse.

Kepler's decision to trust the data over his preconceived beliefs marked an important transition point in the history of science. Once he abandoned perfect circles in favor of ellipses, Kepler soon came up with a model that could predict planetary positions with far greater accuracy than Ptolemy's Earth-centered model. Kepler's model withstood the test of time and became accepted not only as a model of nature but also as a deep, underlying truth about planetary motion.

(MA) Orbits and Kepler's Laws Tutorial, Lessons 2–4

What are Kepler's three laws of planetary motion?

Kepler summarized his discoveries with three simple laws that we now call **Kepler's laws of planetary motion**. He published the first two laws in 1609 and the third in 1619.

Kepler's First Law Kepler's first law tells us that *the orbit of each planet around the Sun is an ellipse with the Sun at one focus* (**FIGURE 3.17**). (Nothing is at the other focus.) In essence,

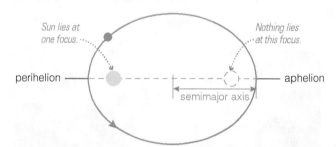

FIGURE 3.17 **interactive figure** Kepler's first law: The orbit of each planet about the Sun is an ellipse with the Sun at one focus. (The eccentricity shown here is exaggerated compared to the actual eccentricities of the planets.)

this law tells us that a planet's distance from the Sun varies during its orbit. It is closest at the point called **perihelion** (from the Greek for "near the Sun") and farthest at the point called **aphelion** (from the Greek for "away from the Sun"). The *average* of a planet's perihelion and aphelion distances is the length of its semimajor axis. We will refer to this simply as the planet's average distance from the Sun.

Kepler's Second Law Kepler's second law states that *as a planet moves around its orbit, it sweeps out equal areas in equal times*. As shown in **FIGURE 3.18**, this means the planet moves a greater distance when it is near perihelion than it does in the same amount of time near aphelion. That is, the planet travels faster when it is nearer to the Sun and slower when it is farther from the Sun.

Kepler's Third Law Kepler's third law tells us that *more distant planets orbit the Sun at slower average speeds, obeying a precise mathematical relationship*. The relationship is written

$$p^2 = a^3$$

where p is the planet's orbital period in years and a is its average distance from the Sun in astronomical units. **FIGURE 3.19a** shows the $p^2 = a^3$ law graphically. Notice that

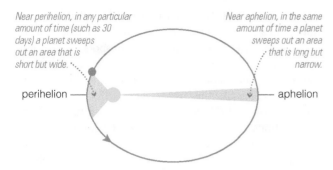

Near perihelion, in any particular amount of time (such as 30 days) a planet sweeps out an area that is short but wide.

Near aphelion, in the same amount of time a planet sweeps out an area that is long but narrow.

perihelion — ⋯ — aphelion

FIGURE 3.18 interactive figure Kepler's second law: As a planet moves around its orbit, an imaginary line connecting it to the Sun sweeps out equal areas (the shaded regions) in equal times.

the square of each planet's orbital period (p^2) is indeed equal to the cube of its average distance from the Sun (a^3). Because Kepler's third law relates a planet's orbital distance to its orbital time (period), we can use the law to calculate a planet's average orbital speed.* **FIGURE 3.19b** shows the result, confirming that more distant planets orbit the Sun more slowly.

The fact that more distant planets move more slowly led Kepler to suggest that planetary motion might be the result of a force from the Sun. He even speculated about the nature of this force, guessing that it might be related to magnetism. (This idea, shared by Galileo, was first suggested by William Gilbert [1544–1603], an early believer in the Copernican system.) Kepler was right about the existence of a force but wrong in his guess of magnetism. A half century later, Isaac Newton finally explained planetary motion as a consequence of gravity [**Section 4.4**].

---

*To calculate orbital speed from Kepler's third law, remember that speed = distance/time. For a planetary orbit, the distance is the orbital circumference, or $2\pi a$ (where a is the semimajor axis, roughly the "radius" of the orbit), and the time is the orbital period p, so the orbital speed is $(2\pi a)/p$. From Kepler's third law, $p = a^{3/2}$. Plugging this value for p into the orbital speed equation, we find that a planet's orbital speed is $2\pi/\sqrt{a}$; the graph of this equation is the curve in Figure 3.19b.

THINK ABOUT IT

Suppose a comet has an orbit that brings it quite close to the Sun at its perihelion and beyond Mars at its aphelion, but with an average distance (semimajor axis) of 1 AU. According to Kepler's laws, how long does the comet take to complete each orbit? Does it spend most of its time close to the Sun, far from the Sun, or somewhere in between? Explain.

How did Galileo solidify the Copernican revolution?

The success of Kepler's laws in matching Tycho's data provided strong evidence in favor of Copernicus's placement of the Sun, rather than Earth, at the center of the solar system. Nevertheless, many scientists still voiced reasonable objections to the Copernican view. There were three basic objections, all rooted in the 2000-year-old beliefs of Aristotle and other ancient Greeks.

■ First, Aristotle had held that Earth could not be moving because, if it were, objects such as birds, falling stones, and clouds would be left behind as Earth moved along its way.

■ Second, the idea of noncircular orbits contradicted Aristotle's claim that the heavens—the realm of the Sun, Moon, planets, and stars—must be perfect and unchanging.

■ Third, no one had detected the stellar parallax that should occur if Earth orbits the Sun [**Section 2.4**].

Galileo Galilei (1564–1642), usually known by only his first name, answered all three objections.

Galileo's Evidence Galileo defused the first objection with experiments that almost single-handedly overturned the Aristotelian view of physics. In particular, he used experiments with rolling balls to demonstrate that a moving object remains in motion *unless* a force acts to stop it (an idea now codified in Newton's first law of motion [**Section 4.2**]). This

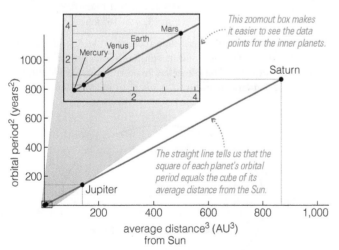

a This graph shows that Kepler's third law ($p^2 = a^3$) holds true; the graph shows only the planets known in Kepler's time.

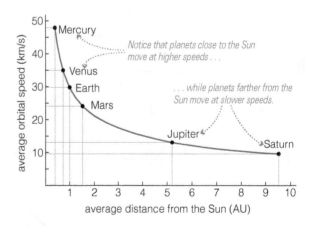

b This graph, based on Kepler's third law and modern values of planetary distances, shows that more distant planets orbit the Sun more slowly.

FIGURE 3.19 Graphs based on Kepler's third law.

Galileo (1564–1642)

insight explained why objects that share Earth's motion through space—such as birds, falling stones, and clouds—should *stay* with Earth rather than falling behind as Aristotle had argued. This same idea explains why passengers stay with a moving airplane even when they leave their seats.

The second objection had already been challenged by Tycho's supernova and comet observations, which proved that the heavens could change. Galileo then shattered the idea of heavenly perfection after he built a telescope in late 1609. (Galileo did not invent the telescope; it was patented by Hans Lippershey in 1608. However, Galileo took what was little more than a toy and turned it into a scientific instrument.) Through his telescope, Galileo saw sunspots on the Sun, which were considered "imperfections" at the time. He also used his telescope to prove that the Moon has mountains and valleys like the "imperfect" Earth by noticing the shadows cast near the dividing line between the light and dark portions of the lunar face (FIGURE 3.20). If the heavens were in fact not perfect, then the idea of elliptical orbits (as opposed to "perfect" circles) was not so objectionable.

The third objection—the absence of observable stellar parallax—had been of particular concern to Tycho. Based on his estimates of the distances of stars, Tycho believed that his naked-eye observations were sufficiently precise to detect stellar parallax if Earth did in fact orbit the Sun. Refuting Tycho's argument required showing that the stars were more distant than Tycho had thought and therefore too distant for him to have observed stellar parallax. Although Galileo didn't actually prove this fact, he provided strong evidence in its favor. For example, he saw with his telescope that the Milky Way

MATHEMATICAL INSIGHT 3.1

Eccentricity and Planetary Orbits

We describe how much a planet's orbit differs from a perfect circle by stating its orbital eccentricity. There are several equivalent ways to define the eccentricity of an ellipse, but the simplest is shown in FIGURE 1. We define c to be the distance from each focus to the center of the ellipse and a to be the length of the semimajor axis. The eccentricity, e, is then defined to be

$$e = \frac{c}{a}$$

Notice that $c = 0$ for a perfect circle, because a circle is an ellipse with both foci *in* the center, so this formula gives an eccentricity of 0 for a perfect circle, just as we expect.

You can find the orbital eccentricities for the planets in tables such as Table E.2 in Appendix E of this book. Once you know the eccentricity, the following formulas allow you to calculate the planet's perihelion and aphelion distances (FIGURE 2):

$$\text{perihelion distance} = a(1 - e)$$
$$\text{aphelion distance} = a(1 + e)$$

EXAMPLE: What are Earth's perihelion and aphelion distances?

SOLUTION:

Step 1 Understand: To use the given formulas, we need to know Earth's orbital eccentricity and semimajor axis length. From Table E.2, Earth's orbital eccentricity is $e = 0.017$ and its semimajor axis (average distance from the Sun) is 1 AU, or $a = 149.6$ million km.

Step 2 Solve: We plug these values into the equations:

$$\begin{aligned}
\text{Earth's perihelion distance} &= a(1 - e) \\
&= (149.6 \times 10^6 \text{ km})(1 - 0.017) \\
&= 147.1 \times 10^6 \text{ km}
\end{aligned}$$

$$\begin{aligned}
\text{Earth's aphelion distance} &= a(1 + e) \\
&= (149.6 \times 10^6 \text{ km})(1 + 0.017) \\
&= 152.1 \times 10^6 \text{ km}
\end{aligned}$$

Step 3 Explain: Earth's perihelion (nearest to the Sun) distance is 147.1 million kilometers and its aphelion (farthest from the Sun) distance is 152.1 million kilometers. In other words, Earth's distance from the Sun varies between 147.1 and 152.1 million kilometers.

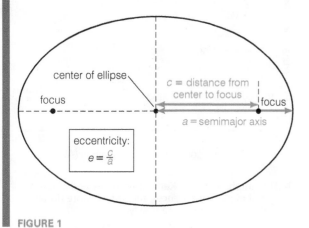

FIGURE 1

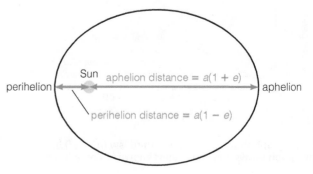

FIGURE 2

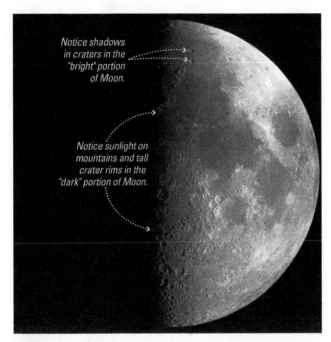

Notice shadows in craters in the "bright" portion of Moon.

Notice sunlight on mountains and tall crater rims in the "dark" portion of Moon.

FIGURE 3.20 The shadows cast by mountains and crater rims near the dividing line between the light and dark portions of the lunar face prove that the Moon's surface is not perfectly smooth.

resolved into countless individual stars. This discovery helped him argue that the stars were far more numerous and more distant than Tycho had believed.

Sealing the Case In hindsight, the final nails in the coffin of the Earth-centered model came with two of Galileo's earliest discoveries through the telescope. First, he observed four moons clearly orbiting Jupiter, *not* Earth (**FIGURE 3.21**). By itself, this observation still did not rule out a stationary, central Earth. However, it showed that moons can orbit a moving planet like Jupiter, which overcame some critics' complaints that the Moon could not stay with a moving Earth. Soon thereafter, he observed that Venus goes through phases in a

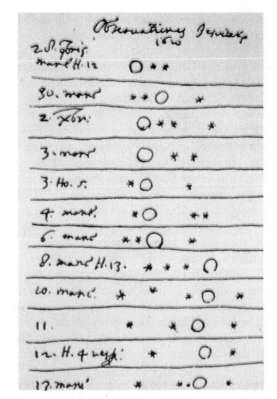

FIGURE 3.21 A page from Galileo's notebook written in 1610. His sketches show four "stars" near Jupiter (the circle) but in different positions at different times (with one or more sometimes hidden from view). Galileo soon realized that the "stars" were actually moons orbiting Jupiter.

way that makes sense only if it orbits the Sun and not Earth (**FIGURE 3.22**).

With Earth clearly removed from its position at the center of the universe, the scientific debate turned to the question of whether Kepler's laws were the correct model for our solar system. The most convincing evidence came in 1631, when astronomers observed a transit of Mercury across the Sun's

Ptolemaic View of Venus

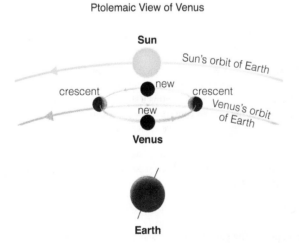

a In the Ptolemaic system, Venus orbits Earth, moving around a smaller circle on its larger orbital circle; the center of the smaller circle lies on the Earth-Sun line. If this view were correct, Venus's phases would range only from new to crescent.

Copernican View of Venus

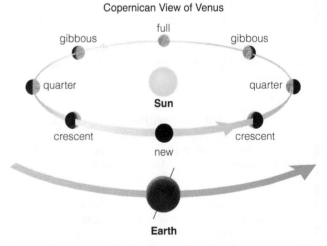

b In reality, Venus orbits the Sun, so from Earth we can see it in many different phases. This is just what Galileo observed, allowing him to prove that Venus orbits the Sun.

FIGURE 3.22 Galileo's telescopic observations of Venus proved that it orbits the Sun rather than Earth.

face. Kepler's laws had predicted the transit with overwhelmingly better success than any competing model.

Galileo and the Church Although we now recognize that Galileo won the day, the story was more complex in his own time, when Catholic Church doctrine still held Earth to be the center of the universe. On June 22, 1633, Galileo was brought before a Church inquisition in Rome and ordered to recant his claim that Earth orbits the Sun. Nearly 70 years old and fearing for his life, Galileo did as ordered and his life was spared. However, legend has it that as he rose from his knees he whispered under his breath, *Eppur si muove*—Italian for "And yet it moves." (Given the likely consequences if Church officials had heard him say this, most historians doubt the legend; see Special Topic, page 74.)

The Church did not formally vindicate Galileo until 1992, but Church officials gave up the argument long before that: In 1757, all works backing the idea of a Sun-centered solar system were removed from the Church's index of banned books. Today, Catholic scientists are at the forefront of much astronomical research, and official Church teachings are compatible not only with Earth's planetary status but also with the theories of the Big Bang and the subsequent evolution of the cosmos and of life.

3.4 THE NATURE OF SCIENCE

The story of how our ancestors gradually figured out the basic architecture of the cosmos exhibits many features of what we now consider "good science." For example, we have seen how

models were formulated and tested against observations and modified or replaced when they failed those tests. The story also illustrates some classic mistakes, such as the apparent failure of anyone before Kepler to question the belief that orbits must be circles. The ultimate success of the Copernican revolution led scientists, philosophers, and theologians to reassess the various modes of thinking that played a role in the 2000-year process of discovering Earth's place in the universe. Let's examine how the principles of modern science emerged from the lessons learned in the Copernican revolution.

How can we distinguish science from nonscience?

It's surprisingly difficult to define the term *science* precisely. The word comes from the Latin *scientia*, meaning "knowledge," but not all knowledge is science. For example, you may know what music you like best, but your musical taste is not a result of scientific study.

Approaches to Science One reason science is difficult to define is that not all science works in the same way. For example, you've probably heard that science is supposed to proceed according to something called the "scientific method." As an idealized illustration of this method, consider what you would do if your flashlight suddenly stopped working. In hopes of fixing the flashlight, you might *hypothesize* that its batteries have died. This type of tentative explanation,

---

MATHEMATICAL INSIGHT 3.2

Kepler's Third Law

When Kepler discovered his third law, $p^2 = a^3$, he did so only by looking at planet orbits. In fact, it applies much more generally. We'll see its most general form in Mathematical Insight 4.3, but even in its original form we can apply it to any object *if*

1. the object is *orbiting the Sun* or another star of the same mass as the Sun and
2. we measure orbital *periods in years* and *distances in AU*.

EXAMPLE 1: What is the orbital period of the dwarf planet (and largest asteroid) Ceres, which orbits the Sun at an average distance (semimajor axis) of 2.77 AU?

SOLUTION:

Step 1 Understand: We can apply Kepler's third law because both conditions above are met. The first is met because Ceres orbits the Sun. The second is met because we are given the orbital distance in AU, which means Kepler's third law will tell us the orbital period in years.

Step 2 Solve: We want the period p, so we solve Kepler's third law for p by taking the square root of both sides; we then substitute the given value $a = 2.77$ AU:

$$p^2 = a^3 \implies p = \sqrt{a^3} = \sqrt{2.77^3} = 4.6$$

Note that because of the special conditions attached to the use of Kepler's third law in its original form, we do *not* include units when

working with it; we know we'll get a period in years as long as we start with a distance in AU.

Step 3 Explain: Ceres has an orbital period of 4.6 years, meaning it takes 4.6 years to complete each orbit around the Sun.

EXAMPLE 2: A new planet is discovered to be orbiting a star with the same mass as our Sun. The planet orbits the star every 3 months. What is its average distance from its star?

SOLUTION:

Step 1 Understand: We can use Kepler's third law in its original form if the problem meets the two conditions above. The first condition is met because the planet is orbiting a star with the same mass as our Sun. To meet the second condition, we must convert the orbital period from 3 months to $p = 0.25$ year.

Step 2 Solve: We want the distance a, so we solve Kepler's third law for a by taking the cube root of both sides; we then substitute the orbital period $p = 0.25$ year:

$$p^2 = a^3 \implies a = \sqrt[3]{p^2} = \sqrt[3]{0.25^2} = 0.40$$

Step 3 Explain: The planet orbits its star at an average distance of 0.4 AU. By comparing this result to the distances of planets in our own solar system given in Table E.2, we find that this planet's average orbital distance is just slightly larger than that of the planet Mercury in our own solar system.

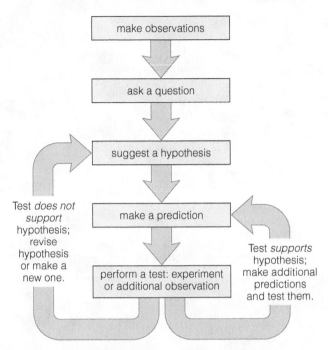

FIGURE 3.23 This diagram illustrates what we often call the scientific method.

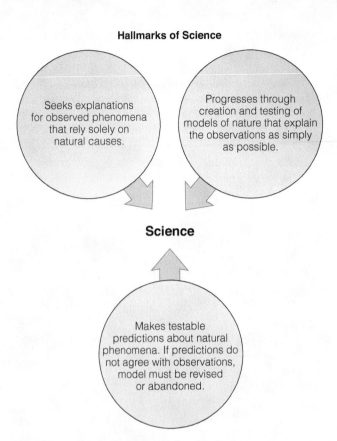

FIGURE 3.24 **interactive figure** Hallmarks of science.

or **hypothesis**, is sometimes called an *educated guess*—in this case, it is "educated" because you already know that flashlights need batteries. Your hypothesis allows you to make a simple prediction: If you replace the batteries with new ones, the flashlight should work. You can test this prediction by replacing the batteries. If the flashlight now works, you've confirmed your hypothesis. If it doesn't, you must revise or discard your hypothesis, perhaps in favor of some other one that you can also test (such as that the bulb is burned out). FIGURE 3.23 illustrates the basic flow of this process.

The scientific method can be a useful idealization, but real science rarely progresses in such an orderly way. Scientific progress often begins with someone going out and looking at nature in a general way, rather than conducting a careful set of experiments. For example, Galileo wasn't looking for anything in particular when he pointed his telescope at the sky and made his first startling discoveries. Furthermore, scientists are human beings, and their intuition and personal beliefs inevitably influence their work. Copernicus, for example, adopted the idea that Earth orbits the Sun not because he had carefully tested it but because he believed it made more sense than the prevailing view of an Earth-centered universe. While his intuition guided him to the right general idea, he erred in the specifics because he still held Plato's ancient belief that heavenly motion must be in perfect circles.

Given that the idealized scientific method is an overly simplistic characterization of science, how can we tell what is science and what is not? To answer this question, we must look a little deeper into the distinguishing characteristics of scientific thinking.

Hallmarks of Science One way to define scientific thinking is to list the criteria that scientists use when they judge competing models of nature. Historians and philosophers of

science have examined (and continue to examine) this issue in great depth, and different experts express different viewpoints on the details. Nevertheless, everything we now consider to be science shares the following three basic characteristics, which we will refer to as the "hallmarks" of science (FIGURE 3.24):

- Modern science seeks explanations for observed phenomena that rely solely on natural causes.

- Science progresses through the creation and testing of models of nature that explain the observations as simply as possible.

- A scientific model must make testable predictions about natural phenomena that will force us to revise or abandon the model if the predictions do not agree with observations.

Each of these hallmarks is evident in the story of the Copernican revolution. The first shows up in the way Tycho's careful measurements of planetary motion motivated Kepler to come up with a better explanation for those motions. The second is evident in the way several competing models were compared and tested, most notably those of Ptolemy, Copernicus, and Kepler. We see the third in the fact that each model could make precise predictions about the future motions of the Sun, Moon, planets, and stars in our sky. Kepler's model gained acceptance because it worked, while the competing models lost favor because their predictions failed to match the observations. The Cosmic Context spread in FIGURE 3.25 summarizes the key scientific changes that occurred with the Copernican revolution and explains how they illustrate the hallmarks of science.

Ancient Earth-centered models of the universe easily explained the simple motions of the Sun and Moon through our sky, but had difficulty explaining the more complicated motions of the planets. The quest to understand planetary motions ultimately led to a revolution in our thinking about Earth's place in the universe that illustrates the process of science. This figure summarizes the major steps in that process.

(1) Night by night, planets usually move from west to east relative to the stars. However, during periods of *apparent retrograde motion*, they reverse direction for a few weeks to months [Section 2.4]. The ancient Greeks knew that any credible model of the solar system had to explain these observations.

This composite photo shows the apparent retrograde motion of Mars.

(2) Most ancient Greek thinkers assumed that Earth remained fixed at the center of the solar system. To explain retrograde motion, they therefore added a complicated scheme of circles moving upon circles to their Earth-centered model. However, at least some Greeks, such as Aristarchus, preferred a Sun-centered model, which offered a simpler explanation for retrograde motion.

The Greek geocentric model explained apparent retrograde motion by having planets move around Earth on small circles that turned on larger circles.

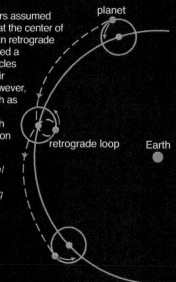

HALLMARK OF SCIENCE   A scientific model must seek explanations for observed phenomena that rely solely on natural causes. The ancient Greeks used geometry to explain their observations of planetary motion.

(Left page)
A schematic map of the universe from 1539 with Earth at the center and the Sun (Solis) orbiting it between Venus (Veneris) and Mars (Martis).

(Right page)
A page from Copernicus's De Revolutionibus, published in 1543, showing the Sun (Sol) at the center and Earth (Terra) orbiting between Venus and Mars.

LIBRI COSMO.   Fo.V.

Schema huius præmiſſæ diuiſionis

Sphærarum.

3 By the time of Copernicus (1473–1543), predictions based on the Earth-centered model had become noticeably inaccurate. Hoping for improvement, Copernicus revived the Sun-centered idea. He did not succeed in making substantially better predictions because he retained the ancient belief that planets must move in perfect circles, but he inspired a revolution continued over the next century by Tycho, Kepler, and Galileo.

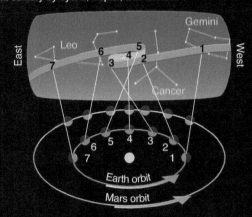

Apparent retrograde motion is simply explained in a Sun-centered system. Notice how Mars appears to change direction as Earth moves past it.

HALLMARK OF SCIENCE **Science progresses through creation and testing of models of nature that explain the observations as simply as possible.** Copernicus developed a Sun-centered model in hopes of explaining observations better than the more complicated Earth-centered model.

4 Tycho exposed flaws in both the ancient Greek and Copernican models by observing planetary motions with unprecedented accuracy. His observations led to Kepler's breakthrough insight that planetary orbits are elliptical, not circular, and enabled Kepler to develop his three laws of planetary motion.

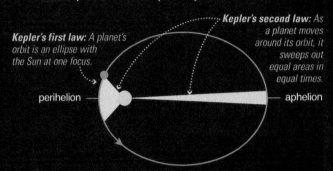

Kepler's first law: A planet's orbit is an ellipse with the Sun at one focus.

Kepler's second law: As a planet moves around its orbit, it sweeps out equal areas in equal times.

perihelion — — aphelion

Kepler's third law: More distant planets orbit at slower average speeds, obeying $p^2 = a^3$.

HALLMARK OF SCIENCE **A scientific model makes testable predictions about natural phenomena. If predictions do not agree with observations, the model must be revised or abandoned.** Kepler could not make his model agree with observations until he abandoned the belief that planets move in perfect circles.

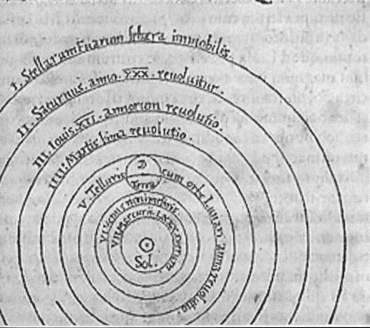

5 Galileo's experiments and telescopic observations overcame remaining scientific objections to the Sun-centered model. Together, Galileo's discoveries and the success of Kepler's laws in predicting planetary motion overthrew the Earth-centered model once and for all.

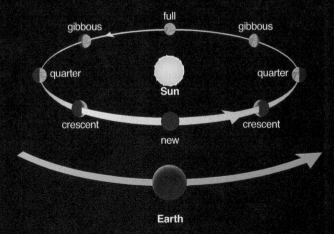

With his telescope, Galileo saw phases of Venus that are consistent only with the idea that Venus orbits the Sun rather than Earth.

Occam's Razor The criterion of simplicity in the second hallmark deserves additional explanation. Remember that the original model of Copernicus did *not* match the data noticeably better than Ptolemy's model. If scientists had judged Copernicus's model solely on the accuracy of its predictions, they might have rejected it immediately. However, many scientists found elements of the Copernican model appealing, such as its simple explanation for apparent retrograde motion. They therefore kept the model alive until Kepler found a way to make it work.

If agreement with data were the sole criterion for judgment, we could imagine a modern-day Ptolemy adding millions or billions of additional circles to the geocentric model in an effort to improve its agreement with observations. A sufficiently complex geocentric model could in principle reproduce the observations with almost perfect accuracy—

but it still would not convince us that Earth is the center of the universe. We would still choose the Copernican view over the geocentric view because its predictions would be just as accurate but follow a much simpler model of nature. The idea that scientists should prefer the simpler of two models that agree equally well with observations is called *Occam's razor,* after the medieval scholar William of Occam (1285–1349).

Verifiable Observations The third hallmark of science forces us to face the question of what counts as an "observation" against which a prediction can be tested. Consider the claim that aliens are visiting Earth in UFOs. Proponents of this claim say that thousands of eyewitness observations of UFO encounters provide evidence that it is true. But do these personal testimonials count as *scientific* evidence? On the

SPECIAL TOPIC

And Yet It Moves

The case of Galileo is often portrayed as a simple example of conflict between science and religion, but the reality was much more complex, with deep divisions inside the Church hierarchy. Perhaps the clearest evidence for a more open-minded Church comes from the case of Copernicus, whose revolutionary work was strongly supported by many Church officials. A less-well-known and even earlier example concerns Nicholas of Cusa (1401–1464), who published a book arguing for a Sun-centered solar system in 1440, more than a century before Copernicus. Nicholas was ordained a priest in the same year that his book was published, and he was later elevated to Cardinal. Clearly, his views caused no problems for Church officials of the time. (Copernicus probably was not aware of this work by Nicholas of Cusa.)

Many other scientists received similar support from within the Church. In fact, for most of his life, Galileo counted Cardinals (and even the Pope who later tried him) among his friends. Some historians suspect that Galileo got into trouble less for his views than for the way in which he portrayed them. In 1632—just a year before his famous trial—he published a book in which two fictional characters debated the geocentric and Sun-centered views. He named the character taking the geocentric position Simplicio—essentially "simple-minded"—and someone apparently convinced the Pope that the character was meant to represent him.

If it was personality rather than belief that got Galileo into trouble, he was not the only one. Another early supporter of Copernicus, Giordano Bruno (1548–1600), drew the wrath of the Church after essentially writing that no rational person could disagree with him (not just on the Copernican system but on other matters as well). Bruno was branded a heretic and burned at the stake.

The evidence supporting the idea that Earth rotates and orbits the Sun was quite strong by the time of Galileo's trial in 1633, but it was still indirect. Today, we have much more direct proof that Galileo was correct when he supposedly whispered of Earth, *Eppur si muove*—"And yet it moves."

French physicist Jean Foucault provided the first direct proof of rotation in 1851. Foucault built a large pendulum that he carefully started swinging. Any pendulum tends to swing always in the same plane, but Earth's rotation made Foucault's pendulum appear to twist slowly in a circle. Today, *Foucault pendulums* are a popular attraction at many science centers and museums (**FIGURE 1**). A second direct proof that Earth rotates is provided by the *Coriolis effect,* first described by French physicist Gustave Coriolis (1792–1843). The Coriolis effect [**Section 10.2**], which would not occur if Earth were not rotating, is responsible for things such as the swirling of hurricanes and the fact that missiles that travel great distances on Earth deviate from straight-line paths.

The first direct proof that Earth orbits the Sun came from English astronomer James Bradley (1693–1762). To understand Bradley's proof, imagine that starlight is like rain, falling straight down. If you are standing still, you should hold your umbrella straight over your head, but if you are walking through the rain, you should tilt your umbrella forward, because your motion makes the rain appear to be coming down at an angle. Bradley discovered that observing light from stars requires that telescopes be tilted slightly in the direction of Earth's motion—just like the umbrella. This effect is called the *aberration of starlight.* Stellar parallax also provides direct proof that Earth orbits the Sun, and it was first measured in 1838 by German astronomer Friedrich Bessel.

FIGURE 1 A Foucault pendulum at the Science Museum of Virginia.

Eggs on the Equinox

One of the hallmarks of science holds that you needn't take scientific claims on faith. In principle, at least, you can always test them for yourself. Consider the claim, repeated in news reports every year, that the spring equinox is the only day on which you can balance an egg on its end. Many people believe this claim, but you'll be immediately skeptical if you think about the nature of the spring equinox. The equinox is merely a point in time at which sunlight strikes both hemispheres equally (see Figure 2.15). It's difficult to see how sunlight could affect an attempt to balance eggs (especially if the eggs are indoors), and the strength of either Earth's gravity or the Sun's gravity is no different on that day than on any other day.

More important, you can test this claim directly. It's not easy to balance an egg on its end, but with practice you can do it on any day of the year, not just on the spring equinox. Not all scientific claims are so easy to test for yourself, but the basic lesson should be clear: Before you accept any scientific claim, you should demand at least a reasonable explanation of the evidence that backs it up.

surface, the answer isn't obvious, because all scientific studies involve eyewitness accounts on some level. For example, only a handful of scientists have personally made detailed tests of Einstein's theory of relativity, and it is their personal reports of the results that have convinced other scientists of the theory's validity. However, there's an important difference between personal testimony about a scientific test and an observation of a UFO: The first can be verified by anyone, at least in principle, while the second cannot.

Understanding this difference is crucial to understanding what counts as science and what does not. Even though you may never have conducted a test of Einstein's theory of relativity yourself, there's nothing stopping you from doing so. It might require several years of study before you had the necessary background to conduct the test, but you could then confirm the results reported by other scientists. In other words, while you may currently be trusting the eyewitness testimony of scientists, you always have the option of verifying their testimony for yourself.

In contrast, there is no way for you to verify someone's eyewitness account of a UFO. Without hard evidence such as photographs or pieces of the UFO, there is nothing that you could evaluate for yourself, even in principle. (And in those cases where "hard evidence" for UFO sightings has been presented, scientific study has never yet found the evidence to be strong enough to support the claim of alien space-craft [**Section 24.5**].) Moreover, scientific studies of eyewitness testimony show it to be notoriously unreliable, because different eyewitnesses often disagree on what they saw even immediately after an event has occurred. As time passes, memories of the event may change further. In some cases in which memory has been checked against reality, people have reported vivid memories of events that never happened at all. This explains something that virtually all of us have experienced: disagreements with a friend about who did what and when. Since both people cannot be right in such cases, at least one person must have a memory that differs from reality.

The demonstrated unreliability of eyewitness testimony explains why it is generally considered insufficient for a

Logic and Science

In science, we attempt to acquire knowledge through logical reasoning. A logical argument begins with a set of premises and leads to one or more conclusions. There are two basic types of logical argument: deductive and inductive.

In a *deductive argument,* the conclusion follows automatically from the premises, as in this example:

> PREMISE: All planets orbit the Sun in ellipses with the Sun at one focus.
>
> PREMISE: Earth is a planet.
>
> CONCLUSION: Earth orbits the Sun in an ellipse with the Sun at one focus.

Note that the first premise is a general statement that applies to all planets, and the conclusion is a specific statement that applies only to Earth. In other words, we use a deductive argument to *deduce* a specific prediction from a more general theory. If the specific prediction proves to be false, then something must be wrong with the premises from which it was deduced. If it proves true, then we've acquired a piece of evidence in support of the premises.

Now consider the following example of an *inductive argument:*

> PREMISE: Birds fly up into the air but eventually come back down.

> PREMISE: People who jump into the air fall back down.
>
> PREMISE: Rocks thrown into the air come back down.
>
> PREMISE: Balls thrown into the air come back down.
>
> CONCLUSION: What goes up must come down.

Notice that the inductive argument begins with specific facts that are used to *generalize* to a broader conclusion. In this case, each premise supports the conclusion, which may explain why the conclusion was thought to be true for thousands of years. However, no amount of additional examples could ever prove the conclusion to be true, and we need only a single counterexample—such as a rocket leaving Earth—to prove the conclusion to be false.

Both types of argument are important in science. We use inductive arguments to build scientific theories, because we use them to *infer* general principles from observations and experiments. We use deductive arguments to make specific predictions from hypotheses and theories, which we can then test. This explains why theories can never be proved true beyond all doubt—they can only be shown to be consistent with ever larger bodies of evidence. Theories *can* be proved false, however, if they fail to account for observed or experimental facts.

conviction in criminal court; at least some other evidence, such as motive, is required. For the same reason, we cannot accept eyewitness testimony by itself as evidence in science, no matter who reports it or how many people offer similar testimony.

Science and Pseudoscience It's important to realize that science is not the only valid way of seeking knowledge. For example, suppose you are shopping for a car, learning to play drums, or pondering the meaning of life. In each case, you might make observations, exercise logic, and test hypotheses. Yet these pursuits clearly are not science, because they are not directed at developing testable explanations for observed natural phenomena. As long as nonscientific searches for knowledge make no claims about how the natural world works, they do not conflict with science.

However, you will often hear claims about the natural world that seem to be based on observational evidence but do not treat evidence in a truly scientific way. Such claims are often called **pseudoscience**, which literally means "false science." To distinguish real science from pseudoscience, a good first step is to check whether a particular claim exhibits all three hallmarks of science. Consider the example of people who claim a psychic ability to "see" the future and use it to make specific, testable predictions. In this sense, "seeing" the future sounds scientific, since we can test it. However, numerous studies have tested the predictions of "seers" and have found that their predictions come true no more often than would be expected by pure chance. If the "seers" were scientific, they would admit that this evidence undercuts their claim of psychic abilities. Instead, they generally make excuses, such as saying that the predictions didn't come true because of "psychic interference." Making testable claims but then ignoring the results of the tests marks the claimed ability to see the future as pseudoscience.

Objectivity in Science The idea that science is objective, meaning that all people should be able to find the same results, is very important to the validity of science as a means of seeking knowledge. However, there is a difference between the overall objectivity of science and the objectivity of individual scientists.

Science is practiced by human beings, and individual scientists may bring their personal biases and beliefs to their scientific work. For example, most scientists choose their research projects based on personal interests rather than on some objective formula. In extreme cases, scientists have even been known to cheat—either deliberately or subconsciously—to obtain a result they desire. For example, in the late 19th century, astronomer Percival Lowell claimed to see a network of artificial canals in blurry telescopic images of Mars, leading him to conclude that there was a great Martian civilization [**Section 9.4**]. But no such canals actually exist, so Lowell must have allowed his beliefs about extraterrestrial life to influence the way he interpreted what he saw—in essence, a form of cheating, though probably not intentional.

Bias can sometimes show up even in the thinking of the scientific community as a whole. Some valid ideas may not be considered by any scientist because the ideas fall too far outside the general patterns of thought, or **paradigm**, of the time. Einstein's theory of relativity provides an example. Many scientists in the decades before Einstein had gleaned hints of the theory but did not investigate them, at least in part because they seemed too outlandish.

The beauty of science is that it encourages continued testing by many people. Even if personal biases affect some results, tests by others should eventually uncover the mistakes. Similarly, if a new idea is correct but falls outside the accepted paradigm, sufficient testing and verification of the idea will eventually force a shift in the paradigm. In that sense, *science ultimately provides a means of bringing people to agreement*, at least on topics that can be subjected to scientific study.

What is a scientific theory?

The most successful scientific models explain a wide variety of observations in terms of just a few general principles. When a powerful yet simple model makes predictions that survive repeated and varied testing, scientists elevate its status and call it a **theory**. Some famous examples are Isaac Newton's theory of gravity, Charles Darwin's theory of evolution, and Albert Einstein's theory of relativity.

Note that the scientific meaning of the word *theory* is quite different from its everyday meaning, in which we equate a theory more closely with speculation or a hypothesis. For example, someone might get a new idea and say "I have a new theory about why people enjoy the beach." Without the support of a broad range of evidence that others have tested and confirmed, this "theory" is really only a guess. In contrast, Newton's theory of gravity qualifies as a scientific theory because it uses simple physical principles to explain many observations and experiments.

Despite its success in explaining observed phenomena, a scientific theory can never be proved true beyond all doubt, because future observations may disagree with its predictions. However, anything that qualifies as a scientific theory must be supported by a large, compelling body of evidence.

In this sense, a scientific theory is not at all like a hypothesis or any other type of guess. We are free to change a hypothesis at any time, because it has not yet been carefully tested. In contrast, we can discard or replace a scientific theory only if we have an alternative way of explaining the evidence that supports it.

Again, the theories of Newton and Einstein offer good examples. A vast body of evidence supports Newton's theory of gravity, but in the late 19th century scientists began to discover cases where its predictions did not perfectly match observations. These discrepancies were explained only when Einstein developed his general theory of relativity in the early 20th century. Still, the many successes of Newton's theory could not be ignored, and Einstein's theory would not have gained acceptance if it had not been able to explain these successes equally well. It did, and that is why we now view Einstein's theory as a broader theory of gravity than Newton's theory. Some scientists today are seeking a theory of gravity that will go beyond Einstein's. If any new theory ever gains acceptance, it will have to match all the successes of Einstein's theory as well as work in new realms where Einstein's theory does not.

THINK ABOUT IT

When people claim that something is "only a theory," what do you think they mean? Does this meaning of "theory" agree with the definition of a theory in science? Do scientists always use the word *theory* in its "scientific" sense? Explain.

3.5 ASTROLOGY

We have discussed the development of astronomy and the nature of science in some depth. Now let's talk a little about a subject often confused with the science of astronomy: *astrology*. Although the terms *astrology* and *astronomy* sound very similar, today they describe very different practices. In ancient times, however, astrology and astronomy often went hand in hand, and astrology played an important role in the historical development of astronomy.

How is astrology different from astronomy?

The basic tenet of astrology is that the apparent positions of the Sun, Moon, and planets among the stars in our sky influence human events. The origins of this idea are easy to understand. After all, the position of the Sun in the sky certainly influences our lives, since it determines the seasons and the times of daylight and darkness, and the Moon's position determines the tides. Because planets also move among the stars, it probably seemed natural to imagine that they might also influence our lives, even if the influences were more subtle.

Ancient astrologers hoped to learn how the positions of the Sun, Moon, and planets influence our lives by charting the skies and seeking correlations with events on Earth. For example, if an earthquake occurred when Saturn was entering the constellation Leo, might Saturn's position have been the cause of the earthquake? If the king became ill when Mars appeared in the constellation Gemini and the first-quarter moon appeared in Scorpio, might another tragedy be in store for the king when this particular alignment of the Moon and Mars next recurred? Surely, the ancient astrologers thought, the patterns of influence would eventually become clear, and they would then be able to forecast human events with the same reliability with which astronomical observations of the Sun could be used to forecast the coming of spring.

Because forecasts of the seasons and forecasts of human events were imagined to be closely related, astrologers and astronomers usually were one and the same in the ancient world. For example, in addition to his books on astronomy, Ptolemy published a treatise on astrology called *Tetrabiblios*, which remains the foundation for much of astrology today. Interestingly, Ptolemy himself recognized that astrology stood upon a far shakier foundation than astronomy. In the introduction to *Tetrabiblios*, he wrote:

[Astronomy], which is first both in order and effectiveness, is that whereby we apprehend the aspects of the movements of sun, moon, and stars in relation to each other and to the earth . . . . I shall now give an account of the second and less sufficient method [of prediction (astrology)] in a proper philosophical way, so that one whose aim is the truth might never compare its perceptions with the sureness of the first, unvarying science . . . .

Other ancient scientists also recognized that their astrological predictions were far less reliable than their astronomical ones. Nevertheless, confronted with even a slight possibility that astrologers could forecast the future, no king or political leader would dare to be without one. Astrologers held esteemed positions as political advisers in the ancient world and were provided with the resources they needed to continue charting the heavens and human history. Wealthy political leaders' support of astrology made possible much of the development of ancient astronomy.

Throughout the Middle Ages and into the Renaissance, many astronomers continued to practice astrology. For example, Kepler cast numerous *horoscopes*—the predictive charts of astrology (FIGURE 3.26)—even as he was discovering the laws of planetary motion. However, given Kepler's later descriptions of astrology as "the foolish stepdaughter of astronomy" and "a dreadful superstition," he may have cast the horoscopes solely as a source of much-needed income. Modern-day astrologers also claim Galileo as one of their own, in part for his having cast a horoscope for the Grand Duke of Tuscany. However, while Galileo's astronomical discoveries changed human history, the horoscope was just plain wrong: The Duke died a few weeks after Galileo predicted that he would have a long and fruitful life.

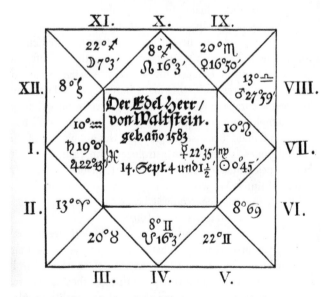

FIGURE 3.26 This chart, cast by Kepler, is an example of a horoscope.

The scientific triumph of Kepler and Galileo in showing Earth to be a planet orbiting the Sun heralded the end of the linkage between astronomy and astrology. Astronomy has since gained status as a successful science that helps us understand our universe, while astrology no longer has any connection to the modern science of astronomy.

Does astrology have any scientific validity?

Although astronomers gave up on it centuries ago, astrology remains popular with the public. Many people read their daily horoscopes, and some pay significant fees to have personal horoscopes cast by professional astrologers. With so many people giving credence to astrology, is it possible that it has some scientific validity after all?

Testing Astrology The validity of astrology can be difficult to assess, because there's no general agreement among astrologers even on such basic things as what astrology is or what it can predict. For example, "Western astrology" is quite different in nature from the astrology practiced in India and China. Some astrologers do not make testable predictions at all; rather, they give vague guidance about how to live one's life. Most daily horoscopes fall into this category. Although your horoscope may seem to ring true at first, a careful read will usually show it to be so vague as to be untestable. For example, a horoscope that says "It is a good day to spend time with your friends" may be good advice but doesn't offer much to test.

SEE IT FOR YOURSELF

Look online for today's local weather forecast and today's horoscope. Contrast the nature of their predictions. At the end of the day, you will know if the weather forecast was accurate. Will you also be able to say whether the horoscope was accurate? Explain.

Nevertheless, most professional astrologers still earn their livings by casting horoscopes that either predict future events in an individual's life or describe characteristics of the person's personality and life. If the horoscope predicts future events, we can check to see whether the predictions come true. If it describes a person's personality and life, the description can be checked for accuracy. A scientific test of astrology requires evaluating many horoscopes and comparing their accuracy to what would be expected by pure chance. For example, suppose a horoscope states that a person's best friend is female. Because roughly half the population of the United States is female, an astrologer who casts 100 such horoscopes would be expected by pure chance to be right about 50 times. We would be impressed with the predictive ability of the astrologer only if he or she were right much more often than 50 times out of 100.

In hundreds of scientific tests, astrological predictions have never proved to be substantially more accurate than expected from pure chance. Similarly, in tests in which astrologers are asked to cast horoscopes for people they have never met, the horoscopes fail to match actual personality profiles more often than expected by chance. The verdict is clear: The methods of astrology are useless for predicting the past, the present, or the future.

Examining the Underpinnings of Astrology In science, observations and experiments are the ultimate judge of any idea. No matter how outlandish an idea might appear, it cannot be dismissed if it successfully meets observational or experimental tests. The idea that Earth rotates and orbits the Sun seemed outlandish for most of human history, yet today it is so strongly supported by the evidence that we consider it a fact. The idea that the positions of the Sun, Moon, and planets among the stars influence our lives might sound outlandish today, but if astrology were to make predictions that came true, adherence to the principles of science would force us to take astrology seriously. However, given that scientific tests of astrology have never found any evidence that its predictive methods work, it is worth looking at its premises to see whether they make sense. Might there be a few kernels of wisdom buried within the lore of astrology?

Let's begin with one of the key premises of astrology: that there is special meaning in the patterns of the stars in the constellations. This idea may have seemed quite reasonable in ancient times, when the stars were assumed to be fixed on an unchanging celestial sphere, but today we know that the patterns of the stars in the constellations are accidents of the moment. Long ago the constellations did not look the same, and they will also look different in the future [**Section 1.3**]. Moreover, the stars in a constellation don't necessarily have any *physical* association, because two stars that are close together in the sky might lie at vastly different distances (see Figure 2.3). Constellations are only *apparent* associations of stars, with no more physical reality than the water in a desert mirage.

Astrology also places great importance on the positions of the planets among the constellations. Again, this idea might have seemed reasonable in ancient times, when it was thought that the planets truly wandered among the stars. Today we know that the planets only *appear* to wander among the stars, much as your hand might appear to move among distant mountains when you wave it. It is difficult to see how mere appearances could have profound effects on our lives.

Many other ideas at the heart of astrology are equally suspect. For example, most astrologers claim that a proper horoscope must account for the positions of *all* the planets. Does this mean that all horoscopes cast before the discovery of Neptune in 1846 were invalid? If so, why didn't astrologers notice that something was wrong with their horoscopes and predict the existence of Neptune? (In contrast, astronomers *did* predict its existence; see the Special Topic on page 312.) Most astrologers have included Pluto since its discovery in 1930; does this mean that they should now stop including it, since it has been demoted to dwarf planet, or that they need to include Eris and other dwarf planets, including some that may not yet have been discovered? And why stop with our own solar system; shouldn't horoscopes also depend on the positions of planets orbiting other stars? Given seemingly unanswerable questions like these, there seems little hope that astrology will ever meet its ancient goal of forecasting human events.

Putting Chapter 3 into Context

In this chapter, we focused on the scientific principles through which we have learned so much about the universe. Key "big picture" concepts from this chapter include the following:

- The basic ingredients of scientific thinking—careful observation and trial-and-error testing—are a part of everyone's experience. Modern science simply provides a way of organizing this thinking to facilitate the learning and sharing of new knowledge.

- Although our understanding of the universe is growing rapidly today, each new piece of knowledge builds on ideas that came before.

- The Copernican revolution, which overthrew the ancient Greek belief in an Earth-centered universe, unfolded over a period of more than a century. Many of the characteristics of modern science first appeared during this time.

- Science exhibits several key features that distinguish it from nonscience and that in principle allow anyone to come to the same conclusions when studying a scientific question.

- Astronomy and astrology once developed hand in hand, but today they represent very different things.

SUMMARY OF KEY CONCEPTS

3.1 THE ANCIENT ROOTS OF SCIENCE

- **In what ways do all humans use scientific thinking?** Scientific thinking relies on the same type of trial-and-error thinking that we use in our everyday lives, but in a carefully organized way.

- **How is modern science rooted in ancient astronomy?**

Ancient astronomers were accomplished observers who learned to tell the time of day and the time of year, to track cycles of the Moon, and to observe planets and stars. The care and effort that went into these observations helped set the stage for modern science.

3.2 ANCIENT GREEK SCIENCE

- **Why does modern science trace its roots to the Greeks?** The Greeks developed **models** of nature and emphasized the importance of agreement between the predictions of those models and observations of nature.

- **How did the Greeks explain planetary motion?** The Greek **geocentric model** reached its culmination with the **Ptolemaic model**, which explained apparent retrograde motion by having each planet move on a small circle whose center moves around Earth on a larger circle.

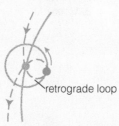

retrograde loop

3.3 THE COPERNICAN REVOLUTION

- **How did Copernicus, Tycho, and Kepler challenge the Earth-centered model?** Copernicus created a Sun-centered model of the solar system designed to replace the Ptolemaic model, but it was no more accurate than Ptolemy's because Copernicus still used perfect circles. Tycho's accurate, naked-eye observations provided the data needed to improve on Copernicus's model. Kepler developed a model of planetary motion that fit Tycho's data.

- **What are Kepler's three laws of planetary motion?** (1) The orbit of each planet is an ellipse with the Sun at one focus. (2) As a planet moves around its orbit, it sweeps out equal areas in

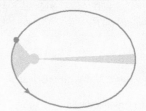

equal times. (3) More distant planets orbit the Sun at slower average speeds, obeying the mathematical relationship $p^2 = a^3$.

- **How did Galileo solidify the Copernican revolution?** Galileo's experiments and telescopic observations overcame remaining objections to the Copernican idea of Earth as a planet

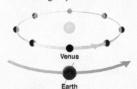

Venus

Earth

orbiting the Sun. Although not everyone accepted his results immediately, in hindsight we see that Galileo sealed the case for the Sun-centered solar system.

3.4 THE NATURE OF SCIENCE

- **How can we distinguish science from nonscience?** Science generally exhibits three hallmarks: (1) Modern science seeks explanations for observed phenomena that rely solely on natural causes. (2) Science progresses through the creation and testing of models of nature that explain the observations as simply as possible. (3) A scientific model must make testable predictions about natural phenomena that would force us to revise or abandon the model if the predictions did not agree with observations.

- **What is a scientific theory?** A scientific **theory** is a simple yet powerful model that explains a wide variety of observations using just a few general principles and has been verified by repeated and varied testing.

3.5 ASTROLOGY

- **How is astrology different from astronomy?** Astronomy is a modern science that has taught us much about the universe. Astrology is a search for hidden influences on human lives based on the apparent positions of planets and stars in the sky; it does not follow the tenets of science.

- **Does astrology have any scientific validity?** Scientific tests have shown that astrological predictions do not prove to be accurate more than we can expect by pure chance, showing that the predictions have no scientific validity.

Use the following questions to check your understanding of some of the many types of visual information used in astronomy. Answers are provided in Appendix J. For additional practice, try the Chapter 3 Visual Quiz at MasteringAstronomy®.

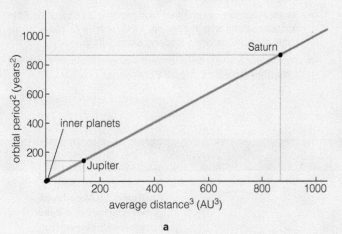

a

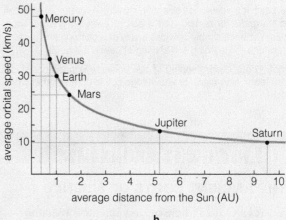

b

Study the two graphs above, based on Figure 3.19. Use the information in the graphs to answer the following questions.

1. Approximately how fast is Jupiter orbiting the Sun?
   a. This cannot be determined from the information provided.
   b. 20 km/s
   c. 10 km/s
   d. a little less than 15 km/s

2. An asteroid with an average orbital distance of 2 AU will orbit the Sun at an average speed that is
   a. a little slower than the orbital speed of Mars.
   b. a little faster than the orbital speed of Mars.
   c. the same as the orbital speed of Mars.

3. Uranus, not shown on graph b, orbits about 19 AU from the Sun. Based on the graph, its approximate orbital speed is between about
   a. 20 and 25 km/s.
   b. 15 and 20 km/s.
   c. 10 and 15 km/s.
   d. 5 and 10 km/s.

4. Kepler's third law is often stated as $p^2 = a^3$. The value a^3 for a planet is shown on
   a. the horizontal axis of graph **a**.   b. the vertical axis of graph **a**.
   c. the horizontal axis of graph **b**.   d. the vertical axis of graph **b**.

5. On graph **a**, you can see Kepler's third law ($p^2 = a^3$) from the fact that
   a. the data fall on a straight line.
   b. the axes are labeled with values for p^2 and a^3.
   c. the planet names are labeled on the graph.

6. Suppose graph **a** showed a planet on the red line directly above a value of 1000 AU³ along the horizontal axis. On the vertical axis, this planet would be at
   a. 1000 years².
   b. 1000² years².
   c. $\sqrt{1000}$ years².
   d. 100 years.

7. How far does the planet in question 6 orbit from the Sun?
   a. 10 AU
   b. 100 AU
   c. 1000 AU
   d. $\sqrt{1000}$ AU

MasteringAstronomy®

For instructor-assigned homework go to MasteringAstronomy®.

REVIEW QUESTIONS

Short-Answer Questions Based on the Reading

1. In what way is scientific thinking natural to all of us, and how does modern science build upon this everyday type of thinking?

2. Why did ancient peoples study astronomy? Describe an astronomical achievement of at least three ancient cultures.

3. Describe the astronomical origins of our day, week, month, and year.

4. What is a lunar calendar? How can it be kept roughly synchronized with a solar calendar?

5. What do we mean by a *model* in science?

6. Summarize the development of the Greek *geocentric model* to its culmination with Ptolemy. How did this model account for the apparent retrograde motion of planets in our sky?

7. What was the *Copernican revolution*, and how did it change the human view of the universe?

8. What is an *ellipse*? Define its *foci*, *semimajor axis*, and *eccentricity*.

9. State and explain the meaning of each of *Kepler's laws of planetary motion*.

10. Describe the three hallmarks of science and how we can see them in the Copernican revolution. What is *Occam's razor*? Why doesn't science accept personal testimony as evidence?

11. What is the difference between a *hypothesis* and a *theory* in science?
12. What is the basic idea behind *astrology*? Explain why this idea seemed reasonable in ancient times but is no longer accepted by scientists.

TEST YOUR UNDERSTANDING

Science or Nonscience?

Each of the following statements makes some type of claim. Decide in each case whether the claim could be evaluated scientifically or falls into the realm of nonscience. Explain clearly; not all of these have definitive answers, so your explanation is more important than your chosen answer.

13. The Yankees are the best baseball team of all time.
14. Several kilometers below its surface, Jupiter's moon Europa has an ocean of liquid water.
15. My house is haunted by ghosts who make the creaking noises I hear each night.
16. There are no lakes or seas on the surface of Mars today.
17. Dogs are smarter than cats.
18. Children born when Jupiter is in the constellation Taurus are more likely to be musicians than other children.
19. Aliens can manipulate time and memory so that they can abduct and perform experiments on people who never realize they were taken.
20. Newton's law of gravity works as well for explaining orbits of planets around other stars as it does for explaining orbits of the planets in our own solar system.
21. God created the laws of motion that were discovered by Newton.
22. A huge fleet of alien spacecraft will land on Earth and introduce an era of peace and prosperity on January 1, 2025.

Quick Quiz

Choose the best answer to each of the following. Explain your reasoning with one or more complete sentences.

23. In the Greek geocentric model, the retrograde motion of a planet occurs when (a) Earth is about to pass the planet in its orbit around the Sun. (b) the planet actually goes backward in its orbit around Earth. (c) the planet is aligned with the Moon in our sky.
24. Which of the following was *not* a major advantage of Copernicus's Sun-centered model over the Ptolemaic model? (a) It made significantly better predictions of planetary positions in our sky. (b) It offered a more natural explanation for the apparent retrograde motion of planets in our sky. (c) It allowed calculation of the orbital periods and distances of the planets.
25. When we say that a planet has a highly eccentric orbit, we mean that (a) it is spiraling in toward the Sun. (b) its orbit is an ellipse with the Sun at one focus. (c) in some parts of its orbit it is much closer to the Sun than in other parts.
26. Earth is closer to the Sun in January than in July. Therefore, in accord with Kepler's second law, (a) Earth travels faster in its orbit around the Sun in July than in January. (b) Earth travels faster in its orbit around the Sun in January than in July. (c) it is summer in January and winter in July.
27. According to Kepler's third law, (a) Mercury travels fastest in the part of its orbit in which it is closest to the Sun. (b) Jupiter orbits the Sun at a faster speed than Saturn. (c) all the planets have nearly circular orbits.
28. Tycho Brahe's contribution to astronomy included (a) inventing the telescope. (b) proving that Earth orbits the Sun. (c) collecting data that enabled Kepler to discover the laws of planetary motion.

29. Galileo's contribution to astronomy included (a) discovering the laws of planetary motion. (b) discovering the law of gravity. (c) making observations and conducting experiments that dispelled scientific objections to the Sun-centered model.
30. Which of the following is *not* true about scientific progress? (a) Science progresses through the creation and testing of models of nature. (b) Science advances only through the scientific method. (c) Science avoids explanations that invoke the supernatural.
31. Which of the following is *not* true about a scientific theory? (a) A theory must explain a wide range of observations or experiments. (b) Even the strongest theories can never be proved true beyond all doubt. (c) A theory is essentially an educated guess.
32. When Einstein's theory of gravity (general relativity) gained acceptance, it demonstrated that Newton's theory had been (a) wrong. (b) incomplete. (c) really only a guess.

PROCESS OF SCIENCE

Examining How Science Works

33. *What Makes It Science?* Choose a single idea in the modern view of the cosmos as discussed in Chapter 1, such as "The universe is expanding," "The universe began with a Big Bang," "We are made from elements manufactured by stars," or "The Sun orbits the center of the Milky Way Galaxy once every 230 million years." **a.** Describe how this idea reflects each of the three hallmarks of science, discussing how it is based on observations, how our understanding of it depends on a model, and how that model is testable. **b.** Describe a hypothetical observation that, if it were actually made, might cause us to call the idea into question. Then briefly discuss whether you think that, overall, the idea is likely or unlikely to hold up to future observations.
34. *Earth's Shape.* It took thousands of years for humans to deduce that Earth is spherical. For each of the following alternative models of Earth's shape, identify one or more observations that you could make for yourself that would invalidate the model. **a.** A flat Earth **b.** A cylindrical Earth, like that proposed by Anaximander **c.** A football-shaped Earth
35. *Scientific Test of Astrology.* Find out about at least one scientific test of the validity of astrology. Write a short summary of the methods and results of the test.
36. *Your Own Astrological Test.* Devise your own scientific test of astrology. Clearly define your methods and how you will evaluate the results. Carry out the test and write a short report about it.

GROUP WORK EXERCISE

37. *Galileo on Trial.* In this exercise, you will debate the evidence presented by Galileo in favor of the idea that Earth orbits the Sun. Before you begin, assign the following roles to the people in your group: *Scribe* (takes notes on the group's activities), *Galileo* (argues in favor of the idea that Earth orbits the Sun), *Prosecutor* (argues against the idea that Earth orbits the Sun), and *Moderator* (leads group discussion and makes sure the debate remains civil). Then consider each of the following three pieces of evidence: **a.** observations of mountains and valleys on the Moon. **b.** observations of moons orbiting Jupiter. **c.** observations of the phases of Venus. *Galileo* should explain why the evidence indicates that Earth orbits the Sun, and the *Prosecutor* should present a rebuttal. After the discussion, the *Scribe* and *Moderator* should decide whether the evidence is convincing beyond a reasonable doubt, somewhat convincing, or not convincing, and write down their verdict, along with an explanation of their reasoning.

INVESTIGATE FURTHER

In-Depth Questions to Increase Your Understanding

Short-Answer/Essay Questions

38. *Lunar Calendars.*
    a. Find the dates of the Jewish festival of Chanukah for this year and the next three years. Based on what you have learned in this chapter, explain why the dates change as they do. **b.** Find the dates of the Muslim fast for Ramadan for this year and the next three years. Based on what you have learned in this chapter, explain why the dates change as they do.

39. *Copernican Players.* Using a bulleted-list format, make a one-page "executive summary" of the major roles that Copernicus, Tycho, Kepler, and Galileo played in overturning the ancient belief in an Earth-centered universe.

40. *Influence on History.* Based on what you have learned about the Copernican revolution, write a one- to two-page essay about how you believe it altered the course of human history.

41. *Cultural Astronomy.* Choose a particular culture of interest to you, and research the astronomical knowledge and accomplishments of that culture. Write a two- to three-page summary of your findings.

42. *Astronomical Structures.* Choose an ancient astronomical structure of interest to you (e.g., Stonehenge, Templo Mayor, Pawnee lodges), and research its history. Write a two- to three-page summary of your findings. If possible, also build a scale model of the structure or create detailed diagrams to illustrate how the structure was used.

Quantitative Problems

Be sure to show all calculations clearly and state your final answers in complete sentences.

43. *The Metonic Cycle.* The length of our calendar year is 365.2422 days, and the Moon's monthly cycle of phases averages 29.5306 days in length. By calculating the number of days in each, confirm that 19 solar years is almost precisely equal to 235 cycles of the lunar phases. Show your work clearly; then write a few sentences explaining how this fact can be used to keep a lunar calendar roughly synchronized with a solar calendar.

44. *Chinese Calendar.* The traditional Chinese lunar calendar has 12 months in most years but adds a thirteenth month to 22 of every 60 years. How many days does this give the Chinese calendar in each 60-year period? How does this compare to the number of days in 60 years on a solar calendar? Based on your answers, explain how this scheme is similar to the scheme used by lunar calendars that follow the Metonic cycle. (*Hint:* You'll need the data given in Problem 43.)

45. *Method of Eratosthenes I.* You are an astronomer on planet Nearth, which orbits a distant star. It has recently been accepted that Nearth is spherical in shape, though no one knows its size. One day, while studying in the library of Alectown, you learn that on the equinox your sun is directly overhead in the city of Nyene, located 1000 kilometers due north of you. On the equinox, you go outside and observe that the altitude of your sun is 80°. What is the circumference of Nearth? (*Hint:* Apply the technique used by Eratosthenes to measure Earth's circumference.)

46. *Method of Eratosthenes II.* You are an astronomer on planet Tirth, which orbits a distant star. It has recently been accepted that Tirth is spherical in shape, though no one knows its size. One day, you learn that on the equinox your sun is directly overhead in the city of Tyene, located 400 kilometers due north of you. On the equinox, you go outside and observe that the altitude of your sun is 86°. What is the circumference of Tirth? (*Hint:* Apply the technique used by Eratosthenes to measure Earth's circumference.)

47. *Mars Orbit.* Find the perihelion and aphelion distances of Mars. (*Hint:* You'll need data from Appendix E.)

48. *Eris Orbit.* The recently discovered Eris, which is slightly larger than Pluto, orbits the Sun every 557 years. What is its average distance (semimajor axis) from the Sun? How does its average distance compare to that of Pluto?

49. *New Planet Orbit.* A newly discovered planet orbits a distant star with the same mass as the Sun at an average distance of 112 million kilometers. Its orbital eccentricity is 0.3. Find the planet's orbital period and its nearest and farthest orbital distances from its star.

50. *Halley Orbit.* Halley's Comet orbits the Sun every 76.0 years and has an orbital eccentricity of 0.97.
    a. Find its average distance from the Sun (semimajor axis). **b.** Find its perihelion and aphelion distances.

Discussion Questions

51. *The Impact of Science.* The modern world is filled with ideas, knowledge, and technology that developed through science and application of the scientific method. Discuss some of these things and how they affect our lives. Which of these impacts do you think are positive? Which are negative? Overall, do you think science has benefited the human race? Defend your opinion.

52. *The Importance of Ancient Astronomy.* Why was astronomy important to people in ancient times? Discuss both the practical importance of astronomy and the importance it may have had for religious or other traditions. Which do you think was more important in the development of ancient astronomy: its practical or its philosophical role? Defend your opinion.

53. *Astronomy and Astrology.* Why do you think astrology remains so popular around the world even though it has failed all scientific tests of its validity? Do you think the popularity of astrology has any positive or negative social consequences? Defend your opinions.

Web Projects

54. *Easter.* Research when different denominations of Christianity celebrate Easter and why they use different dates. Summarize your findings in a one- to two-page report.

55. *Greek Astronomers.* Many ancient Greek scientists had ideas that, in retrospect, seem well ahead of their time. Choose one ancient Greek scientist to study, and write a one- to two-page "scientific biography" of your chosen person.

56. *The Ptolemaic Model.* This chapter gives only a very brief description of Ptolemy's model of the universe. Investigate this model in greater depth. Using diagrams and text as needed, give a two- to three-page description of the model.

57. *The Galileo Affair.* In recent years, the Roman Catholic Church has devoted a lot of resources to learning more about the trial of Galileo and to understanding past actions of the Church in the Galilean case. Learn more about these studies and write a short report about the Vatican's current view of the case.

58. *Science or Pseudoscience.* Choose a pseudoscientific claim related to astronomy, and learn more about how scientists have "debunked" it. (A good starting point is the Bad Astronomy website.) Write a short summary of your findings.

S1 CELESTIAL TIMEKEEPING AND NAVIGATION
SUPPLEMENTARY CHAPTER

LEARNING GOALS

S1.1 ASTRONOMICAL TIME PERIODS

- How do we define the day, month, year, and planetary periods?
- How do we tell the time of day?
- When and why do we have leap years?

S1.2 CELESTIAL COORDINATES AND MOTION IN THE SKY

- How do we locate objects on the celestial sphere?
- How do stars move through the local sky?
- How does the Sun move through the local sky?

S1.3 PRINCIPLES OF CELESTIAL NAVIGATION

- How can you determine your latitude?
- How can you determine your longitude?

Socrates: Shall we make astronomy the next study? What do you say?

Glaucon: Certainly. A working knowledge of the seasons, months, and years is beneficial to everyone, to commanders as well as to farmers and sailors.

Socrates: You make me smile, Glaucon. You are so afraid that the public will accuse you of recommending unprofitable studies.

—*Plato,* Republic

As the opening quote from Plato shows, ancient astronomy served practical needs for timekeeping and navigation. These ancient uses may no longer seem so important in an age when we tell time with digital watches and navigate with the global positioning system (GPS). But knowing the celestial basis of timekeeping and navigation can help us understand the rich history of astronomical discovery, and occasionally still proves useful in its own right. In this chapter, we will explore the apparent motions of the Sun, Moon, and planets in enough detail to learn the basic principles of keeping time and navigating by the stars.

S1.1 ASTRONOMICAL TIME PERIODS

Although many people do not realize it, modern clocks and calendars are beautifully synchronized to the rhythms of the heavens. Precision measurements allow us to ensure that our clocks keep pace with the Sun's daily trek across our sky, while our calendar holds the dates of the equinoxes and solstices as steady as possible. In earlier chapters, we saw how this synchronicity took root in ancient observations of the sky. In this section, we will look more closely at basic measures of time and our modern, international system of timekeeping.

How do we define the day, month, year, and planetary periods?

By now you know that the length of the day corresponds to Earth's rotation, the length of the month to the cycle of lunar phases, and the length of the year to our orbit around the Sun. However, these correspondences are not quite as simple as we might at first guess, because there is more than one way to define the day, month, year, and planetary periods.

The Length of the Day We usually think of a day as the time it takes for Earth to rotate once. But if you measure Earth's rotation period, you'll find that it is actually about 4 minutes short of 24 hours. What's going on?

Remember that the daily circling of the stars in our sky is an illusion created by Earth's rotation (see Figure 2.9). You can therefore measure Earth's rotation period by measuring how long it takes for any star to go from its highest point in the sky one day to its highest point the next day (FIGURE S1.1a). This time period, which we call a **sidereal** (pronounced *sy-DEAR-ee-al*) **day**, is about 23 hours 56 minutes (more precisely, $23^h\ 56^m\ 4.09^s$). *Sidereal* means "related to the stars"; note that you'll measure the same time no matter what star you choose. For practical purposes, the sidereal day is Earth's precise rotation period.

Our 24-hour day, which we call a **solar day**, is based on the time it takes for the *Sun* to make one circuit around the local sky. You can measure this time period by measuring how long it takes the Sun to go from its highest point in the sky one day to its highest point the next day (FIGURE S1.1b). The solar day is indeed 24 hours on average, although it varies slightly (up to about 25 seconds longer or shorter than 24 hours) over the course of a year.

A simple demonstration shows why the solar day is about 4 minutes longer than the sidereal day. Set an object to represent the Sun on a table, and stand a few steps away to represent Earth. Point at the Sun and imagine that you also happen to be pointing toward a distant star that lies in the same direction. If you rotate (counterclockwise) while standing in place,

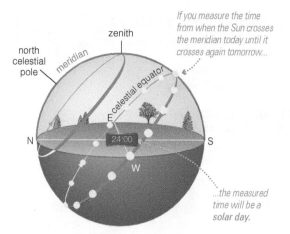

a A sidereal day is the time it takes any star to make a circuit of the local sky. It is about 23 hours 56 minutes.

b A solar day is the time it takes the Sun to make a circuit of the local sky. Its precise length varies over the course of the year, but the average is 24 hours.

FIGURE S1.1 Using the sky to measure the length of a day.

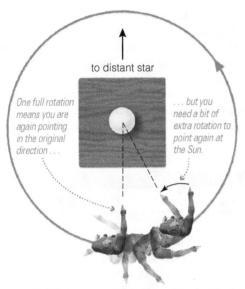

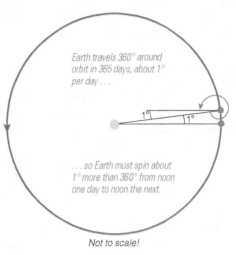

One full rotation means you are again pointing in the original direction . . .

to distant star

. . . but you need a bit of extra rotation to point again at the Sun.

Earth travels 360° around orbit in 365 days, about 1° per day . . .

1°   1°

. . . so Earth must spin about 1° more than 360° from noon one day to noon the next.

Not to scale!

a One full rotation represents a sidereal day and returns you to pointing in your original direction, but you need to rotate a little extra to return to pointing at the Sun.

b Earth travels about 1° per day around its orbit, so a solar day requires about 361° of rotation.

you'll again be pointing at both the Sun and the star after one full rotation. However, to show that Earth also orbits the Sun, you should take a couple of steps around the Sun (counterclockwise) as you rotate (**FIGURE S1.2a**). After one full rotation, you will again be pointing in the direction of the distant star, so this represents a sidereal day. But notice that you need to rotate a little extra to point back at the Sun. In fact, because Earth travels about 1° per day around its orbit, a solar day requires about 1° of extra rotation compared to a sidereal day (**FIGURE S1.2b**). This extra 1° of rotation takes about $\frac{1}{360}$ of Earth's rotation period, which is about 4 minutes.

The Length of the Month As we discussed in Chapter 2, our month comes from the Moon's $29\frac{1}{2}$-day cycle of phases (think "moonth"). More technically, this $29\frac{1}{2}$-day period is called a **synodic month**. The word *synodic* comes from the Latin *synod*, which means "meeting." A synodic month gets its name from the idea that the Sun and the Moon "meet" in the sky with every new moon.

Just as a solar day is not Earth's true rotation period, a synodic month is not the Moon's true orbital period. Earth's motion around the Sun means that the Moon must complete more than one full orbit of Earth from one new moon to the next (**FIGURE S1.3**). The Moon's true orbital period, or a **sidereal month**, is only about $27\frac{1}{3}$ days. Like the sidereal day, the sidereal month gets its name from the fact that it describes how long it takes the Moon to complete an orbit relative to the positions of distant stars.

The Length of the Year We can also define a year in two slightly different ways. The time it takes Earth to complete one orbit relative to the stars is called a **sidereal year**. However, our calendar is based on the cycle of the seasons, which we measure as the time from the spring equinox one year to the spring equinox the next year. This time period,

called a **tropical year**, is about 20 minutes shorter than the sidereal year. A 20-minute difference might not seem like much, but it would make a calendar based on the sidereal year get out of sync with the seasons by 1 day every 72 years—a difference that would add up over centuries.

The difference between the sidereal year and the tropical year arises from Earth's 26,000-year cycle of axis precession [**Section 2.2**]. Precession not only changes the orientation of the axis in space but also changes the locations in Earth's orbit at which the seasons occur. Each year, the location of the equinoxes and solstices among the stars shifts about $\frac{1}{26,000}$ of the way around the orbit. If you do the math, you'll find that $\frac{1}{26,000}$ of a year is about 20 minutes, which explains the 20-minute difference between the tropical year and the sidereal year.

Planetary Periods Although planetary periods are not used in our modern timekeeping, they were important to many ancient cultures. For example, the Mayan calendar was based in part on the apparent motions of Venus. In addition,

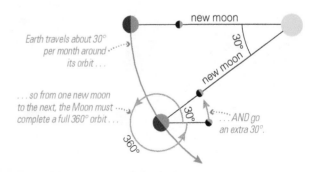

Earth travels about 30° per month around its orbit . . .

new moon

30°

new moon

. . . so from one new moon to the next, the Moon must complete a full 360° orbit . . .

30°

. . . AND go an extra 30°.

360°

FIGURE S1.3 Interactive figure The Moon completes one 360° orbit in about $27\frac{1}{3}$ days (a sidereal month), but the time from new moon to new moon is about $29\frac{1}{2}$ days (a synodic month).

Copernicus's ability to determine orbital periods of planets with his Sun-centered model played an important role in keeping the model alive long enough for its ultimate acceptance (see Mathematical Insight S1.1).

A planet's **sidereal period** is the time the planet takes to orbit the Sun; again, the name comes from the fact that it is measured relative to distant stars. For example, Jupiter's sidereal period is 11.86 years, so it takes about 12 years for Jupiter to make a complete circuit through the constellations of the zodiac. Jupiter therefore appears to move through roughly one zodiac constellation each year. If Jupiter is currently in Gemini (as it is from about July 2013 to July 2014), it will be in Cancer at this time next year and Leo the following year, returning to Gemini in about 12 years.

A planet's **synodic period** is the time from when it is lined up with the Sun in our sky once to the next similar alignment. (As with the Moon, the term *synodic* refers to the planet's "meeting" the Sun in the sky.) FIGURE S1.4 shows that the situation is somewhat different for planets nearer the Sun than Earth (that is, Mercury and Venus) than for planets farther away.

Look first at the situation for the more distant planet in Figure S1.4. As seen from Earth, this planet will sometimes line up with the Sun in what we call a **conjunction**. At other times, it will appear exactly opposite the Sun in our sky, or at **opposition**. We cannot see the planet during conjunction with the Sun because it is hidden by the Sun's glare and rises and sets with the Sun in our sky. At opposition, the planet moves through the sky like the full moon, rising at sunset, reaching the meridian at midnight, and setting at dawn. Note that the planet is closest to Earth at opposition and hence appears brightest in our sky at this time.

Now look at the planet that is *nearer* than Earth to the Sun in Figure S1.4. This planet never has an opposition but instead has two conjunctions—an "inferior conjunction" between Earth and the Sun and a "superior conjunction" when the planet appears behind the Sun as seen from Earth. Two other points are important for the inner planets: their points of **greatest elongation**, when they appear farthest from the Sun in our sky. At its greatest eastern elongation, Venus appears about 46° east of the Sun in our sky, which means it shines brightly in the evening. Similarly, at its greatest

western elongation, Venus appears about 46° west of the Sun and shines brightly before dawn. In between the times when Venus appears in the morning sky and the times when it appears in the evening sky, Venus disappears from view for a few weeks with each conjunction. Mercury's pattern is similar, but because it is closer to the Sun, it never appears more than about 28° from the Sun in our sky. That makes Mercury difficult to see, because it is almost always obscured by the glare of the Sun.

As you study Figure S1.4, you might wonder whether Mercury and Venus ever fall directly in front of the Sun at inferior conjunction, creating a mini-eclipse as they block a little of the Sun's light. They do, but only rarely, because their orbital planes are slightly tilted compared to Earth's orbital plane (the ecliptic plane). As a result, Mercury and Venus usually appear slightly above or below the Sun at inferior conjunction. But on rare occasions, we do indeed see Mercury or Venus appear to pass directly across the face of the Sun during inferior conjunction. Such events are called **transits** (FIGURE S1.5). Mercury transits occur an average of a dozen times per century; the first one in this century occurred on November 8, 2006, and the next will occur on May 9, 2016. Venus transits come in pairs 8 years apart, with more than a century between the second of one pair and the first of the next. If you missed both of the recent transits of Venus, which occurred on June 8, 2004 and June 6, 2012, you have a long wait for the next pair, which will occur in 2117 and 2125.

How do we tell the time of day?

Telling time seems simple, but in fact there are several different ways to define the time of day, even after we agree that time should be based on the 24-hour solar day. Let's explore some of the ways of telling time and see how they ultimately led to our modern system in which we can synchronize clocks anywhere in the world.

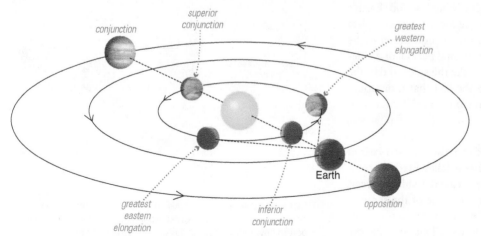

FIGURE S1.4 This diagram shows important positions of planets relative to Earth and the Sun. For a planet farther from the Sun than Earth (such as Jupiter), conjunction occurs when the planet appears aligned with the Sun in the sky, and opposition occurs when the planet appears on our meridian at midnight. Planets nearer the Sun (such as Venus) have two conjunctions and never get farther from the Sun in our sky than at their greatest elongations. (Adapted from *Advanced Skywatching*, by Burnham et al.)

FIGURE S1.5 This photo shows the transit of views that occurred on June 6, 2012— the last Venus transit of this century. It was taken in Germany at dawn. Venus is the small black dot visible near the upper center of the Sun's face.

Apparent Solar Time If we base time on the Sun's *actual* position in the local sky, as is the case when we use a sundial (FIGURE S1.6), we are measuring **apparent solar time**. Noon is the precise moment when the Sun is highest in the sky (on the meridian) and the sundial casts its shortest shadow. Before noon, when the Sun is rising upward through the sky, the apparent solar time is *ante meridiem* ("before the middle of the day"), or a.m. For example, if the Sun will reach the meridian 2 hours from now, the apparent solar time is 10 a.m. After noon, the apparent solar time is *post meridiem* ("after the middle of the day"), or p.m. If the Sun crossed the meridian 3 hours ago, the apparent solar time is 3 p.m. Note that, technically, noon and midnight are *neither* a.m. nor p.m. However, by convention we usually say that noon is 12 p.m. and midnight is 12 a.m.

THINK ABOUT IT
Is it daytime or nighttime at 12:01 a.m.? 12:01 p.m.? Explain.

Mean Solar Time Suppose you set a clock to precisely 12:00 when a sundial shows noon today. If every solar day were precisely 24 hours, your clock would always remain synchronized with the sundial. However, while 24 hours is the *average* length of the solar day, the actual length of the solar day varies throughout the year, so your clock is likely to read a few seconds before or after 12:00 when the sundial reads noon tomorrow, and within a few weeks your clock time may differ from the apparent solar time by several minutes.

If we average the differences between the time your clock would read and the time a sundial would read, we can define **mean solar time** (*mean* is another word for *average*). A clock set to mean solar time reads 12:00 each day at the time the

FIGURE S1.6 A basic sundial consists of a dial marked by numerals, and a stick, or *gnomon*, that casts a shadow. Here, the shadow is on the Roman numeral I, indicating that the apparent solar time is 1:00 p.m. (The portion of the dial without numerals represents nighttime hours.) Because the Sun's path across the local sky depends on latitude, a particular sundial will be accurate only for a particular latitude.

Sun crosses the meridian *on average*. The actual mean solar time at which the Sun crosses the meridian varies over the course of the year in a fairly complex way (see "Solar Days and the Analemma," page 91). The result is that, on any given day, a clock set to mean solar time may read anywhere from about 17 minutes before noon to 15 minutes after noon (that is, from 11:43 a.m. to 12:15 p.m.) when a sundial indicates noon.

Although the lack of perfect synchronization with the Sun might at first sound like a drawback, mean solar time is actually more convenient than apparent solar time (the sundial time)—as long as you have access to a mechanical or electronic clock. Once set, a reliable mechanical or electronic clock can always tell you the mean solar time. In contrast, precisely measuring apparent solar time requires a sundial, which is useless at night or when it is cloudy.

Like apparent solar time, mean solar time is a *local* measure of time. That is, it varies with longitude because of Earth's west-to-east rotation. For example, clocks in New York are set 3 hours ahead of clocks in Los Angeles. If clocks were set precisely to local mean solar time, they would vary even

over relatively short east-west distances. For example, mean solar clocks in central Los Angeles would be about 2 minutes behind mean solar clocks in Pasadena, because Pasadena is slightly to the east.

Standard, Daylight, and Universal Time Clocks displaying mean solar time were once common. But by the late 19th century, particularly in the United States, the growth of railroad travel made mean solar time increasingly problematic. Some states had dozens of different "official" times, usually corresponding to mean solar time in dozens of different cities, and each railroad company made schedules according to its own "railroad time." The many time systems made it difficult for passengers to follow train schedules.

On November 18, 1883, the railroad companies agreed to a new system that divided the United States into four time zones, setting all clocks within each zone to the same time. That was the birth of **standard time**, which today divides the entire world into time zones (FIGURE S1.7, page 90). Depending on where you live within a time zone, your standard time may vary somewhat from your mean solar time. In principle, the

---

MATHEMATICAL INSIGHT S1.1

The Copernican Layout of the Solar System

As discussed in Chapter 3, Copernicus favored the Sun-centered model partly because it allowed him to calculate orbital periods and distances for the planets. Let's see how.

We cannot directly measure a planet's orbital period, because we look at the planet from different points in our orbit at different times. However, we can measure its synodic period simply by seeing how much time passes between one particular alignment (such as opposition or inferior conjunction) and the next. FIGURE 1 shows the geometry for a planet *farther from the Sun than Earth* (such as Jupiter), under the assumption of circular orbits (which Copernicus assumed). Note the following key facts:

■ The dashed brown curve shows the planet's orbit, which takes a time of one orbital period, P_{orb}, to complete.

■ The solid brown arrow shows how far the planet travels along its orbit from one opposition to the next. The time between oppositions is defined as its synodic period, P_{syn}.

■ The dashed blue curve shows Earth's orbit; Earth takes $P_{Earth} = 1$ yr to complete an orbit.

■ The solid red curve and extra red arrow show how far Earth goes during the planet's synodic period; it is *more* than one complete orbit because Earth must travel a little "extra" to catch back up with the planet, and the time required for this "extra" distance (the thick red arrow) is the planet's synodic period minus 1 year, or $P_{syn} - 1$ yr.

Now, notice that the angle that the planet sweeps out during its synodic period is equal to the angle that Earth sweeps out as it travels the "extra" distance. Therefore, the *ratio* of the planet's complete orbital period (P_{orb}) to its synodic period (P_{syn}) must equal the *ratio* of Earth's orbital period (1 yr) to the time required for the "extra" distance (see Appendix C.5 to review ratios). We already

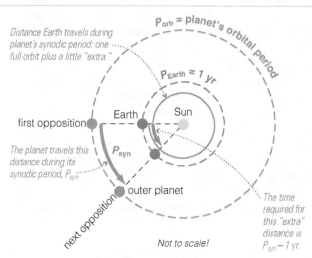

FIGURE 1

found that the time required for this extra distance is $P_{syn} - 1$ yr, so we write

$$\frac{P_{orb}}{P_{syn}} = \frac{1 \text{ yr}}{(P_{syn} - 1 \text{ yr})}$$

Multiplying both sides by P_{syn} gives us the final equation for a planet farther from the Sun than Earth:

$$\text{outer planets: } P_{orb} = P_{syn} \times \frac{1 \text{ yr}}{(P_{syn} - 1 \text{ yr})}$$

The geometry is slightly different for a planet closer to the Sun (Mercury or Venus). FIGURE 2 shows that in this case the equal ratios are 1 yr/$P_{syn} = P_{orb}/(P_{syn} - P_{orb})$, leading to this equation for a planet closer to the Sun than Earth:

$$\text{inner planets: } P_{orb} = P_{syn} \times \frac{1 \text{ yr}}{(P_{syn} + 1 \text{ yr})}$$

standard time in a particular time zone was to be the mean solar time in the *center* of the time zone, so that local mean solar time within a 1-hour-wide time zone would never differ by more than a half-hour from standard time. However, time zones often have unusual shapes to conform to social, economic, and political realities, so larger variations between standard time and mean solar time sometimes occur.

In most parts of the United States, clocks are set to standard time for only part of the year. Between the second Sunday in March and the first Sunday in November, most of the United States changes to **daylight saving time**, which is 1 hour ahead of standard time. Because of the 1-hour advance with daylight saving time, clocks read around 1 p.m. (rather than around noon) when the Sun is on the meridian.

For purposes of navigation and astronomy, it is useful to have a single time for the entire Earth. For historical reasons, this "world" time was chosen to be the mean solar time in Greenwich, England—the place that also defines longitude 0° (see Figure 2.11). Today, this *Greenwich mean time* (*GMT*) is often called **universal time** (**UT**). (Outside astronomy, it is more commonly called *universal coordinated time* [UTC]. Many airlines and weather services call it "Zulu time," because

Greenwich's time zone is designated "Z" and "zulu" is a common way of phonetically identifying the letter *Z*.)

When and why do we have leap years?

Our modern calendar is designed to stay synchronized with the seasons and is therefore based on the tropical year (the time from one spring equinox to the next). Getting this synchronization just right was a long process in human history.

The origins of our modern calendar go back to ancient Egypt. By 4200 B.C., the Egyptians were using a calendar that counted 365 days in a year. However, because the length of a year is about $365\frac{1}{4}$ days (rather than exactly 365 days), the Egyptian calendar drifted out of phase with the seasons by about 1 day every 4 years. For example, if the spring equinox occurred on March 21 one year, 4 years later it occurred on March 22, 4 years after that on March 23, and so on. Over many centuries, the spring equinox moved through many different months. To keep the seasons and the calendar synchronized, Julius Caesar decreed the adoption of a new

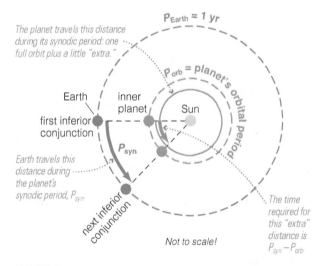

FIGURE 2

Copernicus knew the synodic periods of the planets and therefore could use the above equations (in a slightly different form) to calculate their true orbital periods. He then used the geometry of planetary alignments to compute distances in terms of the Earth-Sun distance. (That is, he calculated distances in AU.) His results were quite close to modern values.

EXAMPLE 1: Jupiter's synodic period is 398.9 days, or 1.092 years. What is its actual orbital period?

SOLUTION:

Step 1 Understand: We are given Jupiter's synodic period (P_{syn}), which is the only value we need to find its orbital period (P_{orb}).

Step 2 Solve: We use the equation for a planet farther from the Sun than Earth, with $P_{syn} = 1.092$ yr:

$$P_{orb} = P_{syn} \times \frac{1 \text{ yr}}{(P_{syn} - 1 \text{ yr})}$$

$$= 1.092 \text{ yr} \times \frac{1 \text{ yr}}{(1.092 \text{ yr} - 1 \text{ yr})} = 11.87 \text{ yr}$$

Step 3 Explain: We have found that Jupiter's orbital period is 11.87 years, or a little less than 12 years. Notice that, as we expect for a planet farther from the Sun, Jupiter's orbital period is longer than Earth's.

EXAMPLE 2: Venus's synodic period is 583.9 days, or 1.599 years. What is its actual orbital period?

SOLUTION:

Step 1 Understand: As in the first example, we can calculate Venus's orbital period from its given synodic period; the only difference is that we'll need the equation for a planet closer to the Sun than Earth.

Step 2 Solve: We use the equation for a planet closer to the Sun, with $P_{syn} = 1.599$ yr:

$$P_{orb} = P_{syn} \times \frac{1 \text{ yr}}{(P_{syn} + 1 \text{ yr})}$$

$$= 1.599 \text{ yr} \times \frac{1 \text{ yr}}{(1.599 \text{ yr} + 1 \text{ yr})} = 0.6152 \text{ yr}$$

Step 3 Explain: Venus takes 0.6152 year to orbit the Sun. This number is easier to interpret if we convert it to days or months; you should confirm that it is equivalent to 224.7 days, or about $7\frac{1}{2}$ months. As we expect, it is shorter than Earth's orbital period of 1 year.

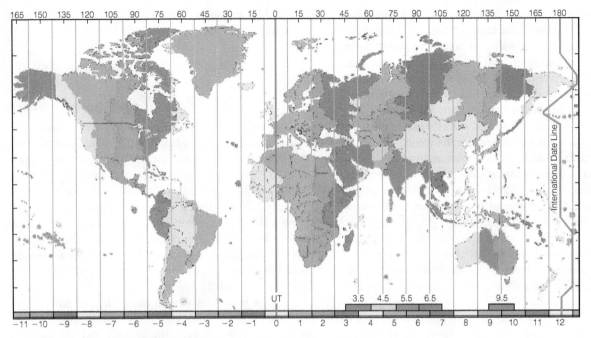

FIGURE S1.7 Time zones around the world. The numerical scale at the bottom shows hours ahead of (positive numbers) or behind (negative numbers) the time in Greenwich, England; the scale at the top is longitude. The vertical lines show standard time zones as they would be in the absence of political considerations. The color-coded regions show the actual time zones. Note, for example, that all of China uses the same standard time, even though the country is wide enough to span several time zones. Note also that a few countries use time zones centered on a half-hour (the upper set of colored bars), rather than an hour, relative to Greenwich time.

calendar in 46 B.C. This **Julian calendar** introduced the **leap year**: Every fourth year has 366 days, rather than 365, so that the average length of the calendar year is $365\frac{1}{4}$ days.

The Julian calendar originally had the spring equinox falling around March 24. If it had been perfectly synchronized with the tropical year, this calendar would have ensured that the spring equinox occurred on the same date every 4 years (that is, every leap-year cycle). It didn't work perfectly, however, because a tropical year is actually about 11 minutes short of $365\frac{1}{4}$ days. As a result, the moment of the spring equinox slowly advanced by an average of 11 minutes per year. By the late 16th century, the spring equinox was occurring on March 11.

Concerned by this drift in the date of the spring equinox, Pope Gregory XIII introduced a new calendar in 1582. This **Gregorian calendar** was much like the Julian calendar, with two important adjustments. First, Pope Gregory decreed that the day in 1582 following October 4 would be October 15. By eliminating the 10 dates from October 5 through October 14, 1582, he pushed the date of the spring equinox in 1583 from March 11 to March 21. (He chose March 21 because it was the date of the spring equinox in A.D. 325, which was the time of the Council of Nicaea, the first ecumenical council of the Christian church.) Second, the Gregorian calendar added an exception to the rule of having leap year every 4 years: Leap year is skipped when a century changes (for example, in years 1700, 1800, 1900) *unless* the century year is divisible by 400. Thus, 2000 was a leap year because it is divisible by 400 (2000 ÷ 400 × 5), but 2100 will *not* be a leap year. These adjustments make the average length of the Gregorian

calendar year almost exactly the same as the actual length of a tropical year, which ensures that the spring equinox will occur on March 21 every fourth year for thousands of years to come.

Today, the Gregorian calendar is used worldwide for international communication and commerce. (Many countries still use traditional calendars, such as the Chinese, Islamic, and Jewish calendars, for cultural purposes.) However, as you might guess, the pope's decree was not immediately accepted in regions not bound to the Catholic Church. For example, the Gregorian calendar was not adopted in England or in the American colonies until 1752, and it was not adopted in China until 1912 or in Russia until 1919.

S1.2 CELESTIAL COORDINATES AND MOTION IN THE SKY

We are now ready to turn our attention from timekeeping to navigation. The goal of celestial navigation is to use the Sun and the stars to find our position on Earth. Before we can do that, we first need to explore the apparent motions of the sky in more detail than we covered in Chapter 2.

How do we locate objects on the celestial sphere?

Recall from Chapter 2 that the celestial sphere is an illusion, but one that is quite useful when looking at the sky. We can make the celestial sphere even more useful by giving it a set of **celestial coordinates** that function much like the coordinates of latitude and longitude on Earth. Just as we can locate a city on Earth by its latitude and longitude, we can use an object's celestial coordinates to describe its precise location on the celestial sphere.

We have already discussed the key starting points for our coordinate system [Section 2.1]: the north and south celestial poles, the celestial equator, and the ecliptic (FIGURE S1.8). It is much easier to visualize the celestial sphere if you make your own model with a simple plastic ball. Use a felt-tip pen to mark the north and south celestial poles on your ball, and then add the celestial equator and the ecliptic. Note that the ecliptic crosses the celestial equator on opposite sides of

the celestial sphere at an angle of $23\frac{1}{2}°$ (because of the tilt of Earth's axis).

Equinoxes and Solstices Recall that the equinoxes and solstices are special moments that occur each year when Earth is at particular positions in its orbit (see Figure 2.15). These positions correspond to the apparent locations of the Sun along the ecliptic shown in Figure S1.8. For example, the spring equinox occurs at the moment when the Sun's path along the ecliptic crosses the celestial equator going from south to north, so we also use the term spring equinox to refer to this point on

---

SPECIAL TOPIC

Solar Days and the Analemma

The precise length of a solar day varies from its average of 24 hours for two reasons. The first is Earth's varying orbital speed. Recall that, in accord with Kepler's second law, Earth moves slightly faster—and therefore moves slightly farther along its orbit each day—when it is closer to the Sun in its orbit. The solar day therefore requires more than the average amount of "extra" rotation (see Figure S1.2) during these periods, making these solar days longer than average. Similarly, the solar day requires less than the average amount of "extra" rotation when it is in the portion of its orbit farther from the Sun, making these solar days shorter than average.

The second reason is the tilt of Earth's axis, which makes the ecliptic inclined $23\frac{1}{2}°$ to the celestial equator. Because the length of a solar day depends on the Sun's apparent *eastward* motion along the ecliptic, the inclination would cause solar days to vary in length even if Earth's orbit were perfectly circular. To see why, suppose the Sun appeared to move exactly 1° per day along the ecliptic. Around the times of the solstices, this motion would be entirely eastward,

making the solar day slightly longer than average. Around the times of the equinoxes, when the motion along the ecliptic has a significant northward or southward component, the solar day would be slightly shorter than average.

Together, the effects of varying orbital speed and tilt mean the actual length of a solar day can be up to about 25 seconds longer or shorter than the 24-hour average. Because the effects accumulate at particular times of year, the apparent solar time can differ by as much as 17 minutes from the mean solar time. The net result is often depicted visually by an **analemma** (FIGURE 1), which looks much like a figure 8. You'll find an analemma printed on many globes, and Figure 2.17 shows a photographic version.

You can use the horizontal scale on the analemma to convert between mean and apparent solar time for any date. (The vertical scale shows the Sun's declination.) For example, the dashed line shows that on November 10, a mean solar clock is about 17 minutes "behind the Sun," or behind apparent solar time; if the apparent solar time is 6:00 p.m. on November 10, the mean solar time is only 5:43 p.m. The discrepancy between mean and apparent solar times is called the **equation of time**. It is often plotted as a graph (FIGURE 2), which gives the same results as reading from the analemma.

The discrepancy between mean and apparent solar time also explains why the times of sunrise and sunset don't follow seasonal patterns perfectly. For example, the winter solstice around December 21 has the shortest daylight hours in the Northern Hemisphere, but the earliest sunset occurs around December 7, when the Sun is still well "behind" mean solar time.

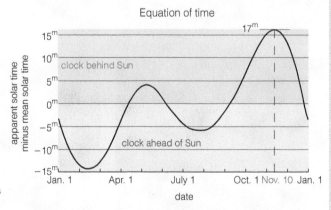

FIGURE 1 The analemma shows the annual pattern of discrepancies between apparent and mean solar time. For example, the dashed red line shows that on November 10, a mean solar clock reads 17 minutes behind (earlier than) apparent solar time.

FIGURE 2 The discrepancies can also be plotted on a graph as the equation of time.

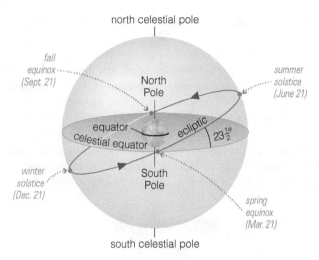

FIGURE S1.8 Schematic diagram of the celestial sphere without stars. The arrow along the ecliptic indicates the direction in which the Sun appears to move over the course of each year.

the celestial sphere. That is, the term *spring equinox* has a dual meaning: It is the *moment* when spring begins and the *point* on the ecliptic at which the Sun appears to be located at that moment. Figure S1.8 shows both the points on the celestial sphere and the approximate dates for each equinox and solstice.

SEE IT FOR YOURSELF

Using your plastic ball as a model of the celestial sphere (which you have already marked with the celestial poles, equator, and ecliptic), mark the locations and approximate dates of the equinoxes and solstices. Based on the dates for these points, approximately where along the ecliptic is the Sun on April 21? On November 21? How do you know?

You can find the locations of the equinoxes and solstices among the constellations with the aid of nearby bright stars (FIGURE S1.9). For example, the point marking the spring equinox is located in the constellation Pisces and can be found with the aid of the four bright stars that make up the "Great Square of Pegasus." Keep in mind that you can find this point any time it is above the horizon on a clear night, even though the Sun is located at this point only once each year (around March 21).

Celestial Coordinates We can now add a system of celestial coordinates to the celestial sphere. Let's begin by reviewing the two other coordinate systems we've used in this book: FIGURE S1.10a shows the coordinates of *altitude* and *direction* (or *azimuth**) that we use in the local sky, and FIGURE S1.10b shows the coordinates of *latitude* and *longitude* that we use on Earth's surface. Our system of celestial coordinates, called **declination (dec)** and **right ascension (RA)**, is shown in FIGURE S1.10c. Notice that declination on the celestial sphere is similar to latitude on Earth, and right ascension is similar to longitude.

To understand the correspondence better, notice the following key points about declination:

- Just as lines of latitude are parallel to Earth's equator, lines of declination are parallel to the celestial equator.

- Just as Earth's equator has lat = 0°, the celestial equator has dec = 0°.

---

*Azimuth is usually measured clockwise around the horizon from due north. By this definition, the azimuth of due north is 0°, of due east is 90°, of due south is 180°, and of due west is 270°.

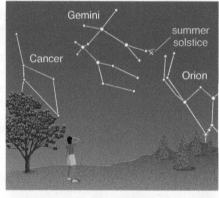

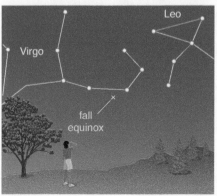

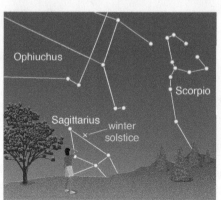

FIGURE S1.9 These diagrams show the locations among the constellations of the equinoxes and solstices. No bright stars mark any of these points, so you must find them by studying their positions relative to recognizable patterns. The time of day or night at which each point is above the horizon depends on the time of year.

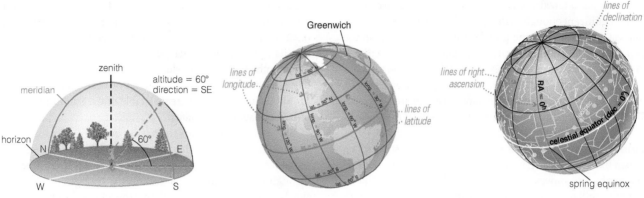

a We use altitude and direction to pinpoint locations in the local sky.

b We use latitude and longitude to pinpoint locations on Earth.

c We use declination and right ascension to pinpoint locations on the celestial sphere.

FIGURE S1.10 Celestial coordinate systems.

- Latitude is labeled *north* or *south* relative to the equator, while declination is labeled *positive* or *negative*. For example, the North Pole has lat = 90°N, while the north celestial pole has dec = +90°; the South Pole has lat = 90°S, while the south celestial pole has dec = −90°.

We find a similar correspondence between right ascension and longitude:

- Just as lines of longitude extend from the North Pole to the South Pole, lines of right ascension extend from the north celestial pole to the south celestial pole.

- Just as there is no natural starting point for longitude, there is no natural starting point for right ascension. By international treaty, longitude zero (the prime meridian) is the line of longitude that runs through Greenwich, England. By convention, right ascension zero is the line of right ascension that runs through the spring equinox.

- Longitude is measured in *degrees* east or west of Greenwich, while right ascension is measured in *hours* (and minutes and seconds) east of the spring equinox. A full 360° circle around the celestial equator goes through 24 hours of right ascension, so each hour of right ascension represents an angle of 360° ÷ 24 = 15°.

As an example of how we use celestial coordinates to locate objects on the celestial sphere, consider the bright star Vega. Its coordinates are dec = +38°44′ and RA = 18^h35^m (**FIGURE S1.11**). The positive declination tells us that Vega is 38°44′ *north* of the celestial equator. The right ascension tells us that Vega is 18 hours 35 minutes east of the spring equinox. Translating the right ascension from hours to angular degrees, we find that Vega is about 279° east of the spring equinox (because 18 hours represents 18 × 15° = 270° and 35 minutes represents $\frac{35}{60}$ × 15° ≈ 9°).

We can also use the Vega example to see the benefit of measuring right ascension in units of time. All objects with a particular right ascension cross the meridian at the same time. For example, all stars with RA = 0^h cross the meridian at the same time the spring equinox crosses the meridian, all objects with RA = 1^h cross the meridian one hour after the spring equinox, and so on. Vega's right ascension of 18^h35^m tells us that it always crosses the meridian 18 hours 35 minutes after the spring equinox crosses the meridian. (This is 18 hours 35 minutes of *sidereal time* later, which is not exactly the same as 18 hours 35 minutes of solar time; see Mathematical Insight S1.2.) Generalizing, an object's right ascension tells us *how long after* the spring equinox the object crosses the meridian.

Note that while we generally think of declination and right ascension as fixed coordinates like latitude and longitude, they are not perfectly constant. Instead, they move slowly relative to distant stars because they are tied to the celestial equator, which moves gradually relative to the constellations with Earth's 26,000-year cycle of axis precession [**Section 2.2**]. (Axis precession does not affect Earth's orbit, so it does not affect the location of the ecliptic among the constellations.)

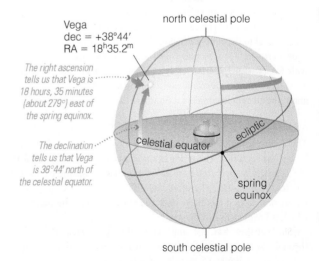

Vega
dec = +38°44′
RA = $18^h35.2^m$

The right ascension tells us that Vega is 18 hours, 35 minutes (about 279°) east of the spring equinox.

north celestial pole

The declination tells us that Vega is 38°44′ north of the celestial equator.

celestial equator

ecliptic

spring equinox

south celestial pole

FIGURE S1.11 This diagram shows how we interpret the celestial coordinates of Vega.

Even over just a few decades, the resulting coordinate changes can be significant enough to make a difference in precise astronomical work, such as aiming a telescope at a particular object. As a result, careful observations require almost continual updating of celestial coordinates. Star catalogs therefore always state the year for which coordinates are given (for example, "epoch 2000"). Astronomical software can automatically calculate day-to-day celestial coordinates for any object in our sky.

Celestial Coordinates of the Sun Unlike stars, which remain fixed in the patterns of the constellations on the celestial sphere, the Sun moves gradually along the ecliptic. It takes a year for the Sun to make a full circuit of the ecliptic, which means it moves through all 24 hours of right ascension over the course of the year. The Sun therefore moves approximately one twelfth of the way around the ecliptic each month, meaning that its right ascension changes by about $24 \div 12 = 2$ hours per month. **FIGURE S1.12** shows the ecliptic marked with the Sun's monthly position and a scale of celestial coordinates. From this figure, we can create a table of the Sun's month-by-month celestial coordinates.

TABLE S1.1 starts from the spring equinox, when the Sun has declination 0° and right ascension 0^h. You can see in the shaded areas of the table that while RA advances steadily through the year, the Sun's declination changes much more slowly around the solstices than around the equinoxes. For

---

MATHEMATICAL INSIGHT S1.2

Time by the Stars

Our everyday clocks are set to solar time, ticking through 24 hours for each day of mean solar time. For astronomical observations, it is also useful to have clocks that tell time by the stars, or **sidereal time**. Just as *solar time* is defined according to the Sun's position relative to the meridian, *sidereal time* is based on the positions of stars relative to the meridian. We define the **hour angle (HA)** of any object on the celestial sphere to be the time *since* it last crossed the meridian (or the higher of its two meridian crossing points for a circumpolar star). For example:

■ If a star is crossing the meridian *now*, its hour angle is 0^h.

■ If a star crossed the meridian 3 hours ago, its hour angle is 3^h.

■ If a star will cross the meridian 1 hour from now, its hour angle is -1^h or, equivalently, 23^h.

By convention, time by the stars is based on the hour angle of the spring equinox. That is, the **local sidereal time (LST)** is

$$\text{LST} = \text{HA}_{\text{spring equinox}}$$

For example, the local sidereal time is 00:00 when the spring equinox is *on* the meridian. Three hours later, when the spring equinox is 3 hours west of the meridian, the local sidereal time is 03:00.

Note that, because right ascension tells us how long after the spring equinox an object reaches the meridian, the local sidereal time is also equal to the right ascension (RA) of objects currently crossing your meridian. For example, if your local sidereal time is 04:30, stars with RA $= 4^h30^m$ are currently crossing your meridian. This idea leads to an important relationship among any object's current hour angle, the current local sidereal time, and the object's right ascension:

$$\text{HA}_{\text{object}} = \text{LST} - \text{RA}_{\text{object}}$$

This formula should make sense: The local sidereal time tells us how long it has been since the *spring equinox* was on the meridian and an object's right ascension tells us how long after the spring equinox it crosses the meridian. Therefore, the difference LST − RA$_{\text{object}}$ must tell us how long it has been *since* the object crossed the meridian, which is the object's hour angle.

Sidereal time has one important subtlety: Sidereal clocks tick through 24 hours of sidereal time in one sidereal day, which is only about 23 hours 56 minutes of solar time. As a result, a sidereal hour is slightly shorter than a "normal" solar hour, and sidereal clocks gain about 4 minutes per day over solar clocks. Therefore, you cannot easily determine sidereal time from a solar clock. That is why astronomical observatories always have special sidereal clocks in addition to clocks that tell solar time.

EXAMPLE 1: Suppose the local solar time is 9:00 p.m. on the spring equinox (March 21). What is the local sidereal time?

SOLUTION:

Step 1 Understand: We are asked to find the local sidereal time, which is the hour angle of the spring equinox. We therefore need to know the current location of the spring equinox in the local sky. The key clue is that it is the day of the spring equinox, which is the one day on which the Sun is located in the same position as the spring equinox in the sky.

Step 2 Solve: We are told that the local solar time is 9:00 p.m., which means that the Sun is 9 hours past the meridian and therefore has an hour angle of 9 hours. Because the spring equinox and the Sun are located in the same place on this date, the spring equinox also has an hour angle of 9 hours.

Step 3 Explain: The hour angle of the spring equinox is 9 hours, which means the local sidereal time is LST $= 09:00$.

EXAMPLE 2: Suppose the local sidereal time is LST $= 04:00$. When will Vega (RA $= 18^h35^m$) cross the meridian?

SOLUTION:

Step 1 Understand: We are given the local sidereal time and Vega's right ascension, so we can use our formula to determine Vega's hour angle, which tells us its current position relative to the meridian.

Step 2 Solve: We put the given values into the formula to find Vega's hour angle:

$$\text{HA}_{\text{Vega}} = \text{LST} - \text{RA}_{\text{Vega}} = 4:00 - 18:35 = -14:35$$

Step 3 Explain: Vega's hour angle is −14 hours 35 minutes, which means Vega will cross your meridian 14 hours and 35 minutes of sidereal time from now. This also means that Vega crossed your meridian 9 hours and 25 minutes ago (because $14^h35^m + 9^h25^m = 24^h$).

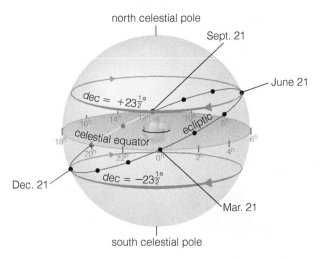

FIGURE S1.12 We can use this diagram of the celestial sphere to determine the Sun's right ascension and declination at monthly intervals.

TABLE S1.1 **The Sun's Approximate Celestial Coordinates at 1-Month Intervals**

Approximate Date	RA	Dec
Mar. 21 (spring equinox)	0^h	$0°$
Apr. 21	2^h	$+12°$
May 21	4^h	$+20°$
June 21 (summer solstice)	6^h	$+23\frac{1}{2}°$
July 21	8^h	$+20°$
Aug. 21	10^h	$+12°$
Sept. 21 (fall equinox)	12^h	$0°$
Oct. 21	14^h	$-12°$
Nov. 21	16^h	$-20°$
Dec. 21 (winter solstice)	18^h	$-23\frac{1}{2}°$
Jan. 21	20^h	$-20°$
Feb. 21	22^h	$-12°$

example, during the 2 months around the summer solstice (that is, between May 21 and July 21), the Sun's declination varies only between $+20°$ and its maximum of $+23\frac{1}{2}°$. In contrast, in the two months around the spring equinox, the Sun's declination changes by about 24°, from $-12°$ on February 21 to $+12°$ on April 21. These facts explain why the number of daylight hours increases rapidly in spring and decreases rapidly in fall, while remaining long and nearly constant for a couple of months around the summer solstice and short and nearly constant for a couple of months around the winter solstice.

SEE IT FOR YOURSELF

On your plastic ball model of the celestial sphere, add dots along the ecliptic to show the Sun's monthly positions. Based on your model, what are the Sun's approximate celestial coordinates on your birthday?

 Seasons Tutorial, Lesson 3

How do stars move through the local sky?

Recall that Earth's rotation makes all celestial objects appear to circle around Earth each day (see Figure 2.9), but what we actually see in the local sky is more complex because we see only half the celestial sphere at one time (the ground blocks our view of the other half). We can now use our understanding of celestial coordinates to gain a deeper understanding of the local sky. As we'll see, the path of any star through your local sky depends only on (1) your latitude and (2) the declination of the star.

The Sky at the North Pole Let's begin by exploring the local sky at the North Pole, where the daily paths of stars are easiest to understand. FIGURE S1.13a shows your orientation relative to the celestial sphere when you are standing at the North Pole. Your "up" points toward the north celestial pole, which therefore marks your zenith. Earth blocks your view of anything south of the celestial equator, which therefore runs along your horizon. To make it easier for you to visualize the local sky, FIGURE S1.13b shows your horizon extending to the celestial sphere. The horizon is marked with directions; note that all directions are south from the North Pole, which means we cannot define a meridian for the North Pole.

Notice that the daily circles of the stars keep them at constant altitudes above or below the North Polar horizon. Moreover, the altitude of any star is equal to its declination. For example, a star with declination $+60°$ circles the sky at an altitude of 60°, and a star with declination $-30°$ remains 30° below your horizon at all times. As a result, all stars north of the celestial equator are circumpolar at the North Pole, meaning that they never fall below the horizon. Stars south of the celestial equator can never be seen at the North Pole. (If you are having difficulty visualizing the star paths, it may help you to watch them as you rotate your plastic ball model of the celestial sphere.)

You should also notice that right ascension does not affect a star's path at all: The path depends only on declination. As we'll see shortly, this rule holds for all latitudes. Right ascension affects only the *time* of day and year at which a star is found in a particular position in your sky.

The Sky at the Equator Imagine that you are standing somewhere on Earth's equator (lat = 0°), such as in Ecuador, in Kenya, or on the island of Borneo. FIGURE S1.14a shows that "up" points directly away from (perpendicular to) Earth's rotation axis. FIGURE S1.14b shows the local sky more clearly by extending the horizon to the celestial sphere and rotating the diagram so the zenith is up. As it does everywhere except at the poles, the meridian extends from the horizon due south, through the zenith, to the horizon due north.

Look carefully at how the celestial sphere appears to rotate in the local sky. The north celestial pole remains stationary on your horizon due north, with its altitude equal to the equator's latitude of 0° [**Section 2.1**], and the south celestial

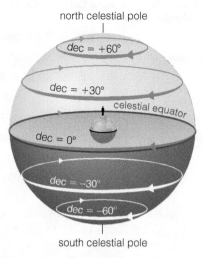

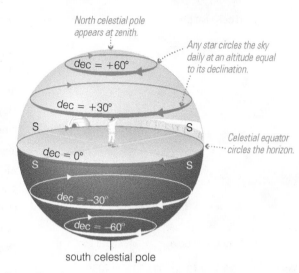

a The orientation of the local sky, relative to the celestial sphere, for an observer at the North Pole.

b Extending the horizon to the celestial sphere makes it easier to visualize the local sky at the North Pole.

FIGURE S1.13 The sky at the North Pole.

pole remains stationary on your horizon due south. Exactly half the celestial equator is visible, extending from the horizon due east, through the zenith, to the horizon due west. (The other half lies below the horizon.) As the equatorial sky appears to turn, all star paths rise straight out of the eastern horizon and set straight into the western horizon, with the following features:

- **Stars with dec = 0°** lie *on* the celestial equator and therefore rise due east, cross the meridian at the zenith, and set due west.

- **Stars with dec > 0°** rise north of due east, reach their highest point on the meridian in the north, and set north of due west. Their rise, set, and highest point depend on their declination. For example, a star with dec = +30° rises

30° north of due east, crosses the meridian 30° to the north of the zenith—that is, at an *altitude* of 90° − 30° = 60° in the north—and sets 30° north of due west.

- **Stars with dec < 0°** rise south of due east, reach their highest point on the meridian in the south, and set south of due west. For example, a star with dec = −50° rises 50° south of due east, crosses the meridian 50° to the south of the zenith—that is, at an *altitude* of 90° − 50° = 40° in the south—and sets 50° south of due west.

Because exactly half of any star's daily circle lies above the horizon, every star at the equator is above the horizon for exactly half of each sidereal day, or just under 12 hours (and below the horizon for the other half of the sidereal day).

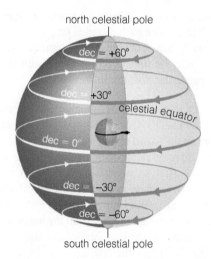

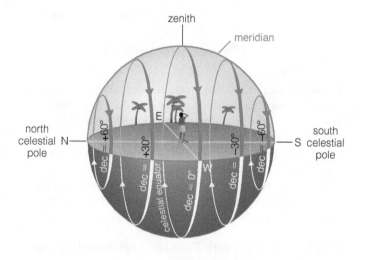

a The orientation of the local sky, relative to the celestial sphere, for an observer at Earth's equator.

b Extending the horizon and rotating the diagram make it easier to visualize the local sky at the equator.

FIGURE S1.14 The sky at the equator.

Are any stars circumpolar at the equator? Are there stars that never rise above the horizon at the equator? Explain.

Skies at Other Latitudes Star tracks may at first seem more complex at other latitudes, with their mixtures of circumpolar stars and stars that rise and set. However, they are easy to understand if we apply the same basic strategy we've used for the North Pole and equator. Let's consider latitude 40°N, such as in Denver, Indianapolis, Philadelphia, or Beijing. First, as shown in FIGURE S1.15a, imagine standing at this latitude on a basic diagram of the rotating celestial sphere. Note that "up" points to a location on the celestial sphere with declination +40°. To make it easier to visualize the local sky, we next extend the horizon and rotate the diagram so that the zenith is up (FIGURE S1.15b).

As we expect, the north celestial pole appears 40° above the horizon due north, since its altitude in the local sky is always equal to your latitude. Half the celestial equator is visible, extending from the horizon due east, to the meridian at an altitude of 50° in the south, to the horizon due west. By comparing this diagram to that of the local sky for the equator, you'll notice the following general rule that applies to all latitudes except the poles:

The celestial equator always extends from due east on your horizon to due west on your horizon, crossing the meridian at an altitude of 90° minus your latitude.

The celestial equator crosses the meridian south of the zenith for locations in the Northern Hemisphere and north of the zenith for locations in the Southern Hemisphere.

If you study Figure S1.15b carefully, you'll notice the following features of the sky for latitude 40°N:

- **Stars with dec = 0°** lie *on* the celestial equator and therefore follow the celestial equator's path through the local sky. For latitude 40°N, these stars rise due east, cross the meridian at altitude 90° − 40° = 50° in the south, and set due west.

- **Stars with dec > (90° − lat)** are circumpolar. For latitude 40°N, stars with declination greater than 90° − 40° = 50° are circumpolar, because they lie *within* 40° of the north celestial pole.

- **Stars with dec > 0° that are not circumpolar** follow paths parallel to but north of the celestial equator: They rise north of due east and set north of due west, and cross the meridian to the north of the place where the celestial equator crosses it by an amount equal to their declination. For example, because the celestial equator at latitude 40° crosses the meridian at altitude 50° in the south, a star with dec = +30° crosses the meridian at altitude 50° + 30° = 80° in the south. Similarly, a star with dec = +60° crosses the meridian 60° farther north than the celestial equator, which means at altitude 70° in the north (because 50° + 60° = 110°, which means 20° past the zenith, which is 90° − 20° = 70°).

- **Stars with dec < (−90° + lat)** never rise above the horizon. For latitude 40°N, stars with declination less than −90° + 40° = −50° never rise above the horizon, because they lie within 40° of the south celestial pole.

- **Stars with dec < 0° that are sometimes visible** follow paths parallel to but south of the celestial equator: They rise south of due east and set south of due west, and cross the meridian south of the place where the celestial equator crosses it by an amount equal to their declination. For example, a star with dec = −30° crosses the meridian at altitude 50° − 30° = 20° in the south.

Note also that the fraction of any star's daily circle that is above the horizon—and hence the amount of time it is above the horizon each day—depends on its declination. Because

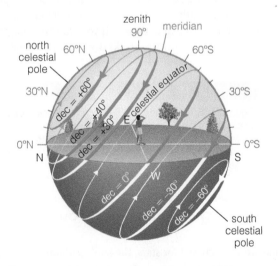

a The orientation of the local sky, relative to the celestial sphere, for an observer at latitude 40°N. Because latitude is the angle to Earth's equator, "up" points to the circle on the celestial sphere with declination +40°.

FIGURE S1.15 The sky at 40°N latitude.

b Extending the horizon and rotating the diagram so that the zenith is up make it easier to visualize the local sky. The blue scale along the meridian shows altitudes and directions in the local sky.

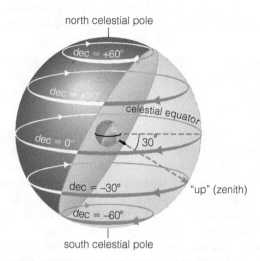

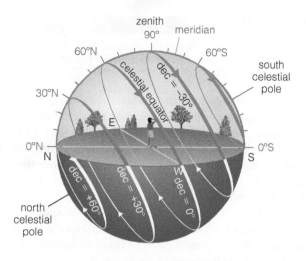

a The orientation of the local sky for an observer at latitude 30°S, relative to the celestial sphere. "Up" points to the circle on the celestial sphere with dec = –30°.

b Extending the horizon and rotating the diagram so that the zenith is up make it easier to visualize the local sky. Note that the south celestial pole is visible at altitude 30° in the south, while the celestial equator stretches across the northern half of the sky.

FIGURE S1.16 The sky at 30°S latitude.

exactly half the celestial equator is above the horizon, stars on the celestial equator (dec = 0°) are above the horizon for exactly half of each sidereal day, or about 12 hours. For northern latitudes like 40°N, stars with positive declinations have more than half their daily circles above the horizon and hence are above the horizon for more than 12 hours each day (with the range extending to 24 hours a day for the circumpolar stars). Stars with negative declinations have less than half their daily circles above the horizon and hence are above the horizon for less than 12 hours each day (with the range going to zero for stars that are never above the horizon).

We can apply the same strategy we used in Figure S1.15 to find star paths for other latitudes. **FIGURE S1.16** shows the local sky for latitude 30°S. Note that the south celestial pole is visible to the south and that the celestial equator passes through the northern half of the sky. If you study the diagram carefully, you can see how star tracks depend on declination.

THINK ABOUT IT

Study Figure S1.16 for latitude 30°S. Describe the path of the celestial equator. Does it obey the *90° – latitude* rule given earlier? Describe how star tracks differ for stars with positive and negative declinations. What declination must a star have to be circumpolar at this latitude?

How does the Sun move through the local sky?

Just as we've discussed for stars, the Sun's path on any particular day depends only on its declination and your latitude. However, because the Sun's declination changes over the course of the year, the Sun's path also changes.

FIGURE S1.17 shows the Sun's path on the equinoxes and solstices for latitude 40°N. On the equinoxes, the Sun is on

the celestial equator (dec = 0°) and therefore follows the celestial equator's path: It rises due east, crosses the meridian at altitude 50° in the south, and sets due west. Like other objects on the celestial equator, it is above the horizon for 12 hours. On the summer solstice, the Sun has dec = $+23\frac{1}{2}°$ (see Table S1.1) and therefore rises well north of due east,* reaches an altitude of $50° + 23\frac{1}{2}° = 73\frac{1}{2}°$ when it crosses the meridian in the south, and sets well north of due west. The daylight hours are long because much more than half the Sun's path is above the horizon. On the winter solstice, when the Sun has dec = $-23\frac{1}{2}°$, the Sun rises well south of due east, reaches an altitude of only $50° - 23\frac{1}{2}° = 26\frac{1}{2}°$ when it crosses the meridian in the south, and sets well south of due west.

---

*Calculating exactly how far north of due east the Sun rises is beyond the scope of this book, but astronomical software and websites can do these calculations for different latitudes.

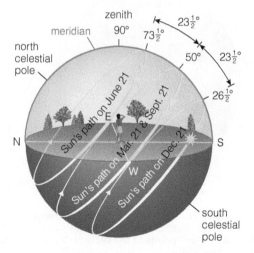

FIGURE S1.17 interactive figure The Sun's daily path on the equinoxes and solstices at latitude 40°N.

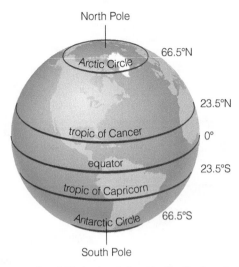

FIGURE S1.18 Special latitudes defined by the Sun's path through the sky.

The daylight hours are short because much less than half the Sun's path is above the horizon.

We could make a similar diagram to show the Sun's path on various dates for any latitude. However, the $23\frac{1}{2}°$ tilt of Earth's axis makes the Sun's path particularly interesting at the special latitudes shown in FIGURE S1.18. Let's investigate.

The Sun at the North and South Poles Recall that the celestial equator circles the horizon at the North Pole. FIGURE S1.19 shows how we use this fact to find the Sun's path in the North Polar sky. Because the Sun appears *on* the celestial equator on the day of the spring equinox, the Sun circles the North Polar sky *on the horizon* on March 21, completing a full circle in 24 hours (1 solar day). Over the next 3 months, the Sun continues to circle the horizon each day, circling at gradually higher altitudes as its declination increases. It reaches its highest point on the summer solstice, when its declination of $+23\frac{1}{2}°$ means that it circles the North Polar sky at an altitude of $23\frac{1}{2}°$. After the summer solstice, the daily circles gradually fall lower over the next 3 months, reaching the horizon on the fall equinox.

Then, because the Sun's declination is negative for the next 6 months (until the following spring equinox), the Sun remains below the North Polar horizon. That is why the North Pole essentially has 6 months of daylight and 6 months of darkness, with an extended twilight that lasts a few weeks beyond the fall equinox and an extended dawn that begins a few weeks before the spring equinox.

The situation is the opposite at the South Pole. Here, the Sun's daily circle first reaches the horizon on the fall equinox. The daily circles then rise gradually higher, reaching a maximum altitude of $23\frac{1}{2}°$ on the *winter* solstice (when it is summer in the Antarctic), and then slowly fall back to the horizon on the spring equinox. That is, the South Pole has the Sun above the horizon during the 6 months it is below the North Polar horizon.

Two important caveats make the actual view from the Poles slightly different than we've described. First, the atmosphere bends light enough so that when the Sun is near the horizon, it *appears* to be about 1° higher than it really is, which means we can see the Sun even when it is slightly below the horizon. Second, the Sun's angular size of about $\frac{1}{2}°$ means that it does not fall below the horizon at a single moment but instead sets gradually. Together, these effects mean that the Sun *appears* above each polar horizon for several days longer than 6 months each year.

The Sun at the Equator At the equator, the celestial equator extends from the horizon due east, through the zenith, to the horizon due west. The Sun therefore follows this path on each equinox, reaching the zenith at local noon (FIGURE S1.20). Following the spring equinox, the Sun's increasing declination means that it follows a daily track that takes it gradually northward in the sky. It is farthest north on the summer solstice, when it rises $23\frac{1}{2}°$ north of due east, crosses the meridian at altitude $90° − 23\frac{1}{2}° = 66\frac{1}{2}°$ in the north, and sets $23\frac{1}{2}°$ north of due west. Over the next 6 months, it gradually tracks southward until the winter solstice, when its path is the mirror image (across the celestial equator) of its summer solstice path.

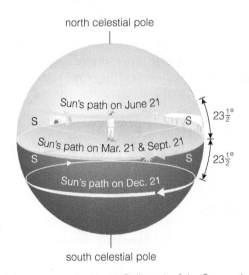

FIGURE S1.19 **interactive figure** Daily path of the Sun on the equinoxes and solstices at the North Pole.

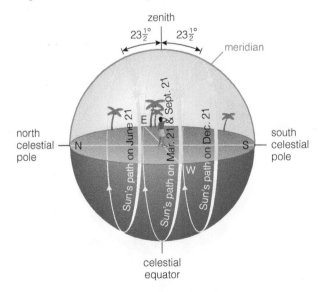

FIGURE S1.20 **interactive figure** Daily path of the Sun on the equinoxes and solstices at the equator.

Like all objects in the equatorial sky, the Sun is always above the horizon for half a day and below it for half a day. Moreover, the Sun's track is highest in the sky on the equinoxes and lowest on the summer and winter solstices. That is why equatorial regions do not have four seasons like temperate regions [**Section 2.2**]. The Sun's path in the equatorial sky also makes it rise and set perpendicular to the horizon every day of the year, making for a more rapid dawn and a briefer twilight than at other latitudes.

The Sun at the Tropics The circles of latitude 23.5°N and 23.5°S are called the **tropic of Cancer** and the **tropic of Capricorn**, respectively (see Figure S1.18). The region between these two circles, generally called the *tropics*, represents the parts of Earth where the Sun can sometimes reach the zenith at noon.

FIGURE S1.21 shows why the tropic of Cancer is special. The celestial equator extends from due east on the horizon to due west on the horizon, crossing the meridian in the south at an altitude of $90° - 23\frac{1}{2}°$ (the latitude) $= 66\frac{1}{2}°$, or $23\frac{1}{2}°$ short of the zenith. Therefore, the Sun reaches the zenith at local noon on the summer solstice, when it crosses the meridian $23\frac{1}{2}°$ northward of the celestial equator. The tropic of Cancer marks the northernmost latitude at which the Sun ever reaches the zenith. Similarly, at the tropic of Capricorn, the Sun reaches the zenith at local noon on the winter solstice (when it is summer for the Southern Hemisphere), making this the southernmost latitude at which the Sun ever reaches the zenith. Between the two tropic circles, the Sun passes through the zenith twice a year; the precise dates vary with latitude.

The Sun at the Arctic and Antarctic Circles At the equator, the Sun is above the horizon for 12 hours each day year-round. At latitudes progressively farther from the equator, the daily time that the Sun is above the horizon varies progressively more with the seasons. The special latitudes at which the Sun remains continuously above the horizon for a full day each year are the polar circles: the **Arctic Circle** at

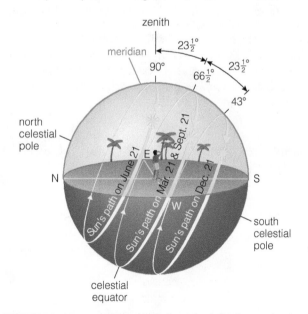

FIGURE S1.21 interactive figure Daily path of the Sun on the equinoxes and solstices at the tropic of Cancer.

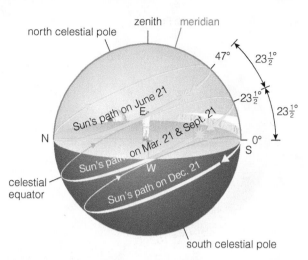

FIGURE S1.22 interactive figure Daily path of the Sun on the equinoxes and solstices at the Arctic Circle.

latitude 66.5°N and the **Antarctic Circle** at latitude 66.5°S (see Figure S1.18). Poleward of these circles, the length of continuous daylight (or darkness) increases beyond 24 hours, reaching the extreme of 6 months at the North and South Poles.

FIGURE S1.22 shows why the Arctic Circle is special. The celestial equator extends from due east on the horizon to due west on the horizon, crossing the meridian in the south at an altitude of $90° - 66\frac{1}{2}°$ (the latitude) $= 23\frac{1}{2}°$. As a result, the Sun's path is circumpolar on the summer solstice: The Sun skims the northern horizon at midnight, rises through the eastern sky to a noon maximum altitude of 47° in the south (which is the celestial equator's maximum altitude of $23\frac{1}{2}°$ plus the Sun's summer solstice declination of $23\frac{1}{2}°$), and then gradually falls through the western sky until it is back on the horizon at midnight (see Figure 2.18). At the Antarctic Circle, the Sun follows the same basic pattern on the winter solstice, except that it skims the horizon in the south and rises to a noon maximum altitude of 47° in the north.

Of course, what we *see* is subject to the same caveats we discussed for the North and South Poles: The bending of light by Earth's atmosphere and the Sun's angular size make the Sun *appear* to be slightly above the horizon even when it is slightly below it. As a result, at the Arctic Circle, the Sun seems not to set for several days around the summer solstice (rather than for a single day) and appears to peek above the horizon momentarily (rather than not at all) around the winter solstice. The same ideas hold for the opposite solstices at the Antarctic Circle.

S1.3 PRINCIPLES OF CELESTIAL NAVIGATION

Imagine that you're on a ship at sea, far from any landmarks. How can you figure out where you are? We now have all the background we need to answer this question.

How can you determine your latitude?

It's easy to determine your latitude if you can find the north or south celestial pole in your sky, because it is equal to the

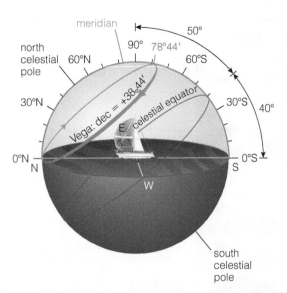

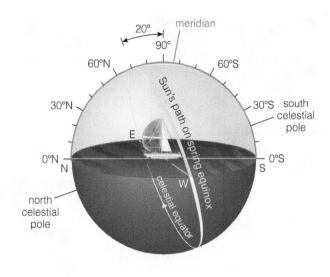

a Because Vega has dec = +38°44′, it crosses the meridian 38°44′ north of the celestial equator. Because Vega crosses the meridian at altitude 78°44′ in the south, the celestial equator must cross the meridian at altitude 40° in the south. Thus, the latitude must be 50°N.

b To determine latitude from the Sun's meridian crossing, you must know the Sun's declination, which you can determine from the date. The case shown is for the spring equinox, when the Sun's declination is 0° and hence the Sun follows the path of the celestial equator through the local sky. Because the celestial equator crosses the meridian at 70° in the north, the latitude must be 20°S.

FIGURE S1.23 Determining latitude from a star and from the Sun.

altitude of the celestial pole. In the Northern Hemisphere at night, you can determine your approximate latitude by measuring the altitude of Polaris, which lies within 1° of the north celestial pole. For example, if Polaris has altitude 17°, your latitude is between 16°N and 18°N.

If you want to be more precise, you can determine your latitude from the altitude of *any* star as it crosses your meridian. For example, suppose Vega happens to be crossing your meridian right now and it appears in your southern sky at altitude 78°44′. Because Vega has dec = +38°44′ (see Figure S1.11), it crosses your meridian 38°44′ north of the celestial equator. As shown in **FIGURE S1.23a**, you can conclude that the celestial equator crosses your meridian at an altitude of precisely 40° in the south. Your latitude must therefore be 50°N, because the celestial equator always crosses the meridian at an altitude of 90° minus the latitude. You know you are in the Northern Hemisphere because the celestial equator crosses the meridian in the south.

In the daytime, you can find your latitude from the Sun's altitude on your meridian if you know the date and the Sun's declination on that date. For example, suppose the date is March 21 and the Sun crosses your meridian at altitude 70° in the north (**FIGURE S1.23b**). Because the Sun has dec = 0° on March 21, you can conclude that the celestial equator also crosses your meridian in the north at altitude 70°. You must be in the Southern Hemisphere because the celestial equator crosses the meridian in the north. From the rule that the celestial equator crosses the meridian at an altitude of 90° minus the latitude, you can conclude that you are at latitude 20°S.

How can you determine your longitude?

You can determine your longitude by comparing the current position of an object in your sky with its position as seen

from some known longitude. As a simple example, suppose you use a sundial to determine that the apparent solar time is 1:00 p.m., which means the Sun passed the meridian 1 hour ago. You immediately call a friend in England and learn that it is 3:00 p.m. in Greenwich (or you carry a clock that keeps Greenwich time). You now know that your local time is 2 hours earlier than the local time in Greenwich, which means you are 2 hours west of Greenwich. (An earlier time means that you are *west* of Greenwich, because Earth rotates from west to east.) Each hour corresponds to 15° of longitude, so "2 hours west of Greenwich" means longitude 30°W.

At night, you can find your longitude by comparing the positions of stars in your local sky and at some known longitude. For example, suppose Vega is on your meridian and a call to your friend reveals that it won't cross the meridian in Greenwich until 6 hours from now. In this case, your local time is 6 hours later than the local time in Greenwich, which means you are 6 hours east of Greenwich, or at longitude 90°E (because 6 × 15° = 90°).

Celestial Navigation in Practice Although celestial navigation is easy in principle, at least three considerations make it more difficult in practice. First, finding either latitude or longitude requires a tool for measuring angles in the sky. One such device, called an *astrolabe*, was invented by the ancient Greeks and significantly improved by Islamic scholars during the Middle Ages. The astrolabe's faceplate (**FIGURE S1.24a**) could be used to tell time, because it consisted of a rotating star map and horizon plates for specific latitudes. Today you can buy similar rotatable star maps, called *planispheres*. Most astrolabes contained a sighting stick on the back that allowed users to measure the altitudes of bright stars in the sky. These measurements could then be correlated

a The faceplate of an astrolabe. Many astrolabes had sighting sticks on the back for measuring positions of bright stars.

b A copper engraving of Italian explorer Amerigo Vespucci (for whom America was named) using an astrolabe to sight the Southern Cross. The engraving by Philip Galle, from the book *Nova Reperta*, was based on an original by Joannes Stradanus in the early 1580s.

c A woodcutting of Ptolemy holding a cross-staff (artist unknown).

d A sextant.

FIGURE S1.24 Navigational instruments.

against special markings under the faceplate (**FIGURE S1.24b**). Astrolabes were effective but difficult and expensive to make. As a result, medieval sailors often measured angles with a simple pair of calibrated perpendicular sticks, called a *cross-staff* or *Jacob's staff* (**FIGURE S1.24c**). A more modern device called a *sextant* allows much more precise angle determinations by incorporating a small telescope for sightings (**FIGURE S1.24d**). Sextants are still used for celestial navigation on many ships. If you want to practice celestial navigation yourself, you can buy an inexpensive plastic sextant at many science-oriented stores.

A second practical consideration is knowing the celestial coordinates of stars and the Sun so that you can determine their paths through the local sky. At night, you can use a table listing the celestial coordinates of bright stars. In addition to knowing the celestial coordinates, you must either know the constellations and bright stars extremely well or carry star charts to help you identify them. For navigating by the Sun in the daytime, you'll need a table listing the Sun's celestial coordinates on each day of the year.

The third practical consideration applies to determining longitude: You need to know the current position of the Sun (or a particular star) in a known location, such as Greenwich,

England. Although you could determine this by calling a friend who lives there, it's more practical to carry a clock set to universal time (the time in Greenwich). In the daytime, the clock makes it easy to determine your longitude. If apparent solar time is 1:00 p.m. in your location and the clock tells you that it is 3:00 p.m. in Greenwich, then you are 2 hours

COMMON MISCONCEPTIONS

Compass Directions

Most people determine direction with the aid of a compass rather than the stars. However, a compass needle doesn't actually point to true geographic north. Instead, the compass needle responds to Earth's magnetic field and points to *magnetic* north, which can be substantially different from true north. If you want to navigate precisely with a compass, you need a special map that takes into account local variations in Earth's magnetic field. Such maps are available at most camping stores. They are not perfectly reliable, however, because the magnetic field also varies with time. In general, celestial navigation is much more reliable for determining direction than using a compass.

west of Greenwich, or at longitude 30°W. The task is more difficult at night, because you must compare the position of a *star* in your sky to its current position in Greenwich. You can do this with the aid of detailed astronomical tables that allow you to determine the current position of any star in the Greenwich sky from the date and the universal time.

Historically, this third consideration created enormous problems for navigation. Before the invention of accurate clocks, sailors could easily determine their latitude but not their longitude. Indeed, most of the European voyages of discovery in the 15th century through the 17th century relied on little more than guesswork about longitude, although some sailors learned complex mathematical techniques for estimating longitude through observations of the lunar phases. More accurate longitude determination, upon which the development of extensive ocean commerce and travel depended, required the invention of a clock that would remain accurate on a ship rocking in the ocean swells. By the early 18th century, solving this problem was considered so important that the British government offered a substantial monetary prize for the solution. John

Harrison claimed the prize in 1761, with a clock that lost only 5 seconds during a 9-week voyage to Jamaica.*

The Global Positioning System Today, a new type of celestial navigation has supplanted traditional methods. It finds positions relative to satellites of the **global positioning system (GPS)**. In essence, these Earth-orbiting satellites function like artificial stars. The satellites' positions at any moment are known precisely from their orbital characteristics, and they transmit radio signals that can be picked up by GPS receivers in cars, smart phones, and other devices. Your GPS receiver locates three or more of the satellites and then does computations to calculate your position on Earth.

Navigation by GPS is so precise that the ancient practice of celestial navigation is in danger of becoming a lost art. Fortunately, many amateur clubs and societies are keeping the skills of celestial navigation alive.

---

*The story of the difficulties surrounding the measurement of longitude at sea and how Harrison finally solved the problem is chronicled in *Longitude*, by Dava Sobel (Walker and Company, 1995).

The Big Picture

Putting Chapter S1 into Context

In this chapter, we built upon concepts from the first three chapters to form a more detailed understanding of celestial timekeeping and navigation. You also learned how to determine paths for the Sun and the stars in the local sky. As you look back at what you've learned, keep in mind the following "big picture" ideas:

- Our modern systems of timekeeping are rooted in the apparent motions of the Sun through the sky. Although it's easy to forget these roots when you look at a clock or a calendar, the sky was the only guide to time for most of human history.

- The term *celestial navigation* sounds a bit mysterious, but it refers to simple principles that allow you to determine your location on Earth. Even if you're never lost at sea, you may find the basic techniques of celestial navigation useful to orient yourself at night (for example, on your next camping trip).

- If you understand the apparent motions of the sky discussed in this chapter and also learn the constellations and bright stars, you'll feel very much "at home" under the stars at night.

SUMMARY OF KEY CONCEPTS

S1.1 ASTRONOMICAL TIME PERIODS

- **How do we define the day, month, year, and planetary periods?** Each of these is defined in two ways. A **sidereal day** is Earth's rotation period, which is about 4 minutes shorter than the 24-hour **solar day** from noon one day to noon the next day. A **sidereal month** is the Moon's orbital period of about $27\frac{1}{3}$ days; a **synodic month** is the $29\frac{1}{2}$ days required for the Moon's cycle of phases. A **sidereal year** is Earth's orbital period, which is about 20 minutes longer than the **tropical year** from one spring

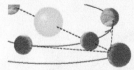
equinox to the next. A planet's **sidereal period** is its orbital period, and its **synodic period** is the time from one opposition or conjunction to the next.

- **How do we tell the time of day?** There are several time measurement systems. **Apparent solar time** is based on the Sun's position in the local sky. **Mean solar time** is also local, but it averages the changes in the Sun's rate of motion over the year. **Standard time** and **daylight saving time** divide the world into

time zones. **Universal time** is the mean solar time in Greenwich, England.

- **When and why do we have leap years?** We usually have a **leap year** every 4 years because the length of the year is about $365\frac{1}{4}$ days. However, it is not exactly $365\frac{1}{4}$ days, so our calendar skips a leap year in century years not divisible by 400.

S1.2 CELESTIAL COORDINATES AND MOTION IN THE SKY

- **How do we locate objects on the celestial sphere?**
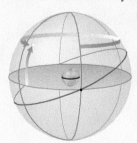
Declination is given as an angle describing an object's position north or south of the celestial equator. **Right ascension**, usually measured in hours (and minutes and seconds), tells us how far east an object is located relative to the spring equinox.

- **How do stars move through the local sky?** A star's path

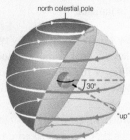

through the local sky depends on its declination and your latitude. Latitude tells you the orientation of your sky relative to the celestial sphere, while declination tells you how a particular star's path compares to the path of the celestial equator through your sky.

- **How does the Sun move through the local sky?** The

Sun's path also depends on its declination and your latitude, but it varies throughout the year because of the Sun's changing declination. The Sun's varying path helps define special latitudes, including the **tropics of Cancer** and **Capricorn** and the **Arctic** and **Antarctic Circles**.

S1.3 PRINCIPLES OF CELESTIAL NAVIGATION

- **How can you determine your latitude?** You can deter-

mine your latitude from the altitude of the celestial pole in your sky or by measuring the altitude and knowing the declination of a star (or the Sun) as it crosses your meridian.

- **How can you determine your longitude?** To determine longitude you must know the position of the Sun or a star in your sky and its position at the same time in the sky of Greenwich, England (or some other specific location). This is most easily done if you have a clock that tells universal time.

VISUAL SKILLS CHECK

Use the following questions to check your understanding of some of the many types of visual information used in astronomy. Answers are provided Appendix J. For additional practice, try the Chapter S1 Visual Quiz at MasteringAstronomy®.

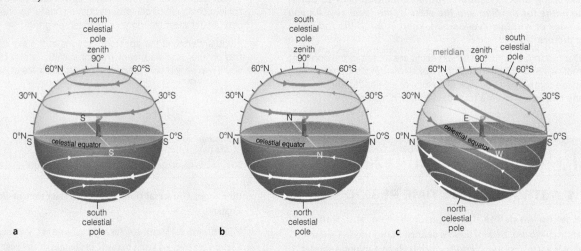

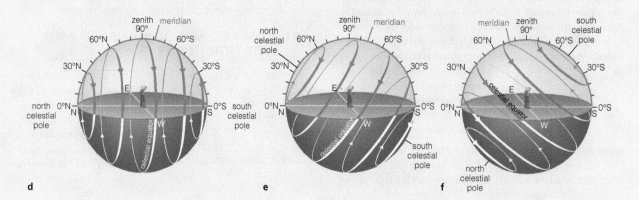

The six diagrams represent the sky at six different latitudes. Answer the following questions about them.

1. Which diagram represents the paths of stars at the North Pole?
2. Which diagram represents the paths of stars at the South Pole?
3. Which diagrams represent Southern Hemisphere skies?
4. What latitude is represented in diagram c?
5. Which diagram(s) represent(s) a latitude at which the Sun sometimes passes directly overhead?
6. Which diagram(s) represent(s) a latitude at which the Sun sometimes remains below the horizon during a full 24-hour period?
7. Each diagram shows five star circles. Look at the first circle to the north of the celestial equator on each diagram. Can you characterize the *declination* of stars on this circle? If so, what is it? Can you characterize the *right ascension* of stars on this circle? If so, what is it?

EXERCISES AND PROBLEMS

For instructor-assigned homework go to MasteringAstronomy®.

REVIEW QUESTIONS

Short-Answer Questions Based on the Reading

1. Briefly explain the differences between (a) a *sidereal day* and a *solar day,* (b) a *sidereal month* and a *synodic month,* (c) a *sidereal year* and a *tropical year,* (d) a planet's *sidereal period* and its *synodic period.*
2. Define *opposition, conjunction,* and *greatest elongation* for planets. Explain both for planets closer than Earth to the Sun and for planets farther than Earth from the Sun.
3. Under what circumstances do we see a *transit* of a planet across the Sun?
4. Distinguish among *apparent solar time, mean solar time, standard time, daylight saving time,* and *universal time.*
5. Describe the origins of the Julian and Gregorian calendars. Which one do we use today?
6. What do we mean when we say the equinoxes and solstices are points on the celestial sphere? How are these points related to the times of year called the equinoxes and solstices?
7. What are *declination* and *right ascension?* How are these celestial coordinates similar to latitude and longitude on Earth? How are they different?
8. How and why do the Sun's celestial coordinates change over the course of each year?
9. Suppose you are at the North Pole. Where is the celestial equator? Where is the north celestial pole? Describe the daily motion of the sky. Do the same for the equator and for latitude 40°N.
10. Describe the Sun's path through the local sky on the equinoxes and on the solstices for latitude 40°N. Do the same for the North Pole, South Pole, and equator.
11. What is special about the tropics of Cancer and Capricorn? Describe the Sun's path on the solstices at these latitudes. Do the same for the Arctic and Antarctic Circles.
12. Briefly describe how you can use the Sun or stars to determine your latitude and longitude.

TEST YOUR UNDERSTANDING

Does It Make Sense?

Decide whether the statement makes sense (or is clearly true) or does not make sense (or is clearly false). Explain clearly; not all of these have definitive answers, so your explanation is more important than your chosen answer. (Hint: For statements that involve coordinates—such as altitude, longitude, or declination—check whether the correct coordinates are used for the situation. For example, it does not make sense to describe a location on Earth by an altitude, because altitude only describes positions of objects in the local sky.)

13. Last night I saw Venus shining brightly on the meridian at midnight.
14. The apparent solar time was noon, but the Sun was just setting.
15. My mean solar clock said it was 2:00 p.m., but a friend who lives east of here had a mean solar clock that said it was 2:11 p.m.
16. When the standard time is 3:00 p.m. in Baltimore, it is 3:15 p.m. in Washington, D.C.
17. Last night around 8:00 p.m., I saw Jupiter at an altitude of 45° in the south.
18. The latitude of the stars in Orion's belt is about 5°N.
19. Today the Sun is at an altitude of 10° on the celestial sphere.
20. Los Angeles is west of New York by about 3 hours of right ascension.
21. The summer solstice is east of the vernal equinox by 6 hours of right ascension.
22. Even though my UT clock had stopped, I was able to find my longitude by measuring the altitudes of 14 different stars in my local sky.

Quick Quiz

Choose the best answer to each of the following. Explain your reasoning with one or more complete sentences.

23. The time from one spring equinox to the next is the (a) sidereal day. (b) tropical year. (c) synodic month.
24. Jupiter is brightest when it is (a) at opposition. (b) at conjunction. (c) closest to the Sun in its orbit.
25. Venus is easiest to see in the evening when it is (a) at superior conjunction. (b) at inferior conjunction. (c) at greatest eastern elongation.
26. In the winter, your wristwatch tells (a) apparent solar time. (b) standard time. (c) universal time.
27. A star that is located 30° north of the celestial equator has (a) declination = 30°. (b) right ascension = 30°. (c) latitude = 30°.
28. A star's path through your sky depends on your latitude and the star's (a) declination. (b) right ascension. (c) both declination and right ascension.
29. At latitude 50°N, the celestial equator crosses the meridian at altitude (a) 50° in the south. (b) 50° in the north. (c) 40° in the south.
30. At the North Pole on the summer solstice, the Sun (a) remains stationary in the sky. (b) reaches the zenith at noon. (c) circles the horizon at altitude $23\frac{1}{2}°$.
31. If you know a star's declination, you can determine your latitude if you also (a) measure its altitude when it crosses the meridian. (b) measure its right ascension. (c) know the universal time.
32. If you measure the Sun's position in your local sky, you can determine your longitude if you also (a) measure its altitude when it crosses the meridian. (b) know its right ascension and declination. (c) know the universal time.

PROCESS OF SCIENCE

Examining How Science Works

33. *Transits and the Geocentric Universe.* Ancient people could not observe transits of Mercury or Venus across the Sun, because they lacked instruments for viewing a small dark spot against the Sun. But suppose they could have seen transits. How would transit observations have affected the debate over an Earth-centered versus Sun-centered solar system? Explain.

34. *Geometry and Science.* As discussed in Mathematical Insight S1.1, Copernicus found that a Sun-centered model led him to a simple geometric layout for the solar system, a fact that gave him confidence that his model was on the right track. Did the mathematics actually prove that the Sun-centered model was correct? Use your answer to briefly discuss the role of mathematics in science.

GROUP WORK EXERCISE

35. *Find Your Way Home.* Assign the following roles to the people in your group: *Scribe* (takes notes on the group's activities), *Proposer* (proposes methods for the group), *Skeptic* (points out weaknesses in proposed methods), and *Moderator* (leads group discussion and makes sure everyone contributes). You are an international spy who has been captured by a criminal mastermind and flown for many hours to a secret compound, which could be anywhere in the world. You escape … but all you have is a watch (set to your previous local time), a star chart, and a world map with longitude and latitude marked on it. How do you figure out where you are? How could you use celestial navigation to find your way back home?

INVESTIGATE FURTHER

In-Depth Questions to Increase Your Understanding

Short-Answer/Essay Questions

36. *Opposite Rotation.* Suppose Earth rotated in a direction opposite to its orbital direction; that is, suppose it rotated clockwise (as seen from above the North Pole) but orbited counterclockwise. Would the solar day still be longer than the sidereal day? Explain.

37. *No Precession.* Suppose Earth's axis did *not* precess. Would the sidereal year still be different from the tropical year? Explain.

38. *The Sun from Mars.* Mars has an axis tilt of 25.2°, only slightly larger than that of Earth. Compared to that on Earth, is the range of latitudes on Mars for which the Sun can reach the zenith larger or smaller? Is the range of latitudes for which the Sun is circumpolar larger or smaller? Make a sketch of Mars similar to the one for Earth in Figure S1.18.

39. *Fundamentals of Your Local Sky.* Answer each of the following for *your* latitude.
a. Where is the north (or south) celestial pole in your sky? **b.** Describe the meridian in your sky, specifying at least three distinct points along it (such as the points at which it meets your horizon and its highest point). **c.** Describe the celestial equator in your sky, specifying at least three distinct points along it. **d.** Does the Sun ever appear at your zenith? If so, when? If not, why not? **e.** What range of declinations makes a star circumpolar in your sky? **f.** What is the range of declinations for stars that you can never see in your sky?

40. *Sydney Sky.* Repeat Problem 39 for the local sky in Sydney, Australia (latitude 34°S).

41. *Local Path of the Sun.* Describe the path of the Sun through your local sky for each of the following days:
a. the spring and fall equinoxes. **b.** the summer (June) solstice. **c.** the winter (December) solstice. **d.** today. (*Hint:* You can estimate the Sun's RA and dec for today's date from data in Table S1.1.)

42. *Sydney Sun.* Repeat Problem 41 for the local sky in Sydney, Australia (latitude 34°S).

Quantitative Problems

Be sure to show all calculations clearly and state your final answers in complete sentences.

43. *Lost at Sea I.* During a vacation, you decide to take a solo boat trip. While contemplating the universe, you lose track of your location. Fortunately, you have some astronomical tables and instruments, as well as a UT clock. You thereby put together the following description of your situation:
  ■ It is the spring equinox.
  ■ The Sun is on your meridian at altitude 75° in the south.
  ■ The UT clock reads 22:00.
  a. What is your latitude? How do you know? **b.** What is your longitude? How do you know? **c.** Consult a map. Based on your position, where is the nearest land? Which way should you sail to reach it?

44. *Lost at Sea II.* Repeat Problem 43 for this situation:
  ■ It is the day of the summer solstice.
  ■ The Sun is on your meridian at altitude $67\frac{1}{2}°$ in the north.
  ■ The UT clock reads 06:00.

45. *Lost at Sea III.* Repeat Problem 43 for this situation:
  ■ Your local time is midnight.
  ■ Polaris appears at altitude 67° in the north.
  ■ The UT clock reads 01:00.

46. *Lost at Sea IV.* Repeat Problem 43 for this situation:
  ■ Your local time is 6 a.m.
  ■ From the position of the Southern Cross, you estimate that the south celestial pole is at altitude 33° in the south.
  ■ The UT clock reads 11:00.

47. *Orbital and Synodic Periods.* Use each object's given synodic period to find its actual orbital period.
  a. Saturn, synodic period = 378.1 days **b.** Mercury, synodic period = 115.9 days **c.** An asteroid with synodic period = 429 days

48. *Using the Analemma.*
  a. It's February 15 and your sundial tells you the apparent solar time is 18 minutes until noon. What is the mean solar time?
  b. It's July 1 and your sundial tells you that the apparent solar time is 3:30 p.m. What is the mean solar time?

49. *HA = LST − RA.*
  a. It is 4 p.m. on the spring equinox. What is the local sidereal time? **b.** The local sidereal time is 19:30. When will Vega cross your meridian? **c.** You observe a star that has an hour angle of 13 hours (13^h) when the local sidereal time is 8:15. What is the star's right ascension? **d.** The Orion Nebula has declination of about −5.5° and right ascension of 5^h25^m. If you are at latitude 40°N and the local sidereal time is 7:00, approximately where does the Orion Nebula appear in your sky?

50. *Meridian Crossings of the Moon and Phobos.* Estimate the time between meridian crossings of the Moon for a person standing on Earth. Repeat your calculation for meridian crossings of the Martian moon Phobos. Use the Appendixes in the back of the book if necessary.

51. *Mercury's Rotation Period.* Mercury's sidereal day is approximately $\frac{2}{3}$ of its orbital period, or about 58.6 days. Estimate the length of Mercury's solar day. Compare it to Mercury's orbital period of about 88 days.

Discussion Questions

52. *Northern Chauvinism.* Why is the solstice in June called the *summer solstice,* when it marks winter for places like Australia, New Zealand, and South Africa? Why is the writing on maps and globes usually oriented so that the Northern Hemisphere is at the top, even though there is no up or down in space? Discuss.

Mineral	Color	Streak	Type of Cleavage	Hardness	Specific Gravity	Symbol
Carbonates						
calcite	variety of colors	colorless	3 directions; not 90°	3	2.7	$CaCO_3$
Sulfates						
gypsum	yellowish, reddish	colorless	2 directions	2	2.3	$CaSO_4 \cdot 2H_2O$
Phosphates						
apatite	variety of colors	white	indistinct	5	3.2	$Ca_5(PO_4)_3$ (Cl,F)
Silicates						
quartz	variety of colors	colorless	none (fracture)	7	2.6	SiO_2
talc	white, greenish-gray	colorless	1 direction	1	2.8	$Mg_3Si_4O_{10}$ $(OH)_2$
olivine	yellowish, greenish	white to light green	none (fracture)	6.5	3.5	$(MgFe)_2$ SiO_4
serpentine	greenish	colorless	none (fracture)	2–5	2.2-2.6	$Mg_3Si_2O_5$ $(OH)_4$
hornblende	green to black	gray to white	2 directions	5–6	3.4	complex structure
muscovite (mica)	white to dark	colorless	1 direction	2–2.5	2.8	complex structure
topaz	variety of colors	colorless	3 directions	8	3.5	complex structure

Glossary

A simple, phonetic spelling is given for words in this book that may be unfamiliar or hard to pronounce.

Stressed syllables are printed in capital letters. Sometimes a word has two stressed syllables. The syllable with the primary stress is printed in full capitals. The syllable with the secondary stress is printed in small capitals.

Example: *Asteroid* is pronounced AS tuh ROYD.

Most of the time, the phonetic spelling can be interpreted without referring to the key. The key to the right gives the pronunciations for letters that are commonly used for more than one sound.

Pronunciation Key

a	cat	ih	pin
ah	hot	oh	grow
ai	care	oo	rule, music
ah	all	ow	now
ay	say, age	oy	voice
ee	meet	u	put
eh	let	uh	sun, about
eye	ice or by	ur	term

A

abrasion Mechanical weathering process that is the result of gravity, wind, or moving water, causing rocks to rub against each other, wear each other down, or break into smaller pieces. (pp. 241, 282)

absolute age The approximate age in years of particular rocks, determined through radiometric dating. (p. 83)

absolute magnitude The brightness a star would appear if it were a standard distance (32.6 light-years) from Earth. (p. 592)

abyssal plain (uh BIHS uhl) Flat areas, covered with layers of sediment, deep on the ocean floor. (p. 374)

adapted Characteristic of a species that makes it able to survive in its environment. (p. 290)

air mass One of six different types of weather conditions in a given area: continental polar, continental tropical, maritime polar, maritime tropical, equatorial, and arctic. (p. 440)

air pressure The pressure exerted by air in a particular area. (p. 397)

alluvial fan (uh LOO vee uhl) Fan-shaped type of sediment deposit formed when a river flows down a steep mountain slope onto a broad, flat, desert area. (p. 268)

altitude A location's distance above sea level. (p. 464)

anthracite (AN thruh syt) The fourth stage of coal formation, anthracite is about 90 percent carbon, generating a great amount of heat while releasing few pollutants. (p. 493)

anticline (ANT ee klyn) A fold that produces an upward bulge. (p. 115)

anticyclonic wind pattern Air, rushing away from a high-pressure center, creates a clockwise wind pattern, resulting in warm, sunny weather. (p. 445)

aphelion (uh FEEL yuhn) The place in the Earth's orbit where Earth is farthest away from the sun. (p. 539)

apogee (AP uh JEE) Point in the moon's orbit where it is farthest away from the Earth. (p. 547)

apparent magnitude The measure of a star's brightness as it appears from Earth. (p. 592)

aquifer (AH kwih fur) A groundwater-containing layer of rock or sediment. (p. 331)

archipelago A chain or cluster of islands. (p. 35)

asteroid (AS tuh ROYD) A small, irregularly-shaped body that revolves counterclockwise around the sun. (p. 575)

asteroid belt In the gap between Mars and Jupiter, a large group of unusually shaped asteroids makes up this belt. (p. 575)

asthenosphere (as THEHN uhs FEER) The hot, semi-liquid layer of the earth's mantle below the lithosphere. (p. 57)

atmosphere An envelope of gases surrounding the earth that extends about 1,000 km above the earth's surface. (p. 402)

atoll (A tohl) The ring of coral left behind when a volcanic island has sunk below the surface of the water. (p. 375)

atom The smallest particle of an element, with all the properties of this element, that can combine with other atoms to form a molecule. (p. 161)

atomic number The number of protons in an element's nucleus that identifies the element. (p. 162)

aurora australis In the Southern Hemisphere, the beautiful display of lights in the sky, caused by charged particles carried by solar wind. (p. 562)

aurora borealis In the Northern Hemisphere, the display of beautiful lights in the sky that is caused by a steady stream of solar wind from the sun's corona, which carries charged particles. (p. 562)

axis An imaginary line extending through the Earth from the North Pole to the South Pole, around which the Earth rotates. (p. 537)

B **barometer** (buh RAHM uh tur) Instrument used to measure air pressure. (p. 443)

barred spiral galaxy A galaxy with a spiral shape, with the arms attached to a straight bar shape. (p. 602)

batholith A large pluton that has been exposed at the earth's surface by erosion. (p. 124)

bathymetric map (BATH uh MEH trihk) Topographic map of the ocean floor. (p. 368)

bathyscaph (BATH ih skaf) A small, submarinelike submersible that scientists use to explore the ocean depths. (p. 370)

beach Shoreline formed when sand, gravel, or other sediments accumulate over a long period of time. (p. 272)

bedrock Layer of solid rock that underlies soil, sand, clay, and gravel layers on the earth's surface. (p. 230)

benthos (BEHN thohs) Organisms, such as clams, crabs, seaweeds, and tube worms, that live on the ocean floor. (p. 380)

big bang theory Theory stating that the universe was at one time one giant fireball that exploded; as the matter cooled, the force of gravity pulled particles together to form stars and galaxies. (p. 604)

binary stars The most common type of star group, this is two stars close to each other, that sometimes appear as one bright star. (p. 603)

biodiversity (BY oh dih VURS uh tee) The wide variety of different species in an ecosystem. (p. 517)

biome A large community of plants and animals whose makeup is determined by soil and climate. (p. 36)

biosphere (BY uhs feer) A life-supporting zone extending from the earth's crust into the atmosphere. (p. 24)

bituminous coal (by TOO mihn uhs) Most common type of coal mined and used in the United States; about 85% carbon, it burns cleaner and releases fewer pollutants than lignite. (p. 493)

black hole The remains of a supernova explosion, it is a dense object with very strong gravity from which nothing can escape, including light. (p. 599)

C **capture theory** Idea proposing that the moon formed elsewhere and was trapped by the Earth's gravity. (p. 547)

carbonation Chemical weathering process produced by carbonic acid, where the rock develops small pits or holes; common in rocks like limestone and marble. (p. 243)

cast Fossil formed by minerals in water that build up in a mold. (p. 295)

cementation Sedimentary process where sediment spaces fill and bind together with minerals. (p. 221)

Cenozoic Era (SEE nuh ZOH ihk) The time from the end of the Mesozoic Era (66 million years ago) up to the present. (p. 85)

chemical bond The force of attraction that holds atoms or ions together. (p. 163)

chemical change Change in the chemical identity of a substance. (p. 168)

chemical formula A combination of chemical symbols used to represent compounds. (p. 166)

chemical rock Rock formed when minerals come out of solution and crystallize. (p. 223)

chemical symbol A one- or two-letter abbreviation for every element, used by scientists worldwide. (p. 166)

chemical weathering Type of weathering that changes the chemical composition of rock. (p. 242)

chromosphere (KROH muh sfeer) The middle layer of the sun's atmosphere, made up mostly of streams of hydrogen gas. (p. 561)

cinder cone volcano A volcano formed from ash, cinder, and other volcanic debris. (p. 147)

cirque (SURK) Large, bowl-shaped hole in the side of a mountain where a glacier began. (p. 276)

clastic rock Rock that is formed when particles of country rock and mineral grains compact together. (p. 222)

cleavage Property of a mineral when it breaks along a flat plane or surface. (p. 194)

climate Characteristic weather for a region over a long period of time, determined by latitude, altitude, distance from the ocean, topography, and prevailing winds. (p. 463)

climate zone A region with a particular range of temperatures, based on latitude. (p. 469)

cold front Weather boundary characterized by strong gusts of wind and rain where cold, dry air displaces warm, moist air. (p. 441)

comet An object made of ice that travels in an orbit around the sun. (p. 578)

compaction Sedimentary rock process where the water is squeezed out of the spaces, and the particles of sediment pack tightly together. (p. 221)

composite volcano A volcano that contains alternating layers of volcanic debris and lava. (p. 147)

composting Creating a garden area where organic material can break down to be reused in the soil as fertilizer. (p. 527)

compound A substance made of two or more chemically combined elements. (p. 165)

compression Type of stress in the earth's crust where rocks are squeezed together. (p.114)

conchoidal Property of a mineral when it breaks and forms a curving surface. (p. 194)

condensation Phase change that occurs when water vapor rises in the air, then cools, forming liquid droplets which make clouds. (p. 320)

condensation nuclei In the atmosphere, small particles of salt, dust, or smoke around which water condenses when the relative humidity reaches 100 percent. (p. 423)

conduction The transfer of heat energy or electrons between objects in direct contact. (p. 398)

conservation The careful use of our natural resources. (p. 523)

constellation Star pattern seen in the sky in the shape of people or animals. (p. 603)

continent One of the seven major landmasses of the earth. (p. 32)

continental drift The theory that all the world's landmasses were at one time joined together in a super-continent called Pangaea. (p. 91)

continental glacier A glacier that covers a large area in a polar region. (p. 274)

continental margin The downward-sloping part of a continent that extends out into the ocean. (p. 372)

continental rise Part of the continental margin; the area from the continental slope to the deep ocean floor. (p. 373)

continental shelf The gently-sloping surface of the continental margin, extending underwater from the shoreline. (p. 373)

continental slope Part of the continental margin, at the edge of the continental shelf, that drops off steeply to the ocean floor, where the boundary between the continental crust and ocean crust occurs. (p. 373)

contour line Line on a topographic map connecting points that have the same elevation. (p. 45)

control A test where all variables are identical to the experiment being performed except the independent variable. (p. 7)

convection (kuhn VEHKT shuhn) Circular flow of matter in currents in a heated material. (p. 59)

convection zone About 400 000 km from the core of the sun, the area where matter expands and rises, then cools, becomes denser, and sinks back. (p. 560)

convergent boundary Boundary where two plates collide. (p. 100)

core The innermost layer of the earth, composed primarily of iron and nickel. Also, the innermost layer of the sun where nuclear fusion occurs. (pp. 56, 560)

Coriolis force (KOR ee OH lihs) Caused by the earth's rotation, this force makes the earth's winds and ocean currents bend and curve. (p. 345)

corona (kuh ROH nuh) The outermost layer of the sun. (p. 560)

country rock Existing body of rock on the earth's surface that is broken down by rain, sun, wind, ice, pollution, and organisms. (p. 220)

crater A hollowed-out area at the top of a volcano; or, a circular indentation on the surface of the moon. (pp. 145, 546)

creep Slow, steady movement along an active fault. Also, the gradual downslope movement of soil. (pp. 140, 264)

crest The highest point of a wave. (p. 352)

crust Outermost layer of the earth that covers the mantle. (p. 56)

cumulus cloud (KYOO myuh luhs) Large, puffy cloud common on a warm summer day. (p. 424)

current The flow and movement of water in the ocean. (p. 345)

cyclone A hurricane that forms over the Indian Ocean. (p. 450)

cyclonic wind pattern (sy CLAH nihk) Counter-clockwise wind pattern that surrounds a low-pressure area, creating hurricanes and major winter storms. (p.445)

 data Information from which analyses and conclusions can be made. (p. 3)

database A large collection of organized material in a computer. (p. 520)

daughter theory Idea that suggests that the moon was formed from a piece of the Earth that split off at some time. (p. 547)

decay Process where an atom of a radioactive isotope breaks down and releases matter and energy from its nucleus. (p. 300)

deflation Process of wind carrying away loose sediment. (p. 282)

deforestation The systematic cutting down of forests. (p. 518)

deformation A change in the shape or structure of the earth's crustal material resulting from bending, folding, breaking, sliding, or tilting. (p. 113)

delta Triangular-shaped sediment deposit formed at the mouth of a river. (p. 268)

density Measure of how much matter exists in a given volume; density = mass/volume. (p. 16)

dependent variable The observed variable in an experiment that changes in response to the independent variable. (p. 7)

deposition (DEHP uh ZIH shuhn) The buildup of sediments on the bottoms of lakes, valleys, and the ocean floor. (pp. 78, 263)

desert pavement Hard, pebbly surface that is left behind after the wind carries away any loose sediment. (p. 282)

dew point Certain temperature at which the air becomes saturated with water vapor. (p. 416)

diatomaceous earth (DY uh tuh MAY shuhs) Powdery material, made of glasslike skeletons of diatoms. (p. 384)

diurnal tides Pattern of tides with one high tide and one low tide per day. (p. 357)

divergent boundary Any boundary where plates move away from each other, and where new crust is being created. (p. 100)

divide A ridge separating different drainage systems. (p. 325)

domesticated Characteristic of plants and animals that are cared for by agricultural societies. (p. 511)

Doppler effect A change in wave frequency, and therefore in the pitch of sound, caused by movement of either the source or the receiver of the sound. (p. 604)

drainage system A pattern of streams and rivers that flows into the ocean. (p. 325)

dry climate Located on both sides of the equator between 15° and 30° north and south latitudes, this climate includes some of the earth's driest deserts. Dry climates also occur in the middle latitudes between 35° and 50° north latitudes in western North America and the Asian interior, and are characterized by little rainfall, cold winters, and warm to very hot summers. (p. 470)

ductile Able to change shape without breaking. (p. 113)

dune A deposit formed from windblown sand. (p. 283)

earthquake Movement of the earth's crust that occurs when rocks suddenly break and release stored energy. (p. 133)

eclipse (ee KLIHPS) The shadow caused when the moon of one planet passes between the sun and another body. (p. 552)

ecosystem (EEK oh IHS tuhm) Area in which living things interact with each other and the environment. (p. 381)

elastic limit The amount of stress a material can absorb without breaking apart. (p. 134)

electromagnetic spectrum The entire range of visible and invisible electromagnetic waves, from radio waves to gamma rays. (p. 586)

electromagnetic wave Wave of energy that makes up the electromagnetic spectrum. (p. 586)

electron (ee LEHK trahn) A subatomic particle with a negative charge located outside an atom's nucleus. (p. 161)

elevation Distance measured above sea level. (p. 34)

elliptical Referring to an object's orbit in space, which is not in a perfect circle, but rather in the shape of an ellipse. (p. 572)

elliptical galaxy A galaxy shaped like a slightly flattened circle. (p. 602)

El Niño A disturbance of ocean winds and currents off the western coast of South America, occurring every three to eight years, that warms coastal waters, killing many organisms and starving many fishes. (pp. 350, 478)

endangered species Particular species of plant or animal that is in immediate danger of becoming extinct. (p. 517)

epicenter The point on the earth's surface directly above the focus of an earthquake. (p. 134)

epoch Subdivision of a geological period on the geologic timescale. (p. 85)

equator The imaginary line around the earth's center, equidistant from the poles, and perpendicular to the earth's axis of rotation. (p. 38)

equinox (EE kwuh nahks) The first day of spring or fall, when the sun is directly over the equator, called the vernal equinox (spring) or autumnal equinox (fall). (p. 540)

era The largest division of the earth's history; the Precambrian, Paleozoic, Mesozoic, and Cenozoic Eras are measured in millions of years. (p. 84)

erosion (ee ROH zhuhn) Process by which smaller particles of rock are displaced by moving water, wind, or ice. (pp. 77, 263)

estivate (EHS tuh vayt) What amphibians, such as frogs, do when they burrow in the mud and remain dormant for the winter. (p. 541)

estuary (EHS choo AIR ee) A bay or inlet of low salinity, where river water mixes with ocean water. (p. 340)

evaporation Phase change when liquid water turns to vapor by the heat energy of the sun. (p. 320)

evaporite Sedimentary rock formed from the evaporation of ocean or lake waters. (p. 223)

evolution A change in a living population over time. (p. 290)

exfoliation (EHKS foh lee AY shun) Process where outer layers of granite expand, crack, and flake off; caused by extreme changes in temperature. (p. 239)

exosphere Outermost layer of the atmosphere that extends several thousand kilometers above the earth. (p. 403)

exponential growth (EHKS poh NEHN shuhl) Growth of a population that doubles its numbers at regular, predictable intervals. (p. 513)

extinction The dying out of a species that is unable to adapt to its environment. (p. 290)

extrusive rock Igneous rock formed from lava that solidifies on or near the earth's surface. (p. 215)

F **fault** A fracture in the earth's crust where movement has occurred. (p. 117)

fault plane The fracture line of a fault. (p. 117)

fissure Long crack in soil or rock resulting from an earthquake. (p. 141)

floodplain Valley area surrounding the banks of a river that has been built up from sediment left by repeated flooding. (pp. 267, 269)

fluorescence (flor EHS uhns) Property of a mineral that glows when exposed to ultraviolet light. (p. 196)

focus The point along a fault where rocks first break and move, causing an earthquake. (p.134)

fog A cloud that forms on the earth's surface. (p. 426)

folding The bending of rock layers resulting from compressional stress. (p. 115)

foliated rock Striped-looking, metamorphic rock with grains arranged in parallel bands. (p. 228)

food chain Sequence of organisms through which food energy passes. (381)

footwall Formed from the rocks below the fault plane. (p. 117)

fossil Remains or traces of an organism that lived in the past. (p. 79)

fossil fuel An energy source made from the buried remains of decayed plants and animals that lived hundreds of millions of years ago: coal, oil, and natural gas. (p. 492)

fossil record Record of life on the earth provided by fossils. (p. 294)

fracture Property of a mineral that breaks, leaving an uneven or splintered surface. (p. 194)

front The boundary where two different air masses meet, causing sudden weather changes. (p. 441)

G **galaxy** A very large collection of stars, nebulae, gases, dust, and planets, that travels through space bound together by gravity. (p. 601)

gem Rare, beautiful mineral that is cut and polished; used for jewelry and ornamentation. (p. 203)

geode Mineral rock formed when hot, mineral-containing liquid inside the rock evaporates, leaving the rock's interior lined with mineral crystals. (p. 187)

geologic time The time scale of the history of the earth and its life. (p. 76)

geothermal energy Alternative energy source that comes from heat energy within the earth, such as water that has been heated near igneous rocks by magma. (p. 499)

geyser Vent in the ground where superheated water builds up pressure and finally blows out of the small surface opening. (p. 332)

gibbous moon Phase of the moon when more than half of its surface is illuminated. (p. 551)

glacier Formed when the amount of snow is so great that all of the snow is unable to melt. (p. 274)

Gondwanaland (gahnd WAH nuh LAND) The large southern continent formed when the supercontinent of Pangaea broke apart. (p. 92)

gravity The attracting force between the sun and each planet that exists because of their mass, keeping the planets in their orbits. (p. 572)

greenhouse effect A process that traps energy from the sun by allowing radiant energy to enter a given space, but preventing heat energy from escaping. (p. 408)

groundwater Water beneath the earth's surface that soaked into the ground from rain or melted snow. (p. 329)

gully Channel formed from stream erosion when rainwater produces rills, and the rills join together, flowing downhill and removing topsoil. (p. 266)

guyot (GEE oh) Volcanic island that has stopped growing and been flattened by wave action. (p. 375)

gyre (JY ur) Surface current that flows in a circular pattern: clockwise in the Northern Hemisphere, and counterclockwise in the Southern Hemisphere. (p. 347)

H **habitat** (HAB uh tat) The area where an organism naturally lives in an ecosystem. (p. 379)

hachures (HASH oorz) Short lines used on a map to indicate slopes, their degree, and direction. (p. 46)

hail Type of precipitation that forms when small snow pellets or frozen raindrops collide with supercooled water droplets in a cloud, are caught in upward-rising air, and returned to the thundercloud. (p. 431)

half-life Measurement scientists use to describe how long it takes for half of the atoms in a sample to decay. (p. 300)

hanging wall Formed from the rocks above the fault plane. (p. 117)

heft Property of a mineral that is measured by picking the mineral up and comparing its mass to an equal volume of another mineral. (p. 194)

heliocentric Descriptive of something that is centered around the sun, as a model of the solar system. (p. 572)

hemispheres The halves of the earth north and south of the equator; also the halves of the earth east and west of the prime meridian. (p. 38)

highland Bright, mountainous terrain on the surface of the moon. (p. 546)

high tide Highest level the ocean water reaches on the shore. (p. 356)

hominid (HAHM uh nihd) First humanlike organism that appeared between 4 and 8 million years ago. (p. 307)

Homo erectus First upright-walking ancestor of modern man, whose fossils date back about 1.6 million years. (p. 307)

Homo sapiens Species of human that evolved from Homo erectus, and appeared between 500,000 and 130,000 years ago. (p. 307)

horizon One of the three boundary layers of mature soils. Also, the line where the Earth seems to meet the sky. (pp. 248, 540)

horn Sharp peak formed when several cirques are close together. (p. 276)

hot spot An area of frequent volcanic activity on the earth's surface, which develops from an especially hot area of the mantle. (p. 148)

humid cold climate Found in the northern temperate zone, climate characterized by short, warm, wet summers, and long, very cold winters. (p. 471)

humidity Amount of water vapor that is contained in the air. (p. 415)

humus (HYOO muhs) The uppermost, nutrient-rich layer of soil. (p. 248)

hurricane A violent, tropical storm with sustained winds of at least 120 km/h that forms over warm oceans near the equator. (p. 450)

hydroelectric energy Alternative energy resource that produces electricity from water moving through dams; also uses tidal energy to make electricity, but this process has limited use. (p. 499)

hygrometer A device that measures humidity using human hair. (p. 418)

hypothesis (hy PAHTH uh sihs) A possible answer or solution to a particular problem, based on current information. (p. 5)

I **igneous rock** (IHG nee uhs) Rocks produced by the cooling and solidifying of magma. (p. 215)

impermeable Describes a rock with spaces that do not easily conduct water. (p. 329)

independent variable A manipulated variable in an experiment that causes the change in the dependent variable. (p. 7)

inertia The tendency of an object to remain at rest or in motion until acted upon by an external force. (p. 573)

infer To make a conclusion based on available data. (p. 4)

inner planets Mercury, Venus, Earth, and Mars, all of which have a liquid core made of nickel and iron, and a rocky mantle and crust. (p. 570)

interglacial Period of warming that separated the ice ages, when glaciers melted and retreated. (p. 477)

international date line The imaginary line of longitude where the date changes, directly opposite the prime meridian. (p. 39)

intrusive rock Igneous rock formed when magma cools and solidifies beneath the earth's surface. (p. 215)

invertebrate Animal without a backbone common during the early Paleozoic Era. (p. 304)

ion (EYE ahn) An atom or group of atoms having an electric charge as a result of losing or gaining one or more electrons. (p. 161)

ionic bond (eye AHN ihk) A chemical bond between a metal and a nonmetal in which electrons are transferred from one atom to another. (p. 163)

ionosphere (eye AHN oh sfihr) An indistinct layer of air within the upper mesosphere and the thermosphere where solar radiation strips atoms and molecules of their electrons, which then become ions. These ions reflect light and radio signals, and bounce them back to earth. (p. 404)

irregular galaxy The least common type of galaxy, without a regular shape or form. (p. 602)

isobar Line on a weather map that connects points of equal atmospheric pressure. (p. 443)

isobath (EYE soh bath) Contour line on a bathymetric map. (p. 368)

isostasy (eye SAHS teh see) The balance of gravity and buoyancy in the earth's crust. (p. 127)

isotherm (EYE soh thurm) Curving line on a weather map that connects points with the same temperature. (p. 457)

isotope (EYE soh tohp) Atoms of the same element having different numbers of neutrons, with resultant different atomic masses. (p. 162)

J

jet stream A narrow ribbon of winds located 8 000 to 12 000 m above the earth's surface. (p. 445)

K

kettle lake Lake formed when a block of ice breaks off from a glacier, is buried, and melts. (p. 277)

kilogram Basic SI unit of mass; abbreviated kg. (p. 15)

kingdom One of the five major divisions into which all living things can be classified. (p. 291)

L

laccolith A bulge or dome-shaped formation resulting from magma intruding into layers of existing rocks. (p. 217)

landform Main feature of the earth's surface. (p. 34)

landslide Type of mass movement where large amounts of rock and soil move rapidly downhill. (p. 264)

lateral fault A fault characterized by side-to-side movement, caused by shear stress, with little or no up-and-down movement. (p. 117)

laterite (LAYT er YT) Rusty, red tropical soil, heavily leached by frequent rains, with a high content of iron oxide. (p. 257)

latitude Distance measured in degrees north and south of the equator. (pp. 39, 463)

Laurasia (lawr AY zhuh) The large northern continent that was formed when the supercontinent of Pangaea broke apart. (p. 92)

lava Hot liquid rock (magma) which reaches the earth's surface. (p. 144)

layer A single thickness of a material covering a surface, usually horizontally. (p. 55)

leaching Chemical weathering process where rainwater carries dissolved minerals from the surface soil deeper into the ground, resulting in mineral-poor surface soil with a mineral-rich layer below it. (p. 243)

levee Sediment that is deposited in a long ridge along a mature or old riverbank during floods. (p. 269)

light-year The distance light travels in one year at a speed of 310 000 km per second, about 9.5 trillion km. (p. 591)

lignite The second stage of coal development, lignite is a soft brown coal that contains about 40% carbon, and releases harmful pollutants when burned; used in some European countries. (p. 493)

liter Metric unit of volume; abbreviated L. (p. 15)

lithification Process where sediment is hardened into rock. (p. 221)

lithosphere (LITH uhs FEER) The cool, solid, outer layer of the earth extending to a depth of about 100 km. (p. 57)

littoral zone (LIHT uh ruhl) Ocean life zone in the shallow water area between the low-tide line and the high-tide line. (p. 380)

local group A large cluster of galaxies including the Milky Way galaxy. (p. 603)

loess Fine-grained angular particles, formed from rocks during the last ice age, that are deposited by wind erosion to make up prairie soil. (pp. 255, 283)

longitude (LAHN jih tood) Imaginary lines, measured in degrees, running from pole to pole; also called meridians. (p. 39)

longitudinal wave A wave consisting of a series of compressions and rarefactions, that moves through a medium in the same direction as the wave is traveling. (p. 135)

longshore current A continuous back-and-forth motion of wave action that forms a zig-zag current parallel to the shore. (p. 349)

low tide Lowest level that the ocean water reaches on the shore. (p. 356)

lunar eclipse When the moon is darkened by the Earth's shadow blocking sunlight from reaching the moon. (p. 552)

luster The way a mineral reflects light from its surface. (p. 193)

M magnetism Property of a mineral containing iron or nickel that makes the mineral attracted to magnets. (p. 196)

magnetosphere An area in the thermosphere where solar particles are trapped; contains a belt of charged particles called the Van Allen radiation belt. (p. 404)

magnitude (MAG nih tood) A number that indicates the brightness of a star; the smaller the number, the brighter the star. (p. 592)

main-sequence A star that ranges from hot and bright to cool and dim. (p. 593)

mantle The layer of rock in the earth that extends to a depth of about 3,000 km. (p. 56)

maria (MAR ee uh) Dark, broad, flat plains on the surface of the moon. (p. 546)

mass The scientific measurement of the amount of matter that an object contains. (p. 15)

mass number A number used to identify different isotopes, containing the total number of protons and neutrons in an atom's nucleus. (p. 162)

mass movement The action of gravity moving rocks or soil down a slope. (p. 264)

matter Any object or substance that has mass and takes up space. (p. 159)

meander Series of curves formed when a mature river erodes and shifts the sides of its banks. (p. 267)

mechanical weathering Process of weathering resulting from ice wedging, temperature changes, wind and water abrasion, and the abrasions of animals and plants. (pp. 240, 241)

meniscus (meh NIHS kuhs) The curved surface of a liquid in a graduated cylinder. (p. 15)

mesosphere Rigid middle layer inside the earth between the asthenosphere and the core. Also, a layer of the atmosphere that extends from the edge of the stratosphere to about 65 km. (pp. 57, 403)

Mesozoic Era (MEHZ uh ZOH ihk) The era in the earth's history when dinosaurs were the dominant life form, from about 245 million years ago to 66 million years ago. (p. 85)

metamorphic rock Rock that has undergone a change in structure, appearance, and composition from its original state, as a result of heat, pressure, and chemical action. (p. 226)

metamorphism Changes in the structure, appearance, and composition of rock that occur beneath the earth's surface. (p. 226)

meteor The light in the night sky that results from a meteoroid entering the earth's atmosphere. (p. 577)

meteorite (MEE tee uh RYT) A meteoroid that does not completely burn up in the atmosphere, and lands on the earth's surface. (p. 578)

meteoroid (MEE tee uh ROYD) An object entering the Earth's atmosphere, made from a chunk of rock or metal smaller than an asteroid, which causes a meteor (shooting star). (p. 577)

meter Basic SI unit of length; abbreviated m. (p. 14)

microclimate Climate that exists in a very small, limited area. (p. 474)

mineral Naturally-occurring inorganic solid with a definite chemical composition and a particular crystalline structure. (p. 185)

model A small-scale representation of a larger object. (p. 10)

Moho (Mohorovičić discontinuity) The boundary between the earth's crust and mantle, about 30 km below the surface. (p. 62)

Mohs scale Scale of hardness of ten minerals that is used to measure the relative hardness of minerals. (p. 195)

mold Fossil impression left in rock by the hard parts of an organism. (p. 295)

molecule (MAHL ih KYOOL) Two or more chemically bonded atoms; the smallest part of a compound with all the properties of that compound. (p. 164)

monocline (MAHN oh klyn) Type of folding where rock layers on one side of a bend are higher than on the other side. (p. 115)

monsoon A heavy, seasonal rainstorm, particularly in southern Asia. (p. 451)

moraine Sediment that is left when a glacier retreats. (p. 277)

mudflow Mass movement caused when heavy rains mix with sediment and wash down a slope. (p. 264)

N **natural gas** A fossil fuel that is a gaseous mixture of hydrocarbons, often found above petroleum deposits. (p. 494)

natural resource Material from the environment that people use to carry on their daily lives. (p. 489)

natural selection Darwin's theory which states that the traits of a species as a whole change over time. (p. 290)

neap tide Daily tide cycle with the least difference between high and low tides. (pp. 358, 553)

nebula (NEHB yoo luh) A great cloud of dust and gas where stars are born. (p. 596)

nekton Freely-swimming organisms such as fishes, dolphins, squids, and whales. (p. 380)

neritic zone Ocean life zone extending from the low-tide line to the edge of the continental shelf, with plenty of sunlight, fairly constant water temperature, and abundant ocean life. (p. 380)

neutron (NOO trahn) A subatomic particle located in an atom's nucleus, having no electric charge, with a mass similar to that of a proton. (p. 161)

neutron star The tiny core of star that remains after a supernova explosion. (p. 599)

nimbus cloud Dark, threatening rain cloud. (p. 424)

nitrogen cycle Closed cycle in which the total amount of nitrogen on the earth is kept constant. Nitrogen is removed from the air to combine with other elements to form nitrogen compounds, which are used by organisms and then returned to the soil or released into the air. (p. 395)

nitrogen fixation Part of the nitrogen cycle where nitrogen is removed from the air to combine with other elements, forming useful nitrogen compounds. (p. 395)

nonrenewable resource A natural resource, such as petroleum, that cannot be replaced by natural processes. (p. 489)

normal fault A fault where the hanging wall moves downward in relation to the footwall, as a result of tension. (p. 117)

nuclear fission (FIHSH uhn) Controversial alternative energy resource where the nucleus of an atom of uranium is split, producing a great amount of energy. (p. 500)

nuclear fusion The energy process that takes place in the sun where two or more atoms' nuclei join together, releasing an enormous amount of energy. (p. 559)

nucleus (NOO klee uhs) The central region of an atom where neutrons and protons are located. (p. 161)

O **occluded front** (uh KLOOD uhd) Boundary where a cold front overtakes a warm front, producing showers. (p. 442)

optical telescope A telescope that uses a large lens to gather light rays and focus them on one spot, with smaller lenses to magnify the image. (pp. 25, 587)

orbit The path that one body takes as it revolves around another body in space. (p. 539)

ore Mineral-rich rock deposit containing usable amounts of metal; the metal is removed from the ore by the process of smelting. (pp. 200, 489)

organic matter A substance in the soil made from living or dead organisms containing carbon. (p. 178)

organic rock Sedimentary rock, like limestone or coal, that is formed from the remains of living things. (p. 223)

organism The highest level of cell organization. All organisms carry out life processes. (p. 23)

outer planets Jupiter, Saturn, Uranus, Neptune, and Pluto. (p. 570)

outwash The sorted and layered glacial deposit formed when the heaviest sediments drop out first. (p. 277)

outwash plain Deltalike area at the front of a glacier, formed when the melting water deposits sediments. (p. 277)

oxbow lake Type of lake formed when an old river cuts across a meander, and sediments build up at both ends of the meander, cutting it off from the rest of the river. (p. 267)

oxidation Chemical weathering process where oxygen in the air combines with iron in a rock to form rust (iron oxide). (p. 242)

oxygen-carbon dioxide cycle Closed cycle where the amount of carbon and oxygen is kept constant. Carbon moves through the atmosphere and into the earth as fossil fuels, in soil, and the oceans; oxygen is released into the air by plants and green algae. (p. 394)

ozone (OH zohn) Gas that forms a layer in the stratosphere, protecting the earth from excessive ultraviolet radiation. (p. 403)

ozone depletion Chlorofluorocarbons, released into the air in aerosols and air conditioners, break down the layer of ozone that protects the earth from ultraviolet radiation. (p. 409)

P **Paleozoic Era** (PAY lee UH ZOH ihk) Second era in the earth's history, from about 640 million years ago to about 245 million years ago, when plants and animals began to live on land. (p. 84)

Pangaea (pan JEE uh) The giant supercontinent where all the world's landmasses were once joined. (p. 91)

parallax (PAIR uh laks) An apparent change in the position of an object caused by a change in position of the observer. (p. 591)

parent rock The rock that weathers and breaks down into smaller fragments to produce soil. (p. 246)

peat The first stage in the formation of coal, composed of partially decayed plant fibers, and burned for heat in parts of Europe. (p. 493)

penumbra (pee NUHM bruh) In an eclipse, an area of partial shadow caused by the Earth, moon, or other body. (p. 552)

perigee (PEHR uh JEE) Point in the moon's orbit where it is closest to the Earth. (p. 547)

perihelion (pur uh HEEL yuhn) The point in the Earth's orbit where it comes closest to the sun. (p. 539)

period The subdivision of a geologic era. (p. 85)

periodic table A tabular arrangement of the elements according to their atomic numbers; elements with similar properties are in the same column. (p. 176)

period of revolution The time it takes a planet to complete one revolution. (p. 573)

permafrost Permanently frozen, deep layer of subsoil found in the polar regions. (p. 257)

permeability Characteristic that measures how easily water flows through a rock. (p. 329)

petrified (PEHT ruh fyd) Characteristic of bone, wood, or other living material where the matter making up the parts of the once-living thing becomes replaced by mineralized deposits, which eventually turn to stone. (p. 295)

petrochemicals Useful chemical compounds produced from petroleum or natural gas. (p. 495)

petroleum Also known as crude oil, a liquid mixture of hydrocarbons, a fossil fuel made from the decayed remains of once-living plants and animals. (p. 494)

phase change When a substance in a solid, liquid, or gas phase changes from one phase to another (i.e., from gas to liquid), without altering its chemical composition. (p.169)

photosphere (FOHT uh sfeer) The innermost layer of the sun's atmosphere, on which sunspots are sometimes seen from Earth. (p. 561)

photosynthesis Process by which plants use energy from sunlight and raw materials from air and water to make glucose to obtain energy. (p. 322)

physical change A change in a substance's physical properties but not in its chemical identity. (p.168)

plankton A collection of small or microscopic plant organisms that floats on or near the surface of salt or fresh water, producing much of the available oxygen in the atmosphere. (pp. 37, 380)

plasma The fourth phase of matter having some properties of a gas and some unique properties. Formed at very high temperatures. (p. 170)

plasticity Condition of some of the earth's material which is soft and flowing, but not completely liquid. (p. 57)

plateau Flat, elevated area of the earth's crust. (p. 126)

plate tectonics (tehk TAHN ihks) Theory of the formation and movement of the rigid crustal pieces covering the earth's surface. (p. 98)

pluton A raised body of rock formed from magma below the surface of the earth. (p. 124)

podsol Type of forest soil formed as a result of acidic leaching. (p. 254)

polar molecule A molecule whose atoms have a slight negative and positive electric charge. (p. 318)

polar zone Coldest of the three climate zones, located between 60° north and south latitude and the poles. (p. 469)

porosity Percentage of a material's volume that is pore space. (p. 329)

Precambrian Era (pree KAYM bree uhn) First and longest era of the earth's history, from the time of the earth's formation to about 640 million years ago, when many new and different life forms began to appear. (p. 84)

precipitation All forms of water that fall from the atmosphere. Also, the process where liquid in a mineral-containing solution evaporates, leaving the minerals. (pp. 187, 320, 428)

preservation Creating parks, preserves, and reserves to keep the wilderness areas in their natural condition. (p. 522)

prevailing winds Winds that blow from one general direction, frequently carrying rain. (p. 466)

primary wave (or P wave) A seismic wave that travels by back–and–forth movement of rock particles. (pp. 62, 134–135)

prime meridian Zero meridian, passing through Greenwich, England, from which longitude is measured. (p. 39)

principle of superposition Principle stating that younger rock layers are formed on top of older rock layers. (p. 298)

product New substances formed in a chemical reaction. (p. 171)

projection The image of a geometric figure reproduced on a flat surface. (p. 40)

prominence (PRAHM uh nuhnts) Spectacular storms on the sun's surface that may extend 1 million km into space. (p. 562)

proton (PROH tahn) A subatomic particle with a positive charge located in the nucleus of an atom. (p. 161)

protostar A hot, spinning ball of matter that forms in a nebula. (p. 597)

psychrometer (sy KRAHM ih tur) A device that measures humidity by calculating the difference between dry-bulb and wet-bulb temperatures. (pp. 418–419)

 radiation fog Fog that forms when warm air cools. (p. 426)

radiation zone Just outside the sun's core, where heat energy produced in the core radiates outward, spreading from atom to atom. (p. 560)

radio telescope A telescope that picks up radio waves emitted by bodies in space. (pp. 26, 588)

rain shadow The dry region on the leeward side of the mountain, the side facing away from the wind. (p. 467)

reactant The starting materials in a chemical reaction. (p. 171)

reclamation Returning the environment of a mining site to its former natural condition. (p. 491)

recycling Reusing already-used materials, such as aluminum cans. (p. 524)

red giant A cool, medium-bright star. (p. 593)

reflecting telescope A telescope that uses one concave mirror as its objective. (pp. 25, 589)

refraction Bending of a wave caused by the change of speed that occurs when the wave moves from one medium to another. (p. 62)

refracting telescope A telescope that uses a convex lens as its objective. (p. 26)

regolith All of the loose, weathered material, including the soil layer, that covers the earth's surface. (p. 245)

relative age Determining the age of a layer of sedimentary rock, or a fossil in such a layer, by comparing its position to other rock layers around it. (pp. 83, 298)

relative humidity The concentration of water vapor in the air compared to the total amount of water vapor that is possible at a particular temperature. (p. 415)

renewable resource A natural resource, such as trees or soil, that can be replaced by natural cycles or processes. (p. 489)

reservoir Artificial lake formed when a dam is constructed on a river. (p. 326)

restoration Returning a habitat to its natural condition. (p. 523)

reverse fault A fault where the hanging wall moves upward in relation to the footwall, as a result of compression. (p. 117)

revolution In space, the movement of one body around another. (p. 539)

rip current Powerful, narrow stream of water that flows away at a right angle to the shore. (p. 349)

Richter magnitude A number on the Richter scale which reflects the total energy released by an earthquake. (p. 136)

rift valley A long, narrow fracture in the earth's crust. (p. 123)

rill (RIHL) A very small channel formed when rainwater flows downhill. (p. 266)

rille A long, narrow valley cutting across a maria on the surface of the moon. (p. 546)

rock cycle Series of processes involving heat, pressure, melting, cooling, and sedimentaion, whereby rocks change from one type to another. (p. 210)

rogue wave The high crest of an enormous wave formed when the crests of two ordinary waves collide and match up, creating a wave with the combined energy of both waves. (p. 355)

rotation The counterclockwise spinning of the Earth on its axis. (p. 537)

runoff Rainwater that is unable to soak into hard-packed, frozen, or saturated ground. (p. 321)

 salinity (suh LIHN uh tee) A measure of the amount of salt in water (g/kg). (p. 340)

sand bar A spit that extends completely across to the other shore. (p. 272)

scale A proportion used to determine the distance between two points on a map. (p. 43)

scarp Cliff created by sudden earth movements along a fault. (p. 141)

schist Coarse-grained metamorphic rock formed from shale or slate. (p. 226)

scientific method Involves the systemized testing of hypotheses, predictions, and inferences about the scientific world, where scientists constantly exchange ideas and information. (p. 8)

sea-floor spreading The theory claiming that the mid-ocean ridge is a huge crack in the earth's crust where the hot mantle pushes through and spreads the ocean floor apart. (p. 97)

seamount Formed near mid-ocean ridges, a volcanic mountain that rises more than 1,000 meters above the ocean floor. (p. 375)

secondary wave (or S wave) A seismic wave that travels by up–and–down movement of rock. (pp. 62, 134–135)

sediment Particles carried away by erosion. (p. 77)

sedimentary rock Rock formed from layered sediments that pile up and squeeze together, providing clues to the earth's past. (pp. 78, 220)

seismic array (SYZ mihk) Cluster of interconnected seismographs. (p. 65)

seismic wave Shock wave in the earth caused by an earthquake. (pp. 61, 134)

seismograph Instrument used to detect earthquake (seismic) waves. (p. 65)

semidiurnal tides Pattern of tides where there are two high tides and two low tides each day. (p. 357)

shadow zone An area around the earth directly opposite the focus of an earthquake, where no seismic waves can be detected. (p. 63)

shear Type of stress where rocks in the earth's crust are pushing in different horizontal directions. (p. 114)

shield volcano A volcano with a flat, shieldlike top that produces runny, easily-flowing lava. (p. 147)

SI (Système internationale d'unités) The metric system, the most commonly used system of measurement based on the meter. (p. 13)

silicates Rocky materials in the crust and mantle, composed of silicon, oxygen, and other elements, such as aluminum, iron, and magnesium. (p. 56)

sister theory Theory that proposes that the Earth and moon formed at the same time and from the same material. (p. 547)

sleet Type of precipitation formed when raindrops or snowflakes fall through air layers of different temperatures. (p. 430)

slide Rapid downslope movement of soil, debris, and rock. (p. 141)

slope Steepness of a landform. (p. 47)

slump Mass movement caused by weak layers of underlying material moving downslope as a single unit. (p. 264)

smog Air pollution caused by using fossil fuels, which results in air that is unhealthy to breathe. (p. 408)

soil profile A cross section of the layers of soil, such as a hole that is dug in the ground. (p. 248)

solar eclipse When the moon passes between the sun and the Earth, causing the moon's shadow to fall on Earth. (p. 552)

solar energy Energy from the sun used to heat buildings and homes. (p. 502)

solar flare On the sun's surface, a very intense spurt of electromagnetic radiation, lasting from 10 minutes to 1 hour, which interrupts radio communications on Earth. (p. 562)

solar system The Earth and the eight other planets, along with various other bodies that orbit the sun. (p. 559)

solar winds A steady stream of charged particles from the corona of the sun that are responsible for the displays of light in the sky called the aurora borealis and the aurora australis. (p. 562)

solstice In the northern hemisphere first day of winter when the noon sun is directly over 23°N; or, the first day of summer when the noon sun is directly over 23°S. (p. 540)

sonar Devices that bounce sound waves off the ocean floor, providing scientists with an accurate image of the ocean-floor topography. (pp. 96, 366)

species (SPEE sheez) The basic unit of classification, the division of a genus, made of very similar organisms that are able to mate and reproduce offspring of the same type. (p. 290)

specific gravity Ratio of a mineral's density compared to the density of water. (p. 194)

spectrograph Tool used to separate light through a prism, lens, and camera; the spectrum is then recorded on a photographic plate. (p. 588)

spectroscope An instrument used by scientists that disperses a beam of light into a spectrum of its component wavelengths. (p. 588)

spiral galaxy A pinwheel-shaped galaxy like the Milky Way. (p. 602)

spit A deposit of sediment, extending out from a beach across a bay or inlet. (p. 272)

stalactite An icicle-like mineral form that hangs from cavern ceilings. (p. 331)

stalagmite A pillar of minerals that forms on a cavern floor. (p. 331)

star cluster A group of stars close together, but smaller in number than a galaxy. (p. 603)

stationary front Boundary between two nonmoving air masses, generally causing light rain. (p. 442)

steam fog Fog that forms when cold air moves over warm water. (p. 426)

stratosphere Layer of the atmosphere, between the troposphere and the mesosphere, that contains the ozone layer. (p. 403)

stratus cloud (STRA tuhs) Widespread flat, dull gray clouds that frequently produce rain or drizzle. (p. 424)

streak Colored powder that a mineral leaves on a streak plate. (p. 193)

stress Forces that act on the rocks of the earth's crust, causing movement of the crust, or a change in shape or volume. (p. 114)

stromatolite (stroh MAT uh lyt) Oldest known fossil of moneran that lived about 3,500 million years ago. (p. 303)

subduction (suhb DUHK shuhn) The process of one plate moving under another plate. (p.101)

submarine canyon Canyons made from currents, and cut by rivers that carried great amounts of water and sediments to the ocean during the ice ages. (p. 373)

submersible (suhb MUR suh buhl) Underwater research vessels that enable scientists to explore deep in the ocean. (p. 367)

sunspot Cool, black looking storm areas that occur on the sun's surface. (p. 562)

supergiant A very bright star, ranging from cool to medium hot. (p. 593)

supernova The most violent event known to occur in the universe, it is the explosion of a supergiant. (p. 599)

surface tension Property of liquids that makes their molecules tend to stick together in a stretched, cohesive manner like a membrane. (p. 318)

swell Wave energy that forms a series of smooth, rolling hills of water. (p. 352)

syncline (SIHN klyn) Type of folding where a middle area has sunk below the level of its two sides. (p. 115)

synoptic chart A weather map that shows current weather data from many different locations, using symbols for air temperature, type of storm or cloud cover, wind direction and speed, and atmospheric pressure. (p. 457)

T **temperate zone** Mildest of the three climate zones, lying on both sides of the tropical zone and extending to 60° north and south latitude. (p. 469)

tension Type of stress in the earth's crust where rocks are stretched or pulled apart. (p. 114)

theory A set of facts, based on separate but related hypotheses, explaining the behavior of a particular phenomenon. (p. 9)

thermocline (THUR moh KLYN) Zone of rapid temperature change in ocean water beneath the surface zone. (p. 341)

thermosphere Layer of the atmosphere right below the exosphere. (p. 403)

thrust fault Fault where the hanging wall rides up and over the footwall as a result of compression. (p. 117)

thunderstorm Caused when a cumulonimbus cloud, filled with positive and negative ions, has a great enough difference in charges to cause lightning and thunder. (p. 449)

tide Daily ebb and flow of water levels in the oceans and other large bodies of water. (pp. 356, 553)

till Mixture of different sediment sizes in a moraine. (p. 277)

topography A precise description of the surface features of a particular area, including elevation. (pp. 45, 467)

tornado (tor NAY doh) A whirling, funnel-shaped windstorm, with rotating winds of more than 500 km/h, that moves or skips on a narrow path along the ground. (p. 451)

toxin A chemical with the capacity to damage the health of organisms. (p. 519)

trace fossils Footprints, tracks, trails, and burrows left by animals or early humans. (p. 295)

transducer Device that changes energy from one form to another. (p. 202)

transform boundary Boundary where two plates slide in opposite directions beside each other. (p. 100)

transpiration (TRAN spuh RAY shun) Process where water moves up through a plant, eventually exiting through tiny holes in the leaves. (p. 322)

transverse wave A wave in which matter moves at a right angle to the direction of the wave. (p. 135)

trench A deep valley on the ocean floor. (p. 101)

tributary (TRIHB yoo TAIR ee) A small stream that flows into a larger one. (p. 325)

tropical zone Warmest of the three climate zones, located between latitudes 30°N and 30°S, characterized by high temperatures and heavy amounts of rain. (p. 469)

troposphere (TROH puh sfihr) Life-containing layer of the atmosphere that is closest to the surface of the earth. (pp. 403, 439)

trough (TROF) The lowest point of a wave. (p. 352)

tsunami (soo NAHM ee) A giant ocean wave that travels at speeds over 700 km/h, caused by underwater earthquakes, landslides, or volcanic eruptions. (pp. 142, 354)

typhoon A hurricane that forms over the western Pacific Ocean. (p. 450)

umbra In an eclipse, the blackest part of a shadow cast by the Earth, moon, or other body. (p. 552)

unconformity (UHN kuhn FORM uh tee) A definitive line between two rock layers indicating a break in geologic time. (p. 83)

undertow Type of current formed when water, carried to the shore in waves, pulls back toward the ocean. (p. 349)

universal solvent Another name for water, so-named because it can dissolve more substances than any other liquid. (p. 319)

uplift Process by which parts of the earth's crust are raised up higher than other parts, forming mountains and plateaus. (p. 78)

upwelling In the ocean, the upward movement of cold, deep water. (p. 348)

valley glacier Glacier that forms in a high mountain valley. (p. 274)

Van Allen radiation belt A belt of charged particles that surrounds the earth; a part of the magnetosphere, which is part of the thermosphere. (p. 404)

vent An opening in the earth's surface where volcanic material, gas, or steam emerges. (p. 145)

vertebrate Animal with a backbone that appeared during the Ordovician period. (p. 304)

volcano An opening in the earth's crust that has released molten rock. (p. 144)

volume The amount of space that something occupies. (p. 15)

watershed Surrounding land area that supplies runoff to streams in a drainage system. (p. 325)

warm front Boundary where a warm, less dense air mass overtakes a cold, dense air mass, producing cloudy skies, rain, or snow. (p. 442)

water table The boundary between the zone of aeration and the zone of saturation. (p. 330)

wave The periodic up-and-down motion of a body of water. (p. 351)

wave height The vertical distance measured between a wave's crest and its trough. (p. 352)

wavelength The distance measured from the crest of one wave to the crest of another wave. (p. 352)

weathering The process during which rocks are broken up into smaller particles by the action of water, the atmosphere, and organisms. (pp. 77, 239)

white dwarf A low-magnitude, relatively hot star. (p. 593)

x-axis The horizontal line on a graph. (p. 20)

y-axis The vertical line on a graph. (p. 20)

zenith The highest point that the sun reaches in the sky. (p. 540)

Index

Acknowledgments

Photographs

Title page iTL Dan McCoy/Rainbow; iTLC NASA; iTR Robert Caputo/Stock, Boston; iTRC Joyce Photographics/Photo Researchers; iB Geoffrey Nilsen*

Contents iiiB Bjorn Bolstad/Photo Researchers; iiiT Ken Karp*; ivC Kevin Schafer/AllStock; ivLB NASA; ivLT Kevin Schafer & Martha Hill/Tom Stack & Associates; ivR Roger Ressmeyer/Starlight; vBC Geoffrey Nilsen*; vBL Geoffrey Nilsen*; vRC M. Long/Visuals Unlimited; vTL Geoff Tompkinson/SPL/Photo Researchers; vTR Larry Lefever/Grant Heilman Photography; viBL Adam Hart-Davis/SPL/Photo Researchers; viBR Douglas Mazonowicz/Gallery of Prehistoric Art; viC Andrew Leitch/Discover Magazine; viTL David M. Dennis/Tom Stack & Associates; viTR Gregory G. Dimijian/Photo Researchers; viiBC Dave Fleetham/Tom Stack & Associates; viiBR Jeff Simon/Bruce Coleman Inc.; viiCR Jan Hinsch/SPL/Photo Researchers; viiL Jeff Foott/DRK Photo; viiTR F. Stuart Westmorland/AllStock; viiiBL Runk-Schoenberger/Grant Heilman Photography; viiiBR Mike Price/Bruce Coleman Inc.; viiiTL Joel W. Rogers/AllStock; viiiTR Gary Withey/Bruce Coleman Inc.; ixBR William McCoy/Rainbow; ixCR Paul Silverman/Fundamental Photographs; ixL Will & Deni McIntyre/AllStock; ixTR K. H. Switak/Photo Researchers; xBL NASA; xR NASA/Jet Propulsion Lab; xTL Jim Ballard/AllStock; xiBCL Ernst Jahn/Bruce Coleman Inc.; xiBL Tom McHugh/Photo Researchers; xiBR Renee Purse/Photo Researchers; xiBRC George Whiteley/Photo Researchers; xiTR NASA; xiiiL Craig Walker/Rainbow; xiiiR Wetmore/Photo Researchers; xivBR Eric Simmons/Stock, Boston; xivL Michael Fogden/Bruce Coleman Inc.; xivTR John Elk/Bruce Coleman Inc.; xvBC Randy Brandon/Peter Arnold, Inc.; xvBL Bill Gallery/Stock, Boston; xvT Geoffrey Nilsen*; xviBC NASA/Peter Arnold, Inc.; xviBL Breck P. Kent/Animals, Animals; xviBR Runk-Schoenberger/Grant Heilman Photography; xviTR Runk-Schoenberger/Grant Heilman Photography.

Unit 1 xii Stocktrek Photo Agency; 1 Galen Rowell

Chapter 1 2 National Center for Atmospheric Research; 3 Runk-Schoenberger/Grant Heilman Photography; 4B Peter B. Kaplan/Photo Researchers; 4T Tom Bean/DRK Photo; 5 Tom Bean/AllStock; 7 Ken Karp*; 10 Ken Karp*; 14 Ken Karp*; 15 Ken Karp*; 16 Ken Karp*; 17 Ken Karp*; 18 National Institute of Standards & Technology; 25 Ken Karp*; 26L Tom Tracy/The Stock Shop; 26R Greg Hadel/Tony Stone Images

Chapter 2 30 George Hall/Woodfin Camp & Associates; 31 NASA; 37 Richard Kolar/Earth Scenes; 42 NASA; 44 Ken Karp*; 45 Tom Bean/AllStock; 47 Peeter Vilms*; 49 Andy Sacks/Tony Stone Images

Chapter 3 54 Dieter Blum/Peter Arnold, Inc.; 55 Bjorn Bolstad/Photo Researchers; 60 Randall Hyman/Stock, Boston; 61 Will & Deni McIntyre/Photo Researchers; 64 Ocean Drilling Program, Texas A&M University; 65 Vince Streano/The Stock Market; 70-71 Cesar Rubio Photography;

Unit 2 72 Krafft/Photo Researchers; 72-73 Alberto Garcia/Saba

Chapter 4 74 Kim Heacox/AllStock; 75 Chip Carroon/AllStock; 76T David Cannon/Allsport; 77L K. & M. Krafft/Explorer/Photo Researchers; 77R Keith Gunnar/Bruce Coleman Inc; 78L Darrell Gulin/AllStock; 78R Laura Dwight/Peter Arnold, Inc.; 79B SPL/Photo Researchers; 79T Kevin Schafer & Martha Hill/Tom Stack & Associates; 82 Spencer Swanger/Tom Stack & Associates; 83 Albert J. Copley/Visuals Unlimited

Chapter 5 90 Dan McCoy/Rainbow; 91 NASA; 102BL George Hall/Woodfin Camp & Associates; 102BR F. Gohier/Photo Researchers; 102TL David Falconer; 103L David Madison/Bruce Coleman Inc.; 103R Keren Su/Stock, Boston; 104 Dan McCoy/Rainbow; 107 Simon Fraser/SPL/Photo Researchers

Chapter 6 112 Michael Collier/Stock, Boston; 113 Joyce Photographics/Photo Researchers; 116 Collier-Condit/Stock, Boston; 117 Tom Bean/DRK Photo; 118 Fletcher & Bayles/Photo Researchers; 121 Tom Bean/DRK Photo; 122B J. Couffer/Bruce Coleman Inc.; 122T NASA/Grant Heilman Photography; 123 Peter French Photography/DRK Photo; 124 Roy Bishop/Stock, Boston; 125 Steve Vidler/Leo de Wys Inc.; 125B Peeter Vilms*; 126B Tibor Bognar/The Stock Market; 126T David Muench; 128 Keren Su/Stock, Boston

Chapter 7 132 William Waterfall/The Stock Market; 133 Ted Mahieu/The Stock Market; 135 Tim Davis*; 140 Kevin Schafer/AllStock; 141BR Mike Andrews/Earth Scenes; 141L Yoav Levy/Phototake; 141TR Francois Gohier/Photo Researchers; 142B Steve McCutcheon/AllStock; 142T Hank Morgan /Rainbow; 144 Galen Rowell; 146C Dieter & Mary Plage /Bruce Coleman Inc.; 146L Dan McCoy/Rainbow; 146R Keith Murakami/Tom Stack & Associates; 147B Darrell Gulin /AllStock; 147L Lindsay Hebberd/Woodfin Camp & Associates; 147T Breck P. Kent/Earth Scenes; 149B Stella Snead/Bruce Coleman Inc.; 149T Oddo & Sinibaldi/The Stock Market; 150 Roger Ressmeyer/Starlight; 154-155 J. Lotter/Tom Stack & Associates

Unit 3 156 Karl Hartmann/ Sachs/Phototake; 156-157 David Muench

Chapter 8 158 Dan McCoy/Rainbow; 159 Art Wolfe/AllStock; 160BC Dennis Purse/Photo Researchers; 160BL M. Long/Visuals Unlimited; 160BR Ron Watts/Westlight; 160T Kip Peticolas/Fundamental Photographs; 162CL Michael Dalton/Fundamental Photographs; 162CR Geoffrey Nilsen*; 162T Larry Lefever/Grant Heilman Photography; 163 Omikron/Science Source/Photo Researchers; 164 Geoffrey Nilsen*; 165BL Paul von Stroheim; 165BR Breck P. Kent; 165CL Michael Dalton/Fundamental Photographs; 165CR Paul Silverman/Fundamental Photographs; 168B Geoffrey Nilsen*; 169 Geoffrey Nilsen*; 170BC Kent Wood/Peter Arnold, Inc.; 170T Chlaus Lotscher/Peter Arnold, Inc.; 171 Erwin & Peggy Bauer/Bruce Coleman Inc.; 172 Geoffrey Nilsen*; 173 Geoff Tompkinson/SPL/Photo Researchers; 175 Geoffrey Nilsen*; 178B John Gerlach/Visuals Unlimited; 178T Kevin Schafer/ Peter Arnold, Inc.; 179 F. Stuart Westmorland/Tom Stack & Associates

Chapter 9 184 Martin Land/SPL/Photo Researchers; 185 Geoffrey Nilsen*; 186 Geoffrey Nilsen*; 187 Geoffrey Nilsen*; 188 Geoffrey Nilsen*; 190 Breck P. Kent; 192 Geoffrey Nilsen*; 193 Geoffrey Nilsen*; 194 Geoffrey Nilsen*; 195 M. Courtney-Clarke/Photo Researchers; 196 E. R. Degginger; 198 Geoffrey Nilsen*; 199 E. R. Degginger; 200 Gene Stein/ Westlight; 201 Richard Hutchings/Photo Researchers; 202 Geoffrey Nilsen*; 203B George Holton/Photo Researchers; 203T Geoffrey Nilsen*; 204 Jim Larsen/West Stock

Chapter 10 208 Richard Steedman/The Stock Market; 209 Geoffrey Nilsen*; 210 Geoffrey Nilsen*; 211 Geoffrey Nilsen*; 212 Geoffrey Nilsen*; 214 Joseph Nettis/Stock, Boston; 215 Geoffrey Nilsen*; 216 Geoffrey Nilsen*; 218 Geoffrey Nilsen*; 219 C. J. Allen/Stock, Boston; 220 S. J. Krasemann/Peter Arnold, Inc.; 221B Breck P. Kent; 221T J. C. Leacock/West Stock; 222B Grant Heilman/Grant Heilman Photography; 222C John Cancalosi/Peter Arnold, Inc.; 222T Runk-Schoenberger/Grant Heilman Photography; 223B Kevin Schafer/Tom Stack & Associates; 223T Barbara Filet/Tony Stone Images; 224 Frank Fisher/West Stock; 226 Geoffrey Nilsen*; 228 Geoffrey Nilsen*; 229B Ernst Jahn/Bruce Coleman Inc.; 229BL Geoffrey Nilsen*; 229BR Geoffrey Nilsen*; 229CL Geoffrey Nilsen*; 229CR Geoffrey Nilsen*; 229TL Geoffrey Nilsen*; 229TR Geoffrey Nilsen*; 230 Steve Leonard/Tony Stone Images; 234-235 Ric Ergenbright/ AllStock; 234BL George Whiteley/Photo Researchers; 234BR Renee Purse/Photo Researchers; 234T Geoffrey Nilsen*; 235 Ed Cooper Photo

Unit 4 236 Breck P. Kent/Earth Scenes; 236-237 John Shaw/ Tom Stack & Associates

Chapter 11 238 Richard Weymouth Brooks/Photo Researchers; 239 Craig Walker/Rainbow; 240C Tom Bean/DRK Photo; 240L Copr. Jim Cummins/AllStock; 240R Len Rue Jr./Stock, Boston; 241C Stan Osolinski/The Stock Market; 241L David M. Dennis/Tom Stack & Associates; 241R Andy Levin/Photo Researchers; 242BL GHP Studio*; 242BR GHP Studio*; 242L Charlie Ott/Photo Researchers; 242TR Robert Harding Picture Library; 243C Adam Hart-Davis/SPL/Photo Researchers; 243L Gerald Davis/Phototake; 243R Gregory G. Dimijian/ Photo Researchers; 244B Runk-Schoenberger/Grant Heilman Photography; 244T Carlos V. Causo/Bruce Coleman Inc.; 245 John Coletti/Stock, Boston; 248 Kenneth W. Fink/Photo Researchers; 249C Runk-Schoenberger/Grant Heilman Photography; 249L Jeff Foott /Bruce Coleman Inc.; 249R Kim Taylor/Bruce Coleman Inc.; 251 J. C. Carton/Bruce Coleman Inc.; 254B James B. Sanderson/The Stock Market; 254TL Michael P. Gadomski/ Earth Scenes; 255BL David Muench; 255BRC Tom Bean/ AllStock; 256BL Manfred Gottschalk/ Westlight; 256TL K. Gunar/Bruce Coleman Inc.; 257L Charlie Ott/Photo Researchers; 257R Randall Hyman/Stock, Boston; 258 Gary R. Zahm/DRK Photo

Chapter 12 262 Don Mason/The Stock Market; 263 Robert Caputo/Stock, Boston; 264BL Brian Parker/Tom Stack & Associates; 264BR Owen Franken/Stock, Boston; 264C Dick Canby/Positive Images; 264T Barbara Alper/Stock, Boston; 265 Smolan/Stock, Boston; 267B Steve McCutcheon/Visuals Unlimited; 267C Kim Heacox/DRK Photo; 267T Breck P. Kent; 268B Keith Gunnar/Bruce Coleman Inc.; 268T Bill Ross/AllStock; 269B Thomas G. Rampton/Grant Heilman Photography; 269T Jack

Couffer/Bruce Coleman Inc.; 271B Michael Ventura/Bruce Coleman Inc.; 271C Randy Brandon/ Peter Arnold, Inc.; 271TL Brian Parker/Tom Stack & Associates; 271TR W. Cody/Westlight; 272L Keith Gunnar/ Bruce Coleman Inc.; 272R T. Kitchin/Tom Stack & Associates; 273 Fred Whitehead/Earth Scenes; 274L Breck P. Kent; 274R Dr. E. R. Degginger; 275 Douglas Mazonowicz; 278 Ann Hawthorne/Black Star; 280 Jerry Howard/Stock, Boston; 281 Peter Pickford/DRK Photo; 282B David Epperson/ AllStock; 282T Tom Bean/DRK Photo; 283B Annie Griffiths Belt/DRK Photo; 283C Dr. E. R. Degginger; 283T Francois Gohier/Photo Researchers

Chapter 13 288 John Cancalosi/Tom Stack & Associates; 289B Ken Lucas/Biological Photo Service; 289T Francois Gohier; 294 Jack Helle/AllStock; 295L Jeff Gnass/West Stock, Inc.; 295R Breck P. Kent; 296 Breck P. Kent; 297 Breck P. Kent; 298 Richard Kolar/Earth Scenes; 301 Andrew Leitch/Discover Magazine; 307B Tom McHugh/Photo Researchers; 307T John Reader/SPL/Photo Researchers; 312-313 Dallas & Jim Heaton/Westlight

Unit 5 314 Johnny Johnson/DRK Photo; 314-315 Ed Cooper

Chapter 14 316 Stephen Frisch/Photo 20-20; 319 Steve Solum/Bruce Coleman Inc.; 322 Runk-Schoenberger/Grant Heilman Photography; 324 Bill Horsman/Stock, Boston; 325L USGS EROS Data Center; 326B Doug Wilson/Westlight; 326C Milton Rand/Tom Stack & Associates; 326T Rich Buzzelli/Tom Stack & Associates; 328 C. C. Lockwood/ Cactus Clyde Productions; 329B Geoffrey Nilsen*; 329T Runk-Schoenberger/Grant Heilman Photography; 332B Holt Confer/Grant Heilman Photography; 332T Prisma/Westlight; 333 Jeff Amberg/Gamma-Liaison

Chapter 15 338 Steve Lissau/Rainbow; 339 Tom Van Sant/ Geosphere Project, Santa Monica/SPL/Photo Researchers; 342B Jan Hinsch/SPL/Photo Researchers; 342TL F. Stuart Westmorland/AllStock; 342TR Zig Leszczynski/ Animals, Animals; 343 Grant Heilman/Grant Heilman Photography; 357L Breck P. Kent; 357R Breck P. Kent/Earth Scenes; 359B George Post/CA Maritime Academy; 359T Jeff Foott/DRK Photo; 360 Jean Pierre Ducatez

Chapter 16 364 Runk-Schoenberger/Grant Heilman Photography; 365 Jeff Simon/Bruce Coleman Inc.; 366C Rona/Bruce Coleman Inc.; 366L Barry L. Runk/Grant Heilman Photography; 366R Dr. Ken C. MacDonald et. al./UCSB; 367B NASA; 367C NASA; 367T Richard Pasley/Stock, Boston; 370 Rona/Bruce Coleman Inc.; 372 Charles Preitner/ Visuals Unlimited; 376 Dr. Peter W. Sloss/NOAA/ NGDC; 378 C. C. Lockwood/Animals, Animals; 379 Dave B. Fleetham/ Tom Stack & Associates; 382R Dr. E. R. Degginger; 282L Scott Blackman/Tom Stack & Associates; 383L Helen Elizabeth Carr/Biological Photo Service; 383R Tom McHugh/Photo Researchers; 384 Runk-Schoenberger/Grant Heilman Photography; 388-389 David Muench

Unit 6 Runk-Schoenberger/Grant Heilman Photography; 390-391 Richard Kaylin/AllStock

Chapter 17 392 Brett Baunton/AllStock; 402 Joyce Photographics/ Photo Researchers; 405 Will McIntyre/Photo Researchers; 408 Owen Franken/Stock, Boston; 409B Philippe Plailly/SPL/Photo Researchers; 409T NASA/Jet Propulsion Lab

AllStock; 426 Owen Franken/Stock, Boston; 427 A. Glauberman/ Photo Researchers; 430BR E. R. Degginger; 430CB Charles Feil/Stock, Boston; 430TL David C. Hauston/ Bruce Coleman Inc.; 430TR Mike Price/Bruce Coleman Inc.; 431 Nuridsany & Perennou/Photo Researchers; 432B Link/ Visuals Unlimited; 432T Stephen Frisch*; 434 Judy Canty/ Stock, Boston

Chapter 19 438 European Space Agency/SPL/Photo Researchers; 443B Richard Palsey/Stock, Boston; 443T Runk-Schoenberger/Grant Heilman Photography; 445 Peeter Vilms*; 446 USDA/Grant Heilman Photography; 448 Wetmore/Photo Researchers; 450T Dr. Fred Espenak/ SPL/Photo Researchers; 451B E. R. Degginger/Bruce Coleman Inc.; 451T E. R. Degginger; 452 Chris Brown/Stock, Boston; 453 E. R. Degginger; 454B Mark C. Burnett/Photo Researchers; 454L Phil Degginger; 454R David Parker/SPL/Photo Researchers; 454T Bill Gallery/Stock, Boston; 458 NASA

Chapter 20 462 Brian Parker/Tom Stack & Associates; 463B David Madison/Bruce Coleman Inc.; 463T Carl Purcell/Photo Researchers; 464L Patti Murray/Earth Scenes; 464R Rob Crandall/Stock, Boston; 468B N. Pecnik/Visuals Unlimited; 468T Ben Blankenburg/Stock, Boston; 469 Manfred Gottschalk/Tom Stack & Associates; 472B Leonard Lee Rue III/Stock, Boston; 472BR K. H. Switak/Photo Researchers; 472C Stephen J. Krasemann/DRK Photo; 472TL Chip & Jill Isenhart/Tom Stack & Associates; 472TLC Michael Fogden/ DRK Photo; 472TR Bruce Forster/AllStock; 473BL John Mitchell/Photo Researchers; 473BR Craig Aurness/ Westlight; 473C Jim Zipp/Photo Researchers; 473CR Johnny Johnson/ Earth Scenes; 473TL E. R. Degginger/Bruce Coleman Inc.; 474 Jon Bertsch/Visuals Unlimited; 477L Tom Bean/DRK Photo; 477R Phil Degginger; 478 Tom Nebbia; 479 T. Kitchin/Tom Stack & Associates; 480 Ray Hoffman/USGS; 484-485 Jim Corwin/AllStock; 484B Christopher Arnesen/ AllStock; 484T Brian Parker/Tom Stack & Associates; 485 W. Bertsch/Bruce Coleman Inc.

Unit 7 486 Jim Zuckerman/Westlight; 486-487 Kathleen Campbell/AllStock

Chapter 21 488 Robert Winslow/Tom Stack & Associates; 489B John Cancalosa/Tom Stack & Associates; 489T Paul Silverman/Fundamental Photographs; 490B George Hunter/ Tony Stone Images; 490L Lester Lefkowitz/Tony Stone Images; 490T Larry Lefever/Grant Heilman Photography; 492 Nicholas Devore/Bruce Coleman Inc.; 494L Grant Heilman/ Grant Heilman Photography; 494R Ken Graham/ AllStock; 496 Anne Dowie*; 497B Larry Lefever/ Grant Heilman Photography; 497T Kristin Finnegan/ AllStock; 498 Jerry Howard/Positive Images; 499B E. R. Degginger/Bruce Coleman Inc.; 499T Kevin Schafer/Tom Stack & Associates; 500 Dr. Jeremy Burgess/SPL/Photo Researchers; 501 Will McIntyre/Photo Researchers; 502T Andrew Rakoczy/Bruce Coleman Inc.; 503 William McCoy/Rainbow

Chapter 22 508 Barrie Rokeach; 510C John Eastcott-Yva Momatiuk/DRK Photo; 510L David R. Austen/Stock, Boston; 510R Bruce Davidson/Earth Scenes; 511BR Craig Aurness/ Westlight; 511L Nigel Smith/Animals, Animals; 511TR Tom Nebbia; 512B Peter French/Bruce Coleman Inc.; 512R Andy Sacks/Tony Stone Images; 512TL Anne Dowie*; 513 Tom Nebbia; 514T Waugh/Peter Arnold, Inc.; 515 Bob Daemmrich/

Stock, Boston; 517C George H. Harrison/Grant Heilman Photography; 517L Tom Walker/Stock, Boston; 517R Tom McHugh/Photo Researchers; 518R Bernard Wolff/Photo Researchers; 518L Tom Bean/AllStock; 519 Kevin Morris/ AllStock; 520 Alan D. Carey/Photo Researchers; 521 Chip & Jill Isenhart/Tom Stack & Associates; 522 Runk-Schoenberger/ Grant Heilman Photography; 523B Larry Lefever/Grant Heilman Photography; 523T Greg Vaughn/Tom Stack & Associates; 524B Will & Deni McIntyre/AllStock; 524R Anne Dowie*; 524L GHP Studio*; 524TC J. Cancalosi/DRK Photo; 525BR Jerry Howard/Positive Images; 525C Dewitt Jones/ Woodfin Camp & Associates; 525TR Joe Sohm/Chromosohm/ AllStock; 526L Robert E. Daemmrich/Tony Stone Images; 526R Robert E. Daemmrich/Stock, Boston; 532-533 Greg Ryan-Sally Beyer/AllStock

Unit 8 534 SPL/Photo Researchers; 534-535 Royal Observatory, Edinburgh

Chapter 23 536R NASA/Rainbow; 538T Richard Megna/ Fundamental Photographs; 541BL James P. Rowan/ Tony Stone Images; 541C Breck P. Kent/Animals, Animals; 541CL David Carriere/Tony Stone Images; 541L Carson Baldwin, Jr./Earth Scenes; 541TL Jeff Lepore/ AllStock; 543T George Holton/Photo Researchers; 545 Ed Degginger/Bruce Coleman Inc.; 546BL NASA/Peter Arnold, Inc.; 546R NASA; 548 NASA/Finley Holiday Film; 549 NASA; 551 Lick Observatory; 552B NASA; 552T S. Nielsen/Bruce Coleman Inc.

Chapter 24 558 NASA JPL/Starlight; 559B Eric Simmons/ Stock, Boston; 559T John Elk/Bruce Coleman Inc.; 560 National Optical Astronomy Observatories; 562BL National Optical Astronomy Observatories; 562CT NASA; 562R NASA/Science Source/Photo Researchers; 562TL Johnny Johnson/AllStock; 563 Del Mulkey/Photo Researchers; 566 NASA; 570B F. Rossotto/Stocktrek; 570T NASA; 571 NASA/ Jet Propulsion Lab; 574B Bruce H. Frisch/Photo Researchers; 574T NASA/Grant Heilman Photography; 575 NASA; 576 Lockheed; 577B National Optical Astronomy Observatories; 577T Richard Megna/ Fundamental Photographs; 578B Lowell Observatory/ NOAO; 578T Breck P. Kent/Earth Scenes; 580 NASA

Chapter 25 584 Dr. Jean Lorre/SPL/Photo Researchers; 585 Jim Ballard/AllStock; 587 John Lawlor/Tony Stone Images; 588T Roger Ressmeyer/Starlight; 589 Roger Ressmeyer/ Starlight; 594 Robert E. Daemmrich/Tony Stone Images; 596 Royal Observatory, Edinburgh; 597 Royal Observatory, Edinburgh; 600 Lick Observatory; 602BC Regents, Univ. Hawaii; 602CR National Optical Astronomy Observatories; 602TL National Optical Astronomy Observatories; 602TR U.S. Naval Observatory; 605 G. Robert Bishop/AllStock; 606 NASA/Jet Propulsion Lab; 610-611 National Optical Astronomy Observatories; 610BL NASA; 610BR NASA; 610T NASA

*Photographed expressly for Addison-Wesley Publishing Company, Inc. All rock and mineral specimens photographed expressly for Addison-Wesley Publishing Company, Inc. were provided by The California Academy of Sciences.

Illustrations

Margo Stahl-Pronk
pgs. 14-15, 16, 18, 210-211, 216-217, 221, 227, 70, 71, 154, 155

Precision Graphics
pgs. 19, 20, 29, 53, 62, 66, 69, 85, 89, 111, 131, 135, 153, 178, 179, 183, 189, 205, 213, 233, 247, 261, 270, 289, 293, 300, 302, 311, 317, 337, 355, 357, 363, 371, 387, 393, 407, 413, 416, 456, 461, 483, 495, 507, 513, 518, 525, 531, 557, 583, 593, 603, 609, 612, 613, 614, 615, 616, 617, 618-619, 622, 623, 624-625

Rolin Graphics
pgs. 76, 83, 92, 93, 94, 96, 97, 102-103, 105, 108, 228, 266, 268-269, 275, 276-277, 281, 284, 292, 312325, 341, 344, 345, 349, 351, 352-353, 354, 358, 396, 397, 398, 401, 403, 404, 415, 419, 421, 422, 423, 429, 437, 544, 565, 567, 572, 573, 576, 586, 587, 601

Sarah Woodward
pgs. 22-23, 34-35, 50, 197, 320-321, 318, 319, 394-395, 493, 494, 500, 502, 516, 598-599

Michael Maydak
pgs. 134, 145, 147, 290, 306, 552, 388, 389

Marlene May-Howerton
pgs. 303, 304, 305, 532, 533

John Foerster
pgs. 297, 380, 381, 399, 547, 550-551

Carla Simmons
pgs. 114, 115, 116, 117, 118, 123, 124, 291, 299

Carlyn Iverson
pgs. 162, 163, 165, 170, 246, 247, 248, 250, 252, 254, 255, 256, 257, 439, 441, 441, 442

Warren Budd & Associates
pgs. 38, 39, 41, 56-57, 58, 59, 63, 99, 100, 101, 106, 120, 127, 373, 374-375, 406, 466, 561, 579, 590, 603

Charles Thomas
pgs. 444, 450, 563, 568-569

Larry Hughston
pgs. 538, 539, 540

Mapping Specialists
pgs. 40, 43, 46, 47, 48, 124, 136, 137, 148, 253, 327, 340, 346, 347, 348, 350, 356, 433, 440, 444, 445, 464, 465, 470, 470-471, 477, 542, 612, 616, 617, 620-621

Science and Literature Credits

Unit 1 From *Farewell to Manzanar* by James D. Houston and Jeanne Wakatsuki Houston, pp. 69-71. Copyright © 1973 by James D. Houston. Reprinted by permission of Houghton Mifflin Co. All rights reserved.

Unit 2 From *Legend Days* by Jamake Highwater, pp. 42-44. Copyright ©1984 by Jamake Highwater. Reprinted by permission of HarperCollins Publishers.

Unit 3 From *A Journey to the Centre of the Earth* by Jules Verne, 1864. (NY: Dodd, Mead, 1959, pp. 73, 74, 82.)

Unit 4 From *Tales Of A Dead King* by Walter Dean Myers, pp. 66-69. Copyright ©1983 by Walter Dean Myers. By permission of William Morrow & Co., Inc., Publishers.

Unit 5 From *The Land I Lost* by Huynh Quang Nhuong, pp. 41-45. Copyright ©1982 by Huynh Quang Nhuong. Reprinted by permission of HarperCollins Publishers.

Unit 6 From *Going Home* by Nicholasa Mohr, pp. 3-10. Copyright ©1986 by Nicholasa Mohr. Used by permission of Dial Books for Young Readers, a division of Penguin Books USA, Inc.

Unit 7 From *The Ohlone Way: Indian Life in the San Francisco-Monterey Bay Area* by Malcolm Margolin, pp. 46-49. Copyright ©1978 by Malcolm Margolin. Reprinted by permission of Heyday Books.

Unit 8 From *To Space and Back* by Sally Ride and Susan Okie, pp. 29, 42, 46. Copyright ©1986 by Sally Ride and Susan Okie. By permission of William Morrow & Co., Inc. Publishers.